*

*   *

THE BOOK OF
THE IT

*   *

*

THE BOOK OF
THE IT

by

GEORG GRODDECK, M.D.

✳ ✳ ✳

Introduction by
LAWRENCE DURRELL

VINTAGE BOOKS
A DIVISION OF RANDOM HOUSE
New York

VINTAGE BOOKS
are published by Alfred A. Knopf, Inc.
and Random House, Inc.

Reprinted by arrangement with Vision Press Limited, London.

Authorized translation of *Das Buch vom Es,* by V. M. E.
Collins, M.A. Published in 1923 by the Psychoanalytischer
Verlag, Vienna.

*Manufactured in the United States of America,
by The Colonial Press Inc.*

INTRODUCTION *

Lawrence Durrell

If the work and teachings of Georg Walther Groddeck
(1866-1934) are not as well known today as they deserve
to be it is perhaps largely his own fault. His first job, he
considered, was to heal; the writer and the teacher took
second place. Over and above this, Groddeck also knew
how quickly the disciple can convert the living word into
the dead canon. He knew that the first disciple is also very
often the first perverter of the truth. And this knowledge
informs his written work with that delightful self-deprecat-
ing irony which so many of his readers profess to find out
of place; an irony which says very clearly, "I am not in-
viting you to follow me, but to follow yourself. I am only
here to help if you need me." The age does need its Grod-
decks, and will continue to need them until it can grasp
the full majesty and terror of the "It," which he has talked
so much about in his various books, and particularly in
that neglected masterpiece *The Book of the It.*

In considering Groddeck's place in psychology, however, there are one or two current misunderstandings
which deserve to be cleared up for the benefit of those
who have mistaken, or continue to mistake, him for an
orthodox disciple of Freud. Groddeck was the only analyst whose views had some effect on Freud; and Freud's
The Ego and the Id is a tribute to, though unfortunately a
misinterpretation of, Groddeck's It theory. Yet so great
was his admiration for Freud that the reviewer might well
be forgiven who once described him as "a popularizer of
Freudian theory." No statement, however, could be far-

* This essay originally appeared as Number vi in the series
"Studies in Genius," *Horizon* magazine (London), Vol. xvii
No. 102, edited by Cyril Connolly, June, 1948.

ther from the truth, for Groddeck, while he accepts and employs much of the heavy equipment of the master, is separated forever from Freud by an entirely different conception of the constitution and functioning of the human psyche. His acknowledgments to Freud begin and end with those wonderful discoveries on the nature of the dream, on the meaning of resistance and transference. In his use of these great conceptual instruments, however, Groddeck was as different from Freud as Lao-Tzu was from Confucius. He accepted and praised them as great discoveries of the age; he employed them as weapons in his own way upon organic disease; he revered Freud as the greatest genius of the age; but fundamentally he did not share Freud's views upon the nature of the forces within the human organism which make for health or sickness. And this is the domain in which the doctrines of Groddeck and of Freud part company. In this domain, too, Groddeck emerges as a natural philosopher, as incapable of separating body and mind as he is incapable of separating health and disease.

To Freud the psyche of man was made up of two halves, the conscious and the unconscious parts; but for Groddeck the whole psyche with its inevitable dualisms seemed merely a function of something else—an unknown quantity—which he chose to discuss under the name of the "It." "The sum total of an individual human being," he says, "physical, mental, and spiritual, the organism with all its forces, the microcosmos, the universe which is a man, I conceive of as a self unknown and forever unknowable, and I call this the 'It' as the most indefinite term available without either emotional or intellectual associations. The It-hypothesis I regard not as a truth—for what do any of us know about absolute truth?—but as a useful tool in work and in life; it has stood the test of years of medical work and experiment, and so far nothing has happened which would lead me to abandon it or even to modify it in any essential degree. I assume that man is animated by the It, which directs what he does and what he goes through, and that the assertion 'I live' only expresses a small and superficial part of the total experience 'I am lived by the It.' . . ."

This fundamental divergence of view concerning the nature of health and disease, the nature of the psyche's role, is something which must be grasped at the outset if we are to interpret Groddeck to ourselves with any accuracy. For Freud, as indeed for the age and civilization of which he was both representative and part, the ego is supreme. There it lies, like an iron-shod box whose compartments are waiting to be arranged and packed with the terminologies of psychoanalysis. But to Groddeck the ego appeared as a contemptible mask fathered on us by the intellect, which, by imposing upon the human being, persuaded him that he was motivated by forces within the control of his conscious mind. Yet, asks Groddeck, what decides how the food which passes into the stomach is subdivided? What is the nature of the force which decrees the rate of the heart beat? What persuaded the original germ to divide and subdivide itself and to form objects as dissimilar as brain cortex, muscle, or mucus?

"When we occupy ourselves in any way either with ourselves or with our fellow-man, we think of the ego as the essential thing. Perhaps, however, for a little time we can set aside the ego and work a little with this unknown It instead. . . . We know, for instance, that no man's ego has had anything to do with the fact that he possesses a human form, that he is a human being. Yet as soon as we perceive in the distance a being who is walking on two legs we immediately assume that this being is an ego, that he can be made responsible for what he is and what he does, and, indeed, if we did not do this, everything that is human would disappear from the world. Still we know quite certainly that the humanity of this being was never willed by his ego; he is human through an act of will of the All, or, if you go a little further, of the It. The ego has not the slightest thing to do with it. . . . What has breathing to do with the will? We have to begin as soon as we leave the womb, we cannot choose but breathe. *'I love you so dearly, I could do anything for you.'* Who has not felt that, heard it, or said it? But try to hold your breath for the sake of your love. In ten seconds, or at most in a quarter of a minute, the proof of your love will disappear before the hunger for air. No one has command over the power to sleep. It will come or it will not. No one can regulate the beating of the heart. . . ."

Man, then, is himself a function of this mysterious force which expresses itself through him, through his illness no less than his health. To Groddeck the psychoanalytic equipment was merely a lens by which one might see a little more deeply than heretofore into the mystery of the human being—as an It-self. Over the theory of psychoanalysis, as he used it, therefore, stood the metaphysical principle which expressed itself through man's behavior, through his size, shape, beliefs, wants. And Groddeck set himself up as a watchman, and where possible, as an interpreter of this mysterious force. The causes of sickness or health he decided were unknown; he had already remarked in the course of his long clinical practice that quite often the same disease was overcome by different treatments, and had been finally led to believe that disease *as an entity* did not exist, except inasmuch as it was an expression of a man's total personality, his It, expressing itself through him. Disease was a form of self-expression.

"However unlikely it may seem, it is nevertheless a fact that any sort of treatment, scientific or old-wife's poultice, may turn out to be right for the patient, since the outcome of medical or other treatment is not determined by the means prescribed but by what the patient's It likes to make of the prescription. If this were not the case, then every broken limb which had been properly set and bandaged would be bound to heal, whereas every surgeon knows of obstinate cases which despite all care and attention defy his efforts and refuse to heal. It is my opinion, backed by some experience with cases of this nature, that a beneficent influence may be directed upon the injured parts . . . by psychoanalyzing the general Unconscious, indeed I believe that every sickness of the organism, whether physical or mental, may be influenced by psychoanalysis. . . . Of itself psychoanalysis can prove its value in every department of medicine, although of course a man with pneumonia must be put immediately to bed and kept warm, a gangrened limb must be amputated, a broken bone set and immobilized. A badly built house may have to be pulled down and reconstructed with all possible speed when no alternative accommodation is available, and the architect who built it so badly must be made to see his mistakes. . . . And an It which has damaged its own work, lung, or bone, or whatever it may be, must learn its lesson and avoid such mistakes in future. . . .

"Since everything has at least two sides, however, it can always be considered from two points of view, and so it is my custom to ask a patient who has slipped and broken his arm: '*What was your idea in breaking your arm?*'

whereas if anyone is reported to have had recourse to morphia to get sleep the night before, I ask him: 'How was it the idea of morphine became so important yesterday that you made yourself sleepless, in order to have an excuse for taking it?' So far I have never failed to get a useful reply to such questions, and there is nothing extraordinary about that, for if we take the trouble to make the search we can always find an inward and an outward cause for any event in life."

The sciences of the day have devoted almost the whole of their interest to the outward cause; they have not as yet succeeded in escaping from the philosophic impasse created by the natural belief in causality, and side by side with this, a belief in the ego as being endowed with free will. In all the marvelous pages of Freud we feel the analytical intellect pursuing its chain of cause—and effect; if only the last link can be reached, if only the first cause can be established, the whole pattern will be made clear. Yet for Groddeck such a proposition was false; the Whole was an unknown, a forever unknowable entity, whose shadows and functions we are. Only a very small corner of this territory was free to be explored by the watchful, only the fringes of this universe lay within the comprehension of the finite human mind which is a function of it. Thus while Freud speaks of cure, Groddeck is really talking of something else—liberation through self-knowledge; and his conception of disease is philosophical rather than rational. In the domain of theory and practice he is Freud's grateful and deeply attentive pupil, but he is using Freud for ends far greater than Freud himself could ever perceive. Psychoanalysis has been in danger of devoting itself only to the tailoring of behavior; too heavily weighted down by its superstructure of clinical terminology it has been in danger of thinking in terms of medical entities rather than patients. This is the secret of Groddeck's aversion to technical phrases, his determination to express himself as simply as possible, using only the homely weapons of analogy and comparison to make his points. In The Book of the It, which is cast in the form of letters to a friend, he discusses the whole problem of health and disease from a metaphysical point of view, and with an ironic refusal to dogmatize or tidy his views into a system. But the book itself, brimming over with gay irony and poetry, does succeed in circumscribing this territory of experience with remarkable fidelity; and from it Groddeck emerges not only as a great doctor but also as a philosopher whose It-concept is positively ancient Greek in its clarity and depth. "In vain," says Freud somewhere, "does Groddeck protest that he has nothing to do with science." Yes, in vain, for Groddeck's findings are being daily called upon to supplement the mechanical findings of the science which he respected, but of which he refused to consider himself a part. "Health and sickness," he says, "are among the It's forms of expression, always ready for use. Consideration of these two modes of expression reveals the remarkable fact that the It never uses either of them alone, but always both at once: that is to say, no one is altogether ill, there is always some part which remains sound even in the worst illnesses; and no one is altogether well, there is always something wrong, even in the perfectly healthy. Perhaps the best comparison we could give would be a pair of scales. The It toys with the scales, now putting a weight in the right pan, now in the left, but never leaving either pan empty; this game, which is often puzzling but always significant, never purposeless, is what we know as life. If once the It loses its interest in the game, it lets go of life and dies. Death is always voluntary; no one dies except he has desired death. . . . The It is ambivalent, making mysterious but deep-meaning play with will and counter-will, with wish and counter-wish, driving the sick man into a dual relation with his doctor so that he loves him as his best friend and helper, yet sees in him a menace to that artistic effort, his illness."

The illness, then, bears the same relation to the patient as does his handwriting, his ability to write poetry, his ability to make money; creation, whether in a poem or a cancer, was still creation, for Groddeck, and the life of the patient betrayed for him the language of a mysterious force at work under the surface—behind the ideological scaffolding which the ego had run up around itself. Disease, then, had its own language no less than health, and when the question of the cure came up, Groddeck insisted on approaching his patient, not to meddle with his "disease" but to try and interpret what his It might be trying to express through the disease. The cure, as we have seen above, is for Groddeck always a result of having influenced the It, of having taught it a less painful mode of self-expression. The doctor's role is that of a catalyst, and more often than not his successful intervention is an accident. Thus the art of healing for Groddeck was a sort of spiritual athletic for both doctor and patient, the one through self-knowledge learning to cure his It of its maladjustments, the other learning from the discipline of interpretation how to use what Graham Howe has so magnificently called "the will power of desirelessness": in other words, how to free himself from *the desire to cure*. This will seem a paradox only to those—and today they are very many—who have no inkling of what it is like to become aware of states outside the comfortable and habitual drowsings of the ego. We are still the children of Descartes, and it is only here and there you will find a spirit who dares to re-place that inexorable first proposition, with the words: "I am, therefore I can love."

It was this dissatisfaction with the current acceptance of disease as clinical entity that drove Groddeck finally to abandon, wherever possible, recourse to the pharmaco-poeia or the knife; in his little clinic in Baden-Baden he preferred to work with a combination of diet, deep mas-sage, and analysis as his surest allies. On these years of successful practice his reputation as a doctor was founded, while his writings, with their disturbing, disarming, mock-ing note, brought him as many pupils as patients, as many enemies as admirers. The majority of his theories and opinions, together with the It-concept on which his phi-losophy is based, were already worked out before he had read Freud. Yet he gladly and joyfully accepted the Freudian findings in many cases, and never ceased to re-vere Freud; but whereas the work of Jung, Adler, Rank, Stekel might well be considered as modifications and riders to basic Freudian theory, Groddeck's case is unique and exceptional. He stands beside Freud as a philosopher and healer in his own true right.

"With Groddeck," wrote Keyserling after his death, "has gone one of the most remarkable men I have ever met. He is indeed the only man I have known who con-tinually reminded me of Lao-Tzu; his non-action had just the same magical effect. He took the view that the doctor really knows nothing, and of himself can do nothing, that he should therefore interfere as little as possible, for his very presence can invoke to action the patient's own pow-ers of healing. Naturally he could not run his sanatorium at Baden-Baden purely on this technique of non-intervention, so he healed his patients by a combination of psycho-therapy and massage in which the pain he inflicted must have played some part in the cure, for in self-protection they developed the will-to-life, while the searching questions he put in analysis often touched them on the raw! . . . In this way Groddeck cured me in less than a week of a relapsing phlebitis which other doctors had warned me would keep me an invalid for years, if not for the rest of my life."

For the patient, Groddeck sought to interpret, through the vagaries of outward symptom and clinical manifestation, the hidden language of the It. "I do maintain," he writes, "that man creates his own illnesses for a definite purpose, using the outer world merely as an instrument, finding there an inexhaustible supply of material which he can use for this purpose, today a piece of orange peel, tomorrow the spirochete of syphilis, the day after, a draft of cold air, or anything else that will help him pile up his woes. And always to gain pleasure, no matter how unlikely that may seem, for every human being experiences something of pleasure in suffering; every human being has the feeling of guilt and tries to get rid of it by self-punishment." To Groddeck plainly the ego is only a reflexive instrument to be used as a help in interpreting the motive force which lies behind the actions and reactions of the whole man; it is perhaps this which gives his philosophy its bracing life-giving quality. It is a philosophy with a boundless horizon, whereas the current usages of psychoanalysis plainly show it to have been built upon a cosmogony as limited in scope as that which bounded the universe of Kelvin or of Huxley.

If Freud gives us a calculus for the examination of behavior, the philosophy on which it rests is a philosophy of causes; to Groddeck, however, all causes derive from an unknowable principle which animates our lives and actions. So we are saved from the hubris of regarding ourselves as egos and of limiting our view of man to the geography of his reflexes; by regarding the ego as a function we can reorientate ourselves more easily to the strains and stresses of a reality which too often the ego rejects, because it cannot comprehend, or because it fears it. So much, then, for the basic difference between the philosophies of Freud and Groddeck; it will be evident, if I have stated my case clearly, that they complement one another, that they are not antithetical, as some have believed them to be; for Freud supplies much of the actual heavy machinery of analysis, and Groddeck joyfully accepts it. In return Groddeck offers a philosophy of orientation and humility which justifies the technocratic contributions of Freud, and allows us to understand more clearly the problems and penalties not merely of disease, for that does not exist *per se*, but of suffering itself. With Freud we penetrate more deeply into the cognitive process; with Groddeck we learn the mystery of participation with the world of which we are part, and from which our ego has attempted to amputate us.

And what of the It? Groddeck does not claim that there is any such thing. He is most careful to insist that the It is not a thing-in-itself, but merely a way-of-seeing, a convenient rule-of-thumb method for attacking the real under its many and deceptive masks; indeed, in this his philosophy bears a startling resemblance to the Tao-concept of the Chinese. The It is a way, not a thing, not a principle or a conceptual figment. Having accepted so much, Groddeck is prepared to attempt a half-length portrait of it.

"Some moment of beginning must be supposed for this hypothetical It, and for my own purposes I quite arbitrarily suppose it to start with fertilization . . . and I assume that the It comes to an end with the death of the individual—though the precise moment at which we can say an individual is dead is again not so simple a matter as it seems. . . . Now the hypothetical It-unit, whose origin we have placed at fertilization, contains within itself two It-units, a male and a female. . . . It is perhaps necessary here to comment upon the extent of our ignorance concerning the further development of the fertilized ovule. For my purposes it is sufficient to say that after fertilization the egg divides into two separate beings, two cells as science prefers to call them. The two then divide again into four, into eight, into sixteen, and so on, until finally there comes to be what we commonly designate a human being. . . . Now in the fertilized ovule, minute as it is, there must be something or other—the It, we have assumed?—which is able to take charge of this multitudinous dividing into cells, to give them all distinctive forms and functions, to induce them to group themselves as skin, bones, eyes, ears, brain, etc. What becomes of the original It in the moment of division? It must obviously impart its powers to the cells into which it divides, since we know that each of them is able to exist and redivide independently of the other. . . . It must not be forgotten that the brain, and therefore the intellect, is itself created by the It. . . . Long before the brain comes into existence the It of man is already active and 'thinking' without the brain, since it must first construct the brain before it can use it to think with. This is a fundamental point and one we are inclined to ignore or forget. In the assumption that one thinks only with the brain is to be found the origin of a thousand and one absurdities, the origin also of many valuable discoveries and inventions, much that adorns life and much that makes it ugly. . . . Over and against the It there stands the ego, the I, which I take to be merely the tool of the It, but which we are forced by nature to regard as the It's master; whatever we say in theory there remains always for us men the final verdict 'I am I.' . . . We cannot get away from it, and even while I assert the proposition is false I am obliged to act as if it were true. Yet I am, by no means, I, but only a continuously changing form in which my 'It' displays itself, and the 'I' feeling is just one of its ways of deceiving the conscious mind and making it a pliant tool. . . . I go so far as to believe that every single separate cell has this consciousness of individuality, every tissue, every organic system. In other words every It-unit can deceive itself, if it likes, into thinking of itself as an individuality, a person, an I. This is all very confusing but there it is. I believe that the human hand has its I, that it knows what it does, and knows that it knows. And every kidney cell and every nail cell has its consciousness just the same . . . its 'I' consciousness. I cannot prove this, of course, but as a doctor I believe it, for I have seen how the stomach can respond to certain amounts of nourishment, how it makes careful use of its secretion according to the nature and quantity of the material supplied to it, how it uses eye, nose, and mouth in selecting what it will enjoy. This 'I' which I postulate for cells, organs, etc., like the general-I (or the ego-awareness of the whole man) is by no means the same thing as the It, but is produced by the It as a mode of expression on all fours with a man's gestures, speech, voice, thinking, building, etc. . . . About the It itself we can know nothing."

At this point the orthodox objections of the Rationalist deserve to be stated and considered. They are questions which Groddeck himself did not bother to answer, believing as he did that no hypothesis could be made to cover all the known facts of a case without special pleading or sophistry, and being unwilling to strain for interpretations which might appear to cover the whole of reality and yet in truth yield only barren formulae. Groddeck believed that whatever was posited as fact could sooner or later be disproved; hence his caution in presenting the It-hypothesis not as a truth, but as a method. Yet a critic of the proof-of-the-pudding school would have every right to ask questions along the following lines: "That a case of inoperable cancer, say, which defies every other form of treatment, can be made to yield before a Groddeckian attack by massage and analysis, is within the bounds of belief. Even the It-hypothesis might be conceded as a useful working tool in this case. Freud has so far altered the boundaries between the conscious and unconscious intention that we are inclined to respond to suggestions which fifty years ago would have seemed fantastic. But if a thousand people contract typhoid from a consignment of fruit, are we to assume that the individual It of each and every one of them has chosen this form of self-expression in a desire for self-punishment?" It is the sort of question to which you will find no answer in Groddeck's books; yet if he seems content to present the It as a partial hypothesis, it is because his major interest is in its individual manifestation. Yet there is nothing in the hypothesis as such to preclude a wider application. Had he addressed himself to such a question he might very easily have asserted that just as the cell has its It-ego polarity, and the whole individual his, so also could any body or community develop its own. The conventions of the logic that we live by demand that, while we credit the individual with his individuality, we deny such a thing to concepts such as "state," "community," "nation"—concepts which we daily use as thought-counters. Yet when our newspapers speak of a "community decimated by plague" or a "nation convulsed by hysteria" we accept the idea easily enough, though our consciousness rejects these formations as fictions. Yet in time of war a nation is treated as an individuality with certain specified characteristics; politicians "go to the nation"; *The Times* discusses the "Health of the Nation" with the help of relevant statistics. This unity which we consider a fiction—could it not reflect, in its component parts, the shadows of the individual unity, which is, according to Groddeck, no less a fiction? If a national ego, why not a national It? But I am aware that in widening the sphere of application for the It-hypothesis I am perhaps trespassing, for if Groddeck himself remained silent on the score he no doubt had his reasons.

And what of the domain of pure accident or misadventure? A man hurt by a falling wall? The victim of a railway accident? Are we to assume that his It has made him a victim of circumstances? We know next to nothing about predisposition—yet it is a term much used by medical men to cover cases where the link of causality appears obvious, the effect related satisfactorily to the cause; thus the victim of hereditary syphilis satisfies the syntax of our logic, while the victim of a railway accident seems simply the passive object of fate. And yet we do, unconsciously, recognize predisposition in individuals, in our friends, for how often when the news of the accident reaches us, do we exclaim: "But it *would* happen to someone like X"? The truth is that all relations between events and objects in this world partake of the mystery of the unknown, and we are no more justified in covering one set of events with words like "disease" or "illness," than we are in dismissing another with words like "accident" or "coincidence." Groddeck himself was too wily a metaphysician to put himself at the mercy of words. "I should tell you something," he writes, "of the onset of diseases, but the truth is that on this subject I know nothing. And about their cure. . . . Of that, too, I know just nothing at all. I take both of them as given facts. At the utmost I can say something about the treatment, and that I will do now. The aim of the treatment, of all medical treatment, is to gain some influence over the It. . . . Generally speaking, people have been content with the method called 'symptomatic treatment' because it deals with the phenomena of disease, the symptoms. And nobody will assert that they were wrong. But we physicians, because we are forced by our calling to play at being God Almighty, and consequently to entertain overwhelming ideas, long to invent a treatment which will do away not with the symptoms but with the cause of the disease. We want to develop causal therapy, as we call it. In this attempt we look around for a cause, and first theoretically establish . . . that there are apparently two essentially different causes, an inner one, *causa interna,* which the man contributes of himself, and an outer one, *causa externa,* which springs from his environment. And accepting this clear distinction we have thrown ourselves with raging force upon the external causes, such as bacilli, chills, overheating, overdrinking, work, and anything else. . . . Nevertheless in every age there have always been physicians who raised their voices to declare that man himself produced his diseases, that in him are to be found the *causae internae.* . . . There I have my jumping-off point. One cannot treat in any way but causally. For both ideas are the same; no difference exists between them. . . . In truth, I am convinced that in analyzing I do no differently than I did before when I ordered hot baths, gave massage, issued masterful commands, all of which I still do. The new thing is merely the point of attack in the treatment, *the one symptom which appears to me to be there in all circumstances, the 'I.'* . . . My treatment . . . consists of the attempt to make conscious the unconscious complexes of the 'I.' . . . That is certainly something new, but it originated not with me, but with Freud; all that I have done in this matter is to apply the method to organic diseases, because I hold the view that the object of all medical treatment is the It: and I believe the It can be influenced as deeply by psychoanalysis as it can by a surgical operation."

If we have spent much time and space in letting Groddeck, as far as possible in his own words, define and demarcate the territory of the It, the reason should by now be apparent. Not only is the ego-It polarity the foundation stone upon which his philosophy is built, but without an understanding of it we cannot proceed to frame the portrait of this poet-philosopher-doctor with any adequacy; since his views concerning the function and place of the ego in the world are carried right through, not only in his study of health and disease, but also into the realms of art criticism and cosmology, where his contributions are no less original and beautiful. Groddeck, like Rank, began as a poet and writer, only to turn aside in middle life and embrace the role of healer; lack of first-hand acquaintance with Groddeck's poetry, his one novel, and what his translator describes as "an epic," prevents me from saying anything about this side of his activities; but in his one incomplete volume of art criticism, published here [in

England] under the title of *The World of Man*, the reader will be able to follow Groddeck's study of painting in terms of the It-process—for he believed that man creates the world in his own image, that all his inventions and activities, his science, art, behavior, language, and so on, reflect very clearly the nature of his primitive experience, no less than the confusion between the ego and the It which rules his thoughts and actions. Unfortunately his death in 1934 prevented him from carrying out more than the groundwork of his plan, which was to review every department of science and knowledge in terms of this hypothesis; but in the fragments he has left us on art, language, and poetry, the metaphysical basis of his philosophy is carefully illustrated and discussed. The humor, the disarming simplicity and poetry of his writing cannot be commented upon by one who has not read his books in the original German, but it is sufficient to say that enough of Groddeck's personality comes through in translation to make the adventure of reading him well worth while, both for the doctor and for the contemporary artist—for the knowledge and practice of the one supplement the ardors and defeats of the other; and art and science are linked more closely than ever today by the very terms of the basic metaphysical dilemma which they both face. All paths end in metaphysics.

Groddeck was often approached for permission to set up a society in England bearing his name, on the lines of the Freudian and Adlerian Societies; but he always laughed away the suggestion with the words: "Pupils always want their teacher to stay put." He was determined that his work should not settle and rigidify into a barren canon of law: that his writings should not become molehills for industrious systematizers, who might pay only lip service to his theories, respecting the letter of his work at the expense of the spirit. In a way this has been a pity, for it has led to an undeserved neglect—not to mention the downright ignominy of being produced [in England in 1948] with a dust jacket bearing the fatal words: "Issued in sealed glacine wrapper to medical and psychological students only." And this for *The Book of the It*, which should be on every bookshelf!

There has been no space in this study to quote the many clinical case histories with which Groddeck illustrates his thesis as he goes along; I have been forced to extract, as it were, the hard capsules of theory, and offer them up without their riders and illustrations. But it is sufficient to say that no analyst can afford to disregard Groddeck's views about such matters as resistance and transference any more than he can afford to disregard him on questions like the duration of analysis, the relation of analysis to organic disorders, and the uses of massage. If he whole-heartedly accepted many of Freud's views, there were many reservations, many amendments which he did not hesitate to express. For if Freud's is a philosophy of knowledge, Groddeck's is one of acceptance through understanding.

Another fundamental difference deserves to be underlined—a difference which illustrates the temperamental divergence between Freud and Groddeck as clearly as it does the divergence between the two attitudes to medicine which have persisted, often in opposition, from the time of Hippocrates until today. While Groddeck is campaigning whole-heartedly for the philosophy of non-attachment, he refuses to relinquish his heritage as a European in favor of what he considers an Asiatic philosophy. In his view the European is too heavily influenced by the Christian myth to be capable of really comprehending any other; so it is that his interpretation of the religious attitude to life refers us back to Christ, and if he accepts the Oedipus proposition of Freud, he does not hesitate to say that it seems to him a partial explanation. But Groddeck's Christ differs radically from the attenuated portraits which have been so much in favor with the dreary puritan theologians of our age and time. "Christ was not, neither will He be; He is. He is not real. He is true. It is not within my power to put all this into words; indeed I believe it is impossible for anyone to express truth of this sort in words, for it is imagery, symbol, and the symbol cannot be spoken. It lives and *we are lived by it*. One can only use words that are indeterminate and vague—that is why the term It, completely neutral, was so quickly caught up—for any definite description destroys the symbol." And man, by the terms of Groddeck's psychology, lives by the perpetual symbolization of his It, through art, music, disease, language. The process of his growth—his gradual freeing of himself from disease, which is malorientation toward his true nature, can only come about by a prolonged and patient self-study; but the study not of the ego in him so much as of the Prime Mover, the It which manifests itself through a multiplicity of idiosyncrasies, preferences, attitudes, and occupations. It is this thoroughgoing philosophic surrender of Groddeck's to the It which makes his philosophy relevant both to patient, to artist, and to the ordinary man. Thus the symbol of the mother on which he lays such stress in his marvelous essay on childhood fuses into the symbol of the crucifixion, which expresses, in artistic terms, this profound and tragic preoccupation. "The cross, too, is a symbol of unimaginable antiquity . . . and if you ask anyone to tell you what the Christian cross may seem to him to resemble, he will most invariably answer: 'A *figure with outstretched arms.*' Ask why the arms are outstretched and he will say they are ready to embrace. But the cross has no power to embrace, since it is made of wood, nor yet the man who hangs upon it, for he is kept rigid by the nails; moreover he has his back turned to the cross. . . . What may that cross be to which man is nailed, upon which he must die in order to redeem the world? The Romans use the terms *os sacrum* for the bone which is over the spot where the birth pangs start, and in German it is named the cross-bone, *Kreuzbein.* The mother-cross longs to embrace, but cannot, for the arms are inflexible, yet the longing is there and never ceases. . . . Christ hangs upon the cross, the Son of Man, the man as Son. The yearning arms which yet may not embrace are to me the mother's arms. Mother and son are nailed together, but can never draw near to each other. For the mother there is no way of escape from her longing than to become dead wood . . . but the Son, whose words: 'Woman, what have I to do with thee?' gave utterance to the deepest mystery of our human world, dies of his own Will and in full consciousness upon that cross. . . ."

It is in his writings on the nature of art and myths that we can see, most clearly revealed, the kernel of his thought concerning the nature of symbolism and the relation of man to the ideological web he has built about himself; it is here too that one will see how clearly and brilliantly Groddeck interpreted the role of art in society. He is the only psychoanalyst for whom the artist is not an interesting cripple but someone who has, by the surrender of his ego to the flux of the It, become the agent and translator of the extra-causal forces which rule us. That he fully appreciated the terrible ambivalent forces to which the artist is so often a prey is clear; but he also sees that the artist's dilemma is also that of everyman, and that this dilemma is being perpetually restated in art, just as it is being restated in terms of disease or language. We live (perhaps I should paraphrase the verb as Groddeck does), we are lived by a symbolic process, for which our lives provide merely a polished surface on which it may reflect itself. Just as linguistic relations appear as "effective beliefs" in the dreams of Groddeck's patients, so the linguistic relations of symbolism, expressed in art, place before the world a perpetual picture of the penalties, the terror and magnificence of living—or of being lived by this extra-causal reality whose identity we cannot guess. "However learned and critical we may be," writes Groddeck, "something within us persists in seeing a window as an eye, a cave as the mother, a staff as the father." Traced back along the web of affective relations these symbols yield, in art, a calculus of primitive preoccupation, and become part of the language of the It; and the nature of man, seen by the light of them, becomes something more than a barren ego with its dualistic conflicts between black and white. Indeed the story of the Gospels, as reinterpreted in the light of Groddeck's non-attachment, yields a far more fruitful crop of meanings than is possible if we are to judge it by the dualistic terms of the ego, which is to say, of the will. "Only in the form of Irony can the deepest things of life be uttered, for they lie always outside morality; moreover, truth itself is always ambivalent, both sides are true. Whoever wants to understand the Gospel teachings would do well to bear these things in mind." And Groddeck's Christ, interpreted as an Ironist, is perhaps the Christ we are striving to reinterpret to ourselves today. There is no room here for the long-visaged, long-suffering historical Christ of the contemporary interpretation, but a Christ capable of symbolizing and fulfilling his artistic role, his artistic sacrifice, against the backcloth of a history which, while it can never be fully understood, yet carries for us a deliberate and inexorable meaning disguised in its symbolism.

If we have insisted, in the course of this essay, on the presentation of Groddeck as a philosopher, it is because what he has to say has something more than a medical application. In medicine he might be considered simply another heretical Vitalist, for whom the whole is something more than the sum of its parts: certainly he has often been dismissed as a doctor "who applied psychoanalysis to organic disease with remarkable results." While one cannot deny his contributions to psychoanalysis, it would not be fair to limit his researches to this particular domain, although the whole of his working life was spent in the clinic, and although he himself threw off his writings without much concern for their fate. Yet it would also be unjust to represent him as a philosopher with a foot-rule by which he measured every human activity. The common factor in all his work is the attitude and the It-precept, which was sufficiently large as to include all manifestations of human life; it does not delimit, or demarcate, or rigidify the objects upon which it gazes. In other words, he refused the temptations of an artificial morality in his dealings with life, and preferred to accord it full rights as an Unknown from which it might be possible for the individual to extract an equation for ordinary living; in so doing he has a message not only for doctors but for artists as well, for the sick no less than for the sound. And one can interpret him best by accepting his It-concept (under the terms of the true-false ambivalence on which he insisted so much) both as truth and as poetic figment. And since Groddeck preferred to consider himself a European and a Christian, it would be equally unjust to harp on the Eastern religious systems from which the It may seem to derive, or to which it may seem related. ("The power of the eye to see depends entirely on the power of vision inherent in that Light which sees through the eye, but which the eye does not see; which hears through the ear, but which the ear does not hear; which thinks through the mind, but which the mind does not think. It is the unseen Seer, the unheard Hearer, the unthought Thinker. Other than It there is no seer, hearer, thinker." *Shri Khrishna Prem.*)

Groddeck would have smiled and agreed, for the principle of non-attachment is certainly the kernel of his philosophy; but the temper of his mind is far more Greek than Indian. And his method of exposition combines hard sane clinical fact with theory in exactly balanced quantities. One has the feeling in reading him that however fantastic a proposition may seem, it has come out of the workshop and not out of an ideological hothouse.

Four books bearing his name have been published in England. Of these the only one which pretends to completeness is *The Book of the It*;[1] the three other titles are composed of essays and various papers, strung together by his translator. They are *The World of Man*, *The Unknown Self* and *Exploring the Unconscious*. At the time of writing they are all unfortunately out of print. The first and third volumes contain a thorough exposition of his views on the nature of health and disease; *The World of Man* contains the unfinished groundwork of his projected study on the nature of pictorial art. The last volume also contains some general art criticism, but is chiefly remarkable for an essay entitled "Unconscious Factors in Organic Process," which sets out his views on massage, and contains a sort of new anatomy of the body in terms of psychological processes. Despite the fearfully muddled arrangement of these papers, not to mention a translation which confessedly misses half the poetry and style of the original, these books should all be read if we are to get any kind of full picture of Groddeck's mind at work.

Even Groddeck's greatest opponents in Germany could not but admit to his genius, and to the wealth of brilliant medical observations contained in his books; it is to be sincerely hoped that he will soon occupy his true place in the English-speaking world as a thinker of importance and a doctor with something important to say.

For the purposes of this brief essay, however, I have stuck as far as possible to the philosophy behind his practice, and have not entered into a detailed exposition of his medical beliefs and their clinical application; with a writer as lucid and brilliant as Groddeck, one is always in danger of muddying the clear waters of his exposition with top-heavy glozes and turbid commentaries. In his work, theory and fact are so skillfully woven that one is always in danger of damaging the tissue of his thoughts in attempting to take it to pieces. I am content if I have managed to capture the ego-It polarity of his philosophy, and his conception of man as an organic whole. But as with everything in Groddeck, one feels that manner and matter are

[1] The English version of *The Book of the It* has been cut: it is not the full text of the German edition.

so well married in him that any attempt to explain him in different words must read as clumsily as a schoolboy's paraphrase of *Hamlet*. This fear must excuse my ending here with a final quotation.

"Every observation is necessarily one-sided, every opinion a falsification. The act of observing disintegrates a whole into different fields of observation, whilst in order to arrive at an opinion one must first dissect a whole and then disregard certain of its parts. . . . At the present time we are trying to recover the earlier conception of a unit, the body-mind, and make it the foundation of our theory and action. My own opinion is that this assumption is one we all naturally make and never entirely abandon, and, furthermore, that by our heritage of thought, we Europeans are all led to trace a relationship between the *individuum* and the cosmos. . . . We understand man better when we see the whole in each of his parts, and we get nearer to a conception of the universe when we look upon him as part of the whole."

*
* *

THE BOOK OF
THE IT

* *
*

✻ LETTER I ✻

So, my dear, you want me to write to you, and it is to be nothing personal or gossipy. I am not to make fine phrases but to be serious, instructive, and, as far as possible, scientific. That's tiresome! For what has my humble self to do with science? The small amount one needs as a practicing physician I cannot well display to you, or you would see the holes in the gown with which, as qualified physicians, we are officially endowed. Perhaps, however, I shall meet your wishes if I tell you why I became a doctor, and how I was led to reject the claims of science.

I do not remember that as a boy I had any special liking for the profession of medicine, and I am very certain that, neither then nor later, did I bring any humanitarian feeling into it; if, as may well be, I used to deck myself out with such noble sentiments, you must look upon my lying with a lenient eye—the truth is I became a doctor just because my father was one. He had forbidden all my brothers to follow that career, probably because he wanted to convince himself and other people that his financial difficulties were due to a doctor's wretched remuneration, which was certainly not the case, since his praises were sung by young and old alike and he was correspondingly rewarded. But he liked, just as his son does, and indeed every one of us, to look for outside causes when he knew that something was out of harmony within himself. One day he asked me—I don't know why—whether I would not like to be a doctor, and because I looked upon this inquiry as a mark of distinction which set me above my brothers, I said yes. With that my fate was sealed, both as to my choice of a profession and as to the manner in which I have followed it, for from that moment I consciously imitated my father to such a degree that an old friend of his,

3

when she came to know me many years later, broke out with the words: "Just your father over again, only without a spark of his genius!"

On this occasion my father related to me a story which later, when doubts arose as to my medical capacity, kept me fast to my work. Perhaps I had already heard it before, but I know that it made a deep impression upon me while I was in that exalted mood, fancying myself, like Joseph, raised above my brothers. He had watched me, he said, when as a three-year-old I was playing at dolls with my sister, a little older than myself and my constant playfellow. Lina wanted to pile still another garment on the doll and, after a long dispute, I gave in to her with the words: "All right, but you'll see she'll be smothered!" From this he concluded that I had a gift for medicine, and I myself drew the same conclusion from these slender grounds.

I have mentioned this trivial incident to you because it gives me the opportunity to speak of a propensity of mine to fall a prey to anxiety about quite insignificant matters, suddenly, and without apparent cause. As you know, anxiety is the result of a repressed wish; in that moment when I uttered the thought, "The doll will be smothered," the wish must have been in me to kill someone represented by the doll. Who that was I do not know, but one may surmise that it was this very sister; her delicacy secured for her many privileges from my mother which I, as the baby of the family, wanted for myself. There you have the essential quality of the doctor, a propensity to cruelty which has been just so far repressed as to be useful, and which has for its warder the dread of causing pain. It would be worth while to pursue this subtle interplay between cruelty and anxiety in mankind, for it is extremely important in life, but for the purpose of this letter it is sufficient to establish quite clearly the fact that my relation to my sister had a great deal to do with the development and with the taming of my desire to cause pain. Our favorite game was "Mother and Child," in which the child was naughty and was slapped. My sister's delicacy compelled us to do this gently, and the manner in which I have carried on my professional work reflects our childhood's play. Nearly as great as my aversion to the surgeon's bloody trade is my dislike of the assorted poisons of the pharmacopoeia, and so I came to massage and to mental treatment; these

4

are both not less cruel, but they adapt themselves better to any particular man's desire to suffer. Out of the constantly changing demands made by Lina's heart trouble upon my unconscious sensitivity, there grew the preference for dealing with chronic cases, acute illness making me impatient.

That is, roughly, what I can tell you about my choice of a profession. But if you will only reflect a little, all sorts of things will occur to you in connection with my attitude to science, for anyone who from childhood upwards has had his attention directed to one particular invalid will find it difficult to learn how to classify things systematically according to the rubric. And then, too, there is that very important question of imitation. My father was a heretic in medicine; he was his own authority, went his own ways, right or wrong, and showed no respect for science either in word or in deed. I still remember how he scoffed at the hopes that were raised by the discovery of the tubercle and the cholera bacilli, and with what glee he recounted how, against all physiological teaching, he had fed an infant for a whole year on bouillon. The first medical book which he put into my hands—I was at that time still a lad at the Gymnasium—was the empirical teaching of Rademacher, and since in that book the points conflicting with scientific teaching are heavily underlined and plentifully sprinkled with marginal comments, it is no matter for surprise if already from the beginning of my studies I was disposed to doubt.

This disposition to doubt was in yet other ways determined. When I was six years old I lost for a time the exclusive companionship of my sister. She gave her affection to a school friend called Alma, and, what was terribly hard to bear, she taught our little childish sadistic games to this new friend and shut me out from them. On one solitary occasion I managed to overhear the two girls while they were at their favorite occupation of telling stories. Alma was making up a tale about an angry mother who punished her disobedient child by putting it into a privy pit (one must picture for this a primitive country closet). To this day it sticks in my memory that I did not hear the conclusion of that story. The friendship between the two little girls came to an end, and my sister returned to me, but that period of loneliness was enough to inspire me with a deep distaste for the name of Alma.

5

And here I must certainly remind you that a university calls itself Alma Mater. That gave me a strong prejudice against science, all the greater because the term "Alma Mater" was also used of the Gymnasium in which I followed my classical studies, and where I suffered much that I should have to tell you of, if it were my purpose to make you understand the unfolding of my nature. That, however, is not what is in my mind, but only the fact that I attributed all the hatred and the suffering of my school days to science, because it is more convenient to ascribe one's depression to external events than to seek its roots in the depths of the unconscious.

Later, but only after many years, did it become clear to me that the expression "Alma Mater," nursing mother, recalled the earliest and the hardest conflict of my life. My mother had nursed only her eldest child; at that time she was visited with a severe inflammation of the breasts which atrophied the milk glands. My birth must have taken place a day or two earlier than was expected. In any case, the wet nurse who had been engaged for me was not yet in the house, and for three days I was scantily nourished by a woman who came twice a day in order to feed me. That did me no harm, one might think, but who can judge the feelings of a suckling babe? To have to go hungry is not a kind welcome for a newborn infant. Now and then I have got to know people who have had a like experience, and even if I cannot prove that they suffered mental harm thereby, still it seems to me quite probable that they did. And by comparison with them I think I have come off well.

There is, for instance, the case of a woman—I have known her for many a year—for whom her mother conceived a dislike at her birth, and whom she did not nurse, as she had the other children, but left to a nursemaid and the bottle. The baby, however, preferred going hungry to being suckled through a rubber tube, and so grew more and more sickly, until the doctor roused the mother out of her antipathy. From being callous she now became most attentive to her child: a wet nurse was engaged and never an hour passed without the mother's going to look after the baby. The youngster began to flourish and grew up a healthy woman. The mother made a pet of her and up to the time of her death, tried to win her daughter's love, but in that daughter only hatred survives. Her whole

6

life has been a steady chain of enmity whose separate links are forged by revenge. She plagued her mother as long as she lived, deserted her on her deathbed, persecuted, without realizing what she was doing, everyone who reminded her of her mother, and to the end of her life will be a prey to the envy which hunger bred in her. She is childless. People who hate their mothers create no children for themselves, and that is so far true that one may postulate of a childless marriage, without further inquiry, that one of the two partners is a mother hater. Whoever hates his mother, dreads to have a child of his own, for the life of man is ruled by the law, "As thou to me, so I to thee," yet this woman is consumed by the desire to bear a child. Her gait resembles that of a pregnant woman; when she sees a suckling babe her own breasts swell, and if her friends conceive, her abdomen also becomes enlarged. Though used to luxury and society, she went every day for years to help at a lying-in hospital, where she kept the babies clean, washed their swaddling clothes, and attended to the mothers, from whom in uncontrollable desire she would snatch the newborn infants to lay them to her empty breast. Yet she has twice married men of whom she knew in advance that they could beget no children. Her life is made up of hatred, anxiety, envy and the yearning cry of hunger for the unattainable.

There is also a second woman who went hungry for the first few days after her birth. She has never been able to bring herself to the point of confessing a hatred of her mother, who died young, but she is incessantly tormented by the feeling that she murdered her, though she recognizes this as irrational since her mother died during an operation of which the girl knew nothing beforehand. For years she has sat in her room alone, living on her hatred for all mankind, seeing no one, spurning, hating.

To return to my own story: the nurse finally arrived and stayed in our home for three years. Have you ever pondered over the experiences of a baby who is fed by a wet nurse? The matter is somewhat complicated, at least if the child has a loving mother. On the one hand, there is that mother in whose body the baby has lain for nine months, carefree, warm, in undisturbed enjoyment. Should he not love her? And on the other hand, there is that second woman to whose breast he is put every day, whose milk he drinks, whose fresh, warm skin he feels, and whose odor he inhales. Should he not love her? But to which of them shall he hold? The suckling nourished by a nurse is plunged into doubt, and never will he lose that sense of doubt. His capacity for faith is shaken at its foundation, and a choice between two possibilities for him is always more difficult than for other people. And to such a man, whose emotional life has been divided at the start, who is thereby cheated of full emotional experience, what can the phrase Alma Mater mean, but a lie to scoff at? And knowledge will seem to him from the beginning to be useless. Life says to him, "That woman over there who does not nourish thee is thy mother and claims thee as her own; this other gives thee her breast and yet thou art not her child." He is confronted with a problem which knowledge is unable to solve, from which he must flee, away from whose troublesome questioning he can best take refuge in phantasy. But whoever is familiar with the kingdom of phantasy recognizes, at one time or another, that all science is a kind of phantasy, a specialist type, so to speak, with all the advantages and all the defects of specialization.

There are other people who do not feel at home in this realm, and of one such I will now briefly tell you. It was not intended that he should be born, but he managed it in spite of his father and mother. So the wife's milk dried up, and a wet nurse was procured. The little boy grew up among his happier brothers and sisters who had been nursed at their mother's breast, but always remained a little stranger among them, as indeed he remained a stranger to his parents. And without either knowing it or wishing it, he gradually severed the bond between the parents through the pressure of their half-conscious sense of guilt, clear enough to strangers' eyes in their peculiar treatment of their son, so that they fled from one another, and knew each other no more. The son, however, became a doubter, his life was divided, and because he did not dare to indulge in phantasy—since he must be an honorable man and his dreams were those of an outcast adventurer—he began to drink, a fate that greets many a one who has been deprived of love in babyhood. But as in everything else, so also in his lust for drink he was divided. Only now and then, for a few weeks or a few months the feeling came over him that he must drink, and as I have followed up his wanderings to some extent, I know that some reminder of the nurse of his childhood always comes to his mind before he seizes the glass. That makes me sure that he will be cured. And this is another strange thing: he chose as his wife a girl who has for her parents a hatred as great as his own, who is just as foolishly fond of children as he is himself, and who yet fears to bear children as she fears death. And because she gave his racked soul no assurance that a child might not be born who would punish him, he contracted a venereal disease and infected his wife. So much tragedy is hidden in the lives of men!.

My letter draws to a close, but may I carry the story of my nurse a little further? I cannot recall her appearance. I know nothing more than her name, Bertha, the shining one. But I have a clear recollection of the day she went away. As a parting present she gave me a copper three-pfennig piece, a *Dreier*, and I know very well that instead of buying sweets with it, as she wished, I sat me down on the kitchen step of stone and rubbed the coin on it to make it shine. Since that day I have been pursued by the number three. Words like trinity, triangle, triple alliance, convey something disreputable to me, and not merely the words but the ideas attached to them, yes, and the whole complex of ideas built up around them by the capricious brain of a child. For this reason, the Holy Ghost, as the Third Person of the Trinity, was already suspect to me in early childhood; trigonometry was a plague in my school days, and the once highly esteemed *Drei-bundspolitik* I banned from the beginning. Yes, three is a sort of fatal number for me. When I look back over my emotional life I realize that, in every case where my heart was engaged, I broke in as a third upon a friendship already existing between two persons, that I always separated the one who roused my emotion from the other, and that my affection cooled as soon as I had succeeded in doing so. I can even see that in order to revive this dying affection, I have again brought in a third whom I might again drive away. And so in one direction, and that certainly no unimportant one, without intention and even without knowledge, those feelings are repeated in me that are associated with the double relationship to mother and nurse and with the conflict aroused by the parting—a matter worthy of consideration, since it shows, at least, that in the mind of a three-year-old child there are processes at work which, though extremely involved, yet have a certain unity at the source. I saw my nurse once again later on—I may have been eight years old—for a few minutes only. She was a stranger to me and I had a heavy sense of oppression while she was by.

I have two more little stories to give you, not without significance, connected with this word *Dreier*. One day, when my elder brother was beginning to learn Latin, my father asked him at table to give the Latin for "tear." He didn't know it, but for some reason or other I had noticed the word *lacrima* the evening before whilst he was memorizing his vocabulary, and so I answered in his place. As a reward I was given a five-groschen piece. After the meal my two brothers asked me to exchange this for a smoothly polished three-pfennig piece, which I joyfully did. Besides the desire to put the bigger boys in the wrong, some dim emotional memories must have influenced me in this. I will tell you later, if you like, what the word *lacrima* signifies to me.

The second incident raises my spirits whenever I remember it. As a grown-up man, later, I wrote a story for my children in which there appeared a withered, dried-up old maid, a learned person who taught Greek and was much derided. To this offspring of my fancy, flat-chested and bald, I gave the name *Dreier*. Thus did my flight from the first, forgotten pain of separation make out of that maid, so alive and loving, who had fed me and to whom I clung, the image that represents science to me.

What I have written is certainly serious enough, at least for me, but whether it is what you wished to get from our correspondence, the gods alone can say. However that may be, I am still, as ever, your very faithful,

PATRIK TROLL.

✻ LETTER II ✻

Fair lady, you are not pleased; is there too much of the personal in my letter, and you would have me objective? But I thought I had been! Let us see then; what I wrote about was the choice of a profession, certain aversions, and an inner conflict which lasted from childhood onwards. Certainly I spoke of myself, but these experiences are typical, and if you apply them to others there is much that you will learn to understand. One thing above all will become clear to you, that our lives are governed by forces that do not lie open to the day, but must needs be laboriously sought out. I wanted to show by an example, by my own example, that a great deal goes on in us which lies outside our accustomed thought. But perhaps it would be better if I made my purpose quite clear, and then you will be able to decide whether the theme is sufficiently serious. If once I drop into chit-chat or into fine writing, you must tell me; that will help both of us.

I hold the view that man is animated by the Unknown, that there is within him an "Es," an "It," some wondrous force which directs both what he himself does, and what happens to him. The affirmation "I live" is only conditionally correct, it expresses only a small and superficial part of the fundamental principle, "Man is lived by the It." With this Unknown, this It, my letters will be concerned. Are you agreed?

Yet one thing more. Of the It, we know only so much as lies within our consciousness. Beyond that the greater part of its territory is unattainable, but by search and effort we can extend the limits of our consciousness, and press far into the realm of the unconscious, if we can bring ourselves no more to desire knowledge but only to phantasy. Come then, my pretty Dr. Faust, the mantle is spread for the flight. Forth into the Unknown. . . .

Is it not strange that we should know hardly anything of our three first years of life? Now and then a man pro-

11

duces some faint remembrance of a face, a door, a wallpaper or whatnot, which he claims to have seen in his infancy, but never yet have I met anyone who remembered his first steps, or the manner in which he learned to talk, to eat, to see or to hear. Yet these are all vital experiences. I can well imagine that a child in stumbling across a room for the first time receives a deeper impression than his elders would from a visit to Italy. I can well imagine that a child who realizes for the first time that the person with the kind smile over there is his mother, is more completely gripped by his emotion than the husband who leads his bride home. Why do we forget it all?

There is much to say on that, but one point must be made clear before proceeding to the answer. The question is wrongly put. It is not that we forget those three first years, only the remembrance of them is shut out from our consciousness; in the unconscious it goes on living, and continues to be so active that all we do is fed from this unknown treasure-heap of memory: we walk as we then learned to walk, we eat, we speak, we feel just as we did then. There are matters, then, which are cast out of consciousness although they are essential to life, which, just because they are essential to life, are preserved in regions of our being which have been named the unconscious. But why does the conscious mind forget experiences without which mankind could not exist?

May I leave the question open? I shall often have to put it again. But now it is more in my mind to inquire from you, as a woman, why mothers know so little of their children, and why they too forget the substance of those three first years? Perhaps mothers only act as if they had forgotten it? Or perhaps with them also the essential things do not reach consciousness?

You will chide because once more I am making merry over mothers, but how else can I help myself? A yearning is in me: when I am sad my heart cries for my mother, and she is not to be found. Am I then to grumble at God's world? Better to laugh at myself, at this childishness from which we never emerge, for never do we quite grow up; we manage it rarely, and then only on the surface; we merely play at being grown up as a child plays at being big. So soon as we live intensely we become children. For the It, age does not exist, and in the It is our own real life.

Do but look upon someone in his moments of deepest sorrow or of highest joy: his face is like that of a child, his gestures too, his voice is flexible again, his heart leaps as it did in childhood, his eyes glisten or cloud over. Certainly we attempt to hide all this, but it is clearly there, and if we pay attention we observe it, only we fail to notice in other people those signs that tell so much because we do not want to perceive them in ourselves. No one cries any more after he is grown up? But that is only because it is not the custom, because some silly idiot or other sent it out of fashion. I have always joked about Mars shrieking like ten thousand men when he was wounded, and it is only in the eyes of the would-be great that Achilles is dishonored by his tears over the body of Patroclus. We play the hypocrite, that is the whole story, and never once dare to give a genuine laugh. Still, that does not prevent our looking like schoolboys when we are up against something we can't do, from wearing the same anxious expression as we did in childhood, from showing always the same little mannerisms in walking, lying, speaking, which cry to everyone who has eyes to see, "Behold the child!" Watch anyone when he thinks he is alone; at once you see the child come to the surface, sometimes in very comical fashion. He yawns, or, without embarrassment, he scratches his head or his bottom, or he picks his nose, or even—yes, it has got to be said—he lets out wind. The daintiest lady will do so! Or notice people who are absorbed in thought or in some task; look at lovers, at the sick, at the aged. All of them are children now and again.

If we like, we can think of life as a masquerade at which we don a disguise, perhaps many different disguises, at which nevertheless we retain our own proper characters, remaining ourselves amidst the other revelers in spite of our disguise, and from which we depart exactly as we were when we came. Life begins with childhood, and by a thousand devious paths through maturity attains its single goal, once more to be a child, and the one and only difference between people lies in the fact that some grow childish, and some childlike.

This same phenomenon, that there is something within us which puts on at will the appearance of any possible degree of age, you may observe also in children. Old age is familiar on the face of infancy, and is often remarked.

13

But walk about the streets and watch the little girls of three or four years old—it is more obvious in them than in their brothers, for which good reason can be given— they will sometimes look as if they were in truth their own mothers. Indeed all children, not just one here and there who is prematurely entangled by life, no, every boy and every girl has at times this peculiar look of maturity. One little child has the sullen mouth of an embittered woman, the lips of another show the born gossip, in another you can see the old maid, in still another, the coquette. And then how often do we see the mother in a tiny girl! It is not mere imitation, it is the working of the It which at times overbears physical age, makes out of it what it will, just as we put on this or that garment.

Perhaps in part it is because of envy that I make fun of mothers, envy that I am not myself a woman and cannot be a mother. Only do not laugh at that for it is really true, and true not of me alone, but of all men, even of those who seem most manly. Their speech tells us that already, for the most masculine of men feels no hesitation in telling us that he is pregnant with some thought; he refers to the children of his brain, and speaks of the fulfilling of some laborious task as "a difficult birth." And these are not just tricks of speech. You set great store by science. Well, it is an indubitable scientific fact that man is formed by both man and woman, although in thought and argument we ignore this as we do many another simple truth. And so in the being we call a man there lives also a woman, in the woman too a man, and that a man should think of childbearing is nothing strange, but only that this should be so obstinately denied. The denial, however, does not alter the facts.

This mingling of man and woman is sometimes fateful. There are people whose It remains clogged by doubt, who see two sides to everything, who are always at the mercy of their impressions of doubleness in childhood. Such doubters were the foster children I wrote of. All four of them have, in fact, an It which does not know at times whether it is male or female. From your own memories of me you will know that under some conditions my stomach will swell up and then, if I speak to you about it, will suddenly subside. You know, too, that I refer to this as my pregnancy. But you do not know—or have I perhaps already told you? No matter, I will tell the story again. Nearly twenty years ago a wen developed on my neck. At that time I did not know what I do now, or think I do. In any case, I went about the world for ten years with this thickened neck, in the full belief that I must bear it to the grave with me. Then the day came that I learned to know the It and realized—no matter how—that this wen was a phantasied child. You yourself have often wondered how I managed to rid myself of the monstrous thing, without operation, without treatment, without iodine or thyroid. My view is that the wen disappeared because my It learned to understand, and my conscious mind also, that I am just as other men in having a bisexual nature and life, and that it is unnecessary to emphasize this fact by means of a swelling.

That woman who gave voluntary service at the lying-in hospital has times in which her breasts completely shrink; then her male nature asserts itself and drives her irresistibly to change places with her husband in their games of love. The It of the third, the lonely woman, has produced a growth between her thighs which looks like a small male organ, and strange to say she paints it with iodine, in order, as she thinks, to get rid of it, but actually to give the authentic red appearance to the tip. The case of the last of the foster children of whom I told you is similar to mine, his stomach swells in the phantasy of pregnancy. And then he has attacks of liver colic, deliverances you may say, and most important of all, he has trouble with his appendix—as do all men who would like to be castrated, to be made into women, for the woman is formed from a man, so thinks the childish It, by the cutting off of the tail. Three attacks of appendicitis he has had, to my knowledge. In all three could be discovered the wish to be a woman. Or have I only persuaded him to wish to be a woman? It is hard to tell.

I must now tell you of a fifth foster child, a man who is richly gifted, but who, as a being with two mothers, is in all things of divided mind, and seeks to overcome his distracted state by drug taking. It was due to her superstition, his mother says, that she did not nurse him herself; she had lost two boys, and so this third one she would not suckle. He does not know whether he is truly man or woman, his It does not know. In early childhood the woman in him was active, and for long he lay ill with pericarditis, a fancied pregnancy of the heart. Later this

15

side of his nature showed itself again in pleurisy, and in an irresistible compulsion towards homosexuality.

Laugh as you please over my wild fairy tales. I am used to being laughed at, and like to harden myself anew, now and again. May I tell you yet another little story? I heard it from a man now long since dead, slain in the war. With a light heart he leapt to his doom, for he was of the line of heroes. One day, he said, when he was about seventeen years old, he was watching with interest his sister's dog, a poodle, which was masturbating by rubbing against his leg. And then, when the seminal fluid ran out over his leg, he was suddenly seized by the idea that he would now give birth to puppies, and for weeks and months afterwards this idea remained in his mind.

If it would give you pleasure, we could now betake ourselves to fairyland, and speak of the queens who had young puppies put into the cradles in place of their trueborn sons, and from that we could pass on to various reflections on the curious role played by dogs in the secret life of man, reflections which throw a bright light on man's pharisaical abhorrence of perverse feelings and practices. But that perhaps would be a little too intimate, and we may prefer to continue with the subject of male pregnancies. These are quite common.

The most striking sign of pregnancy is the enlarged stomach. What do you think about my idea, expressed before, that an enlarged stomach betokens the appearance of pregnancy even in the case of a man? Indisputably he carries no child in his body. But his It creates the swollen stomach by means of eating, drinking, flatulency or whatnot, because it wishes to be pregnant, and accordingly believes itself to be so. There are symbolic pregnancies and symbolic births, which arise from the unconscious and persist for a longer or a shorter time, but disappear without fail when the unconscious stimuli of this symbolic expression are revealed. This is not an entirely simple matter, but here and there it can be done, particularly in cases of flatulency or of symbolic birth pangs in the body, the sacrum, or the head. Yes, so wonderful is the It that it cares nothing at all for scientific anatomy or physiology, but in lordly fashion repeats the legend of Athene's birth from the head of Zeus. And I am sufficient of a phantasist to believe that this myth, like others, sprang from the workings of the unconscious.

The expression "to be pregnant with thought" must come from the depths of the mind, must have special significance, since it has been embodied in the form of a legend.

Undeniably, such symbolic pregnancies and births occur also in women capable of childbearing, perhaps even more frequently in their case; but they arise all the same in aged women, and seem to play an important part in various forms of disease during and after the climacteric; yes, even children will play with such phantasies of reproduction, and particularly those of whom their mothers take for granted that they believe in the stork which brought the babies.

Shall I vex you yet a little more by venturing further? By telling you that the secondary disturbances of pregnancy, indigestion and toothache, are sometimes rooted in symbolism? That bleeding of every kind, more particularly, of course, untimely bleeding of the womb, but also nose bleeding, and bleeding from the rectum and the lungs, have a close connection with imagined births? Or that the small intestinal worms which plague some people throughout their lives are to be accounted for by the association of worm and child, and disappear as soon as they are deprived of the nourishment provided by the unconscious symbolizing wish?

I know a lady—she too is one of those child-loving women who are yet childless because they hated their mothers—who for five months missed her menstrual periods; her body swelled and her breasts, and she believed herself to be with child. One day I had a long talk with her about the connection of worms with the idea of birth, exemplified in the case of a mutual friend. On that same day she expelled a worm, and during the night she started her period, and her body subsided.

With this I am led to speak of the occasions which give rise to such thoughts of pregnancy. They are to be found in the sphere of association, whence I have already drawn the example worm-child. Most of these associations are widespread, manifold, and, because they are found in childhood, they can only be made conscious after much trouble. But there are also some striking and simple associations which are immediately evident to everyone. A man I know told me that on the night before his wife's accouchement he attempted in a peculair way to transfer to himself this (in his view) tormenting experience. He dreamed, that is to say, that he himself bore the child—a dream in every detail resembling what he had seen happen on the occasion of previous births, and waked up in the moment when the child came into the world to discover that he had produced, if not a child, still something warm with life, which he had never before done since the days of boyhood.

Now that was only a dream, but if you listen to the talk of your men and women friends, you will discover to your astonishment how common it is for husbands, grandmothers, or children, to carry out at the same time in their own bodies the childbirth which is taking place in the family.

Such a strong stimulus is, however, unnecessary. It is often sufficient to catch sight of a little child, of a cradle, of a milk bottle. It is also sufficient to eat certain particular things. You will yourself have known of men whose bodies swelled up after eating cabbage or peas, beans, carrots or gherkins. Some of them suffer from birth pangs in the form of stomach ache, or they may even bring about a birth in the guise of vomiting or diarrhoea. The connections established in the unconscious by the It seem to our highly prized intelligence—so foolish a thinker—undoubtedly absurd. It sees in the head of a cabbage, for instance, a likeness to a child's head, peas and beans lie in their pods like a child in its cradle or in its mother's body, pea soup and pea pudding remind it of the baby's wrappings, and now carrots and gherkins, what do you make of them? You will not fathom it unless I help you.

When children are playing with a dog and watching all his doings with a lively interest, they may notice at times in the place where he keeps his little toilet apparatus, a small red point will appear which looks like a carrot. They call the attention of their mother, or of whoever happens to be by, to this strange appearance, and learn either from her words or from her embarrassed looks, that one does not speak of such things, one does not even notice them. The unconscious then keeps tight hold of this impression, which is more or less definite, and because it has once identified the carrot with the little red point of the dog, it keeps obstinately to the idea that carrots also are taboo, and it responds to that early experience by eating them with dislike, with disgust, or with the accompaniment of symbolic pregnancy. For in that also is the child-

18

ish It peculiarly stupid in comparison with the much praised intelligence, that it thinks the germ of the child enters through the mouth into the body, inside which it then develops; just as children believe that a cherry stone they have swallowed will grow into a cherry tree in the stomach. But that the dog's red point has something to do with the begetting of children, this they know in their unenlightened childish innocence just as well or just as obscurely as that the germ of their baby brother or sister, before it enters into the mother, somehow and somewhere must lie in that remarkable appendage of the man and the boy, which looks like a tail put in the wrong place, of which one must only speak with caution, and with which only mamma is allowed to play.

You see, the way that leads from carrots to phantasies of pregnancy is rather long and difficult to trace. When one knows that, however, one also knows the significance of a distaste for gherkins, for there you have not only that comically fatal resemblance to the father's organ, but also, inside there are the kernels which artfully symbolize the seeds of future children.

I have wandered dangerously far from my subject, but I venture to hope that out of your personal regard for me, my dear, you will give a second reading to letters so involved as this one. Then it will be clear to you what I am trying to say in all my ramblings; the It, that mysterious something which dominates us, is just as careless of the distinction of sex as it is of differences in age. And with that I think I shall at least have given you some idea of the irrationality of its nature. Perhaps you will also realize how it is that I am sometimes so womanish as to want to bear a child. If, however, I haven't succeeded in making myself intelligible, next time I will try to be clearer.

Affectionately yours,
PATRIK TROLL.

✳ LETTER III ✳

So I haven't been clear, after all; my letter was horribly muddled and you wanted everything neatly arranged; above all you would like to have been given instructive, scientific, well established facts in place of ill-founded theories, some of which—the story of the fat people who are said to be pregnant, for example—one might almost call crackbrained!

Well, dearest of friends, if you want to be instructed, let me advise you to consult a textbook, as they do at the universities. But for my letters you shall have herewith the key; everything in them that sounds reasonable, or perhaps only a little strange, is derived from Professor Freud of Vienna and his colleagues; whatever is quite mad, I claim as my own spiritual property.

My view that mothers really understand very little about their children, you think far-fetched. Certainly, you say, the mother's heart can err, probably errs more often than mothers themselves can ever guess, but if there is anything in the world of emotion on which one can rely, it is on mother love, that deepest of all mysteries.

Shall we speak a little on this subject of mother love? I do not claim to be able to reveal its secret, the depth of which I too acknowledge; yet various things may be said about it which usually are left unsaid. We commonly invoke the voice of Nature in this connection, but the voice of Nature often utters very strange language. We need not discuss the phenomenon of abortions, which have been practiced in every age, and which only conscience-racked brains can imagine will ever be banished from the earth; it is enough just to watch for a day a mother's dealings with her child, to see a certain amount of indifference, of weariness, of hatred. As well as her love for her child then, there exists in every mother an aversion for the child. Man lives under the law: Where love is, there is also hate; where respect, there is also contempt;

where admiration, there is also envy. The authority of this law is inviolable, and even mothers are no exceptions.

Did you know of this law? Or that it held good even for mothers? If you recognize mother love, do you also recognize mother hate?

I repeat my question: Whence comes it that mothers know so little of their children? Consciously know, that is, for the unconscious knows this feeling of hate, and whoever is able to interpret the unconscious will forsake the doctrine of the almightiness of love; he sees that hate is just as strong as love, and that between the two there is indifference which is the norm. And full of that astonishment which is the constant fate of anyone who ventures into the depths of the life of the It, he follows up those tracks that branch off here and there from the trodden ways, and lose themselves in the mysterious gloom of the unconscious. Perhaps these tracks, so faint and so often overlooked, will lead on to the explanation of why the mother knows nothing and wishes to know nothing of her hatred for her child, perhaps even why we forget all our first years of life.

But to begin with, my dear, I must tell you in what fashion this aversion, this mother hatred, reveals itself. For out of friendship alone, without further evidence, you will not accept it.

When the happy pair, in a romance composed according to popular rules, after many vicissitudes are at length united, there comes a day when she blushingly nestles her head upon his manly breast, and whispers to him a holy secret. That is very sweet; but in real life, pregnancy announces itself, after being indicated by the absence of the period, in right evil fashion, by stomach troubles and vomiting; not invariably, let me forestall possible objection by admitting—and I should like to hope that in their married lives these authors have just as little experience of the vomiting of pregnancy as in their novels—but you will allow that it is very commonly the case. And the indigestion arises out of the opposition of the It against something which is within the organism; it expresses the wish to remove this unwelcome thing, and vomiting is the attempt to expel it. In this case, therefore, you have the desire for and the attempt at abortion. What have you to say about that?

At some later time, perhaps, I can tell you of my experience with cases of vomiting occurring outside normal pregnancy, and how in those cases also are to be found noteworthy symbolic connections, strange associations made by the It. But here I should like to point out to you that once again in these digestive troubles the idea is revealed that the germ of the child is received into the mouth of the woman, and there you have also the significance of the other sign of pregnancy, which is brought about by the woman's opposition against the child, that is to say, toothache.

In attacking the tooth the It is saying, in the gentle but persistent voice of the unconscious, "Do not chew; be cautious, spit out what you would like to eat." Certainly, in the case of expectant mothers, the poisoning has already been accomplished in the act of intercourse, but perhaps the unconscious hopes to be able to deal with the small dose if only it is not poisoned afresh. Indeed, precisely by the toothache it is already trying to kill the living poison of the conception, for—and here again the It shows that utter lack of logic, which makes it so inferior to the thinking mind—the unconscious confuses child and tooth. For the unconscious, a tooth *is* a child. And now I come to think of it, I find it possible to regard this idea of the unconscious as not at all so stupid; it is no more absurd than was that thought of Newton's, who saw the universe in a falling apple. And for me it is even very much of a question whether this association, child equals tooth, made by the It, was and is not more important, more fraught with scientific consequences, than were Newton's astronomical deductions. The tooth is the child of the mouth, the mouth is the womb in which it grows, just as the foetus grows within the mother's body. You must know how strongly rooted is this symbol in men's minds, for how else could they have arrived at the terms "vulvae" (German: *Schamlippen*) and "os uteri"?

Toothache, then, is the unconscious desire that the germ of the child shall sicken, shall die. What is my evidence? Well, among other things—for there are many clues to such knowledge—this, that vomiting and toothache disappear when one brings the mother to realize her unconscious desire for the child's death. She is then able to understand how poorly these means serve her purpose; indeed often enough she abandons that purpose so strongly condemned by law and custom, once she sees it before her in all its nakedness.

Even the curious tastes and dislikes of expectant mothers arise in part from this hatred against the child. The former may be traced to the unconscious idea of poisoning the germ by means of particular foods; the latter are founded on some association or other which recalls the fact of pregnancy or conception. For so strong at times is her aversion—and this is true of every woman, and detracts nothing from her love for the coming child—that even the mere thought of her condition has to be repressed.

And so one might go on endlessly. Would you like more? I spoke before of abortion, an act disowned by moral folk with all possible contumely—in public. But the deliberate avoidance of conception, scientifically regarded, and in its result, is nevertheless the same, and you need no enlightenment from me as to how frequent that is, nor even any instruction as to how it is done. At most, it is worth calling your attention to the fact that remaining unmarried is also one way of avoiding the hated child, and this may be quite frequently recognized as the motive of a single and a virtuous life. And even when marriage has once been contracted, one can still always try to keep the husband at arm's length. For that purpose it is enough always, in word and deed—or much more, by lack of deed—to emphasize the sacrifice which the wife is making to her husband. There are plenty of men who believe this silly nonsense, and gaze with shy reverence at these superior beings who so angelically tolerate the contamination of their bodies for the sake of the dear children and the dear husband. God's thoughts thereon cannot be understood by these noble people, but He ordains that the child shall be bred in a pool of filth, and one has therefore to submit. But if one is to show the husband how despicable this all is, one must show him also, otherwise he finds out for himself, how many substitutes there are for his love-making, substitutes which no one willingly gives up. And after one has trained a husband so well that he renounces the pleasure of committing onanism in the body of his wedded wife, one can ascribe to him in a thousand ways the blame for every miserable mood, for the joyless childhood of the offspring, and for the unhappiness of the marriage.

23

And further, what purpose is served by disease? Especially diseases of the abdomen? In many ways these are disagreeable. There is first of all the possibility of avoiding childbirth. There is further the satisfaction of hearing from a doctor that one is suffering on the husband's account, through his wild bachelor life, for one can never have enough weapons in married life. Above all—if I become too intimate you must tell me so—above all, there is the possibility of exhibiting oneself to a stranger. One can get the most thrilling sensations on the consulting-room couch, sensations so strong that they entice the It to create many a form of illness.

Quite recently I ran across a little lady of sprightly wit. "Years ago," she said, "you said to me that people go to a woman's doctor because they want to feel the touch of another hand than their husband's, yes, that people even got ill for this purpose. Since then I have never again been examined, never again been ill." To hear something like that is both pleasing and instructive, and because it is instructive I pass it on to you. For the curious thing about it is this, that I uttered this cynical truth, not with the idea of giving this woman professional advice, but in order to provoke her to laughter or to indignation. But her It made of it a means of healing, did something which neither I nor half a dozen other doctors had been able to accomplish. In the face of such facts, what is one to say of the doctor's intent to help? One keeps a shamed silence and thinks after all everything happens for the best.

Everything essential happens, in gynecology, outside consciousness. You may, with the conscious intelligence, select the doctor whom you wish to examine you. You may have an eye to your lingerie, whether it is sufficiently attractive; you may scrupulously cleanse yourself; yet already, by your manner of lying down, do you betray the absence of conscious control and the rule of the unconscious; and still more in the choice of the disease, and in the desire to become ill. That is solely the work of the It, for it is the unknown It, not the conscious intelligence, which is responsible for various diseases. They do not invade us as enemies from the outside, but are purposeful creations of our microcosmos, our It, just as purposeful as the structure of the nose and the eye, which indeed are also products of the It—or do you find it impossible that a being which has produced from spermatozoön and egg

24

a man with a man's brain and a man's heart, can also bring forth cancer or pneumonia, or a dropping of the womb?

I must explain, by the way, that I do not suppose that women invent their abdominal pains out of anger or jealousy. That is not my meaning. But the It, the unconscious, drives them into illness against their conscious will, because the It is greedy, is malicious, and longs to have its rights. Remind me of that at some opportune moment, that I may tell you something about the way in which the It secures its right to pleasure, whether in good or in evil.

No, my view of the power of the unconscious and the powerlessness of the conscious will is so comprehensive that I take even simulated diseases to be an expression of the unconscious, for to me the voluntary imitation of illness is a screen behind which are hidden wide, unsurveyed tracts of life's dark mysteries. From this point of view it is a matter of indifference for a doctor whether he is told lies or the truth, if only he stays quiet and unbiased, noticing what the patient has to tell with his tongue, his gestures and his symptoms, and working on these with might and main, as best he may.

But I am forgetting that I wanted to tell you about the hatred of the mother against her child. And for that I must point out to you another of the curious ways of the unconscious. Remember, it is possible—and it often happens so—that a woman longs with all her heart to have a child, and yet remains unfruitful, not because her husband or she herself is sterile, but because there is a tide in the It which refuses to turn; it is better that you should not bear a child. And this tide flows so mightily that when there is a possibility of conception, when the seed is actually within the vagina, it prevents fertilization. Perhaps it constricts the os uteri, or it manufactures a poison which destroys the spermatozoa, or it kills the egg, or whatever else you like to think. In any case the result is that no pregnancy is brought about, simply because the It will not have it. One might almost say, because the uterus will not have it, so independent are these processes of the lofty thoughts of men. On that too I must find some opportunity to say a word. Briefly, the wife receives no child until the It, by some means or other, possibly through treatment, becomes convinced of the fact that its aversion to pregnancy is some sort of relic of its childish thinking in the earliest years of life. You cannot imagine, my dear, what strange ideas come to light in the course of investigating such cases of denial of motherhood. I know one lady who is haunted by the thought that she will bear a double-headed child, through a mixing of early memories of a circus, and, more pressing, of scruples about troublous thoughts of two men at the same time.

I called this idea unconscious, but that is not altogether true, for these women who yearn to have a child and do every mortal thing to attain the happiness of motherhood, who do not know, and who absolutely refuse to believe it when they are told, that they themselves refuse to bear a child, these women yet have an uneasy conscience—not, indeed, because they are childless and therefore seem to be despised, for today women are no longer despised for being childless—and this uneasy conscience is not relieved by pregnancy. It only disappears when one succeeds in tracking down and purifying the filthy swarm in the recesses of the soul, the poisonous swarm which corrupts the unconscious.

What a toilsome business it is to speak about the It. One plucks a string at hazard, and there comes the response, not of a single note but of many, confusedly mingling and dying away again, or else awakening new echoes, and ever new again, until such an ungoverned medley of sounds is raging that the stammer of speech is lost. Believe me, one cannot speak about the unconscious, one can only stammer, or rather, one can only point out this and that with caution, lest the hell brood of the unconscious world should rush up out of the depths with their wild clangor.

Is it necessary for me to say that what is true of the woman in this matter of childlessness may also be alleged of the man; that on this account he may choose to remain a bachelor, a monk, or a devotee of chastity, or that he may infect himself somewhere with venereal disease in order to beget no children? Or that he renders his semen sterile, or permits no erection, or whatever else may be done? In any case you are not to think that I want to cast all the responsibility on women. If it appears so, that is only because I am a man myself and therefore want to throw my own burden of guilt on the woman; for that also is a peculiarity of the It, that every conceivable form of guilt is weighing on everyone, so that he has to say of

26

the murderer, the thief, the hypocrite, the betrayer: "Such an one art thou thyself."

At the moment, however, I am dealing with the hatred of the woman against the child, and I must hasten if I am not to overburden this letter quite too heavily. Up till now I have been speaking of the prevention of conception, but now give your attention to the following: A lady who desired a child was visited by her husband while she was away, taking the baths. In mingled hope and fear she awaited her next period. It failed to come and on the second day the lady stumbled and fell over a stair, and quivered with the joyful thought, "Now I have got rid of the child again." That woman kept her child, for the desire of her It was stronger than its aversion. But how many thousand times has such a fall destroyed the scarce-fertilized germ? If you only speak of your own acquaintances you will in a few days have a veritable collection of such occurrences, and if you have what is seldom freely given between people, but must first be won, the confidence of your women friends, you will hear: "I was pleased that it so fell out." And if you penetrate deeper, you will discover that there were unanswerable reasons against pregnancy, and that the fall was intended, not by the conscious mind, be it understood, but by the unconscious. And so it is with lifting, with getting a push, with everything. Believe me or not, there has never been a miscarriage that has not been brought about by the It on easily recognizable grounds. In its hatred, if this wins the mastery, the It compels the woman for this purpose to dance, to ride, or to travel, or to go to people who employ the kindly needle or probe or poison, or to fall or get pushed or knocked about, or to fall ill. Yes, some comical cases occur in which the unconscious does not itself understand what it is doing. And so the pious lady who leads a lofty existence far above the level of sex, takes care to have hot foot-baths in order to procure a guiltless abortion. But the hot bath is merely pleasant for the germ, it helps its growth—you see, now and again, the It is laughing at itself.

Now at the end I can scarcely go further than I have already done today in my bad, mad views, but still I will try. Listen: I am convinced that the child gets born through hatred. The mother has had enough of being

27

swollen and carrying a burden of so many pounds, and so she casts the child out, with more than necessary roughness. If this disgust is not present, the child stays inside the body and petrifies: that can happen.

To be just, I must add that the child also does not want to sit in that dark prison any longer, and for his part takes a share in the labor. But that is another story. Here it is sufficient to establish that there must be in mother and child a common desire for separation, for the birth to come about.

Enough for today.

Always your
PATRIK TROLL.

✳ LETTER IV ✳

My dear, you are quite right: I wanted to write of mother love, and what I did write of was mother hate. But love and hate always exist side by side; they are mutually conditional, and since so much has been said about mother love and everyone thinks he knows all about it, I thought it just as well for once to cut the sausage at the other end. Moreover I am not at all sure that you have ever busied yourself with the subject of mother love otherwise than to feel it, and to express or to listen to some fine phrases about it, of lyrical or tragic import.

Mother love is axiomatic, it is implanted from the first in every mother, it is an instinctive and holy emotion of womanhood. That may very well be, but I should be very much astonished if Nature had left herself to this womanly emotion, without any further effort, if indeed she has any use for feelings which we humans describe as holy. If one looks more closely, one may possibly discover some, though not all of the sources of this primitive emotion. They have, it seems, little to do with the oft-quoted instinct of reproduction. Let yourself for once dismiss from your mind everything that has been said about mother

28

love and see for yourself what goes on between these two beings, mother and child.

First there is the moment of conception, the conscious or unconscious remembrance of a blissful instant, for without this truly heavenly feeling no conception would take place. You question that and quote the numerous instances of detested bridals, of violations, of conceptions accomplished during unconsciousness. But all these cases only show that the conscious mind need take no part in this intoxication; of the It, of the unconscious, they tell us nothing at all. If its feelings are to be confirmed you must turn to the bodily organs through which it speaks, to the woman's means of voluptuous expression, and then you will be amazed to find how little these concern themselves with the conscious feeling of aversion. They answer to stimulation, to purposeful excitation, in their own way, quite irrespective of whether the sexual act is, or is not, agreeable to the conscious mind. Ask of women's doctors, of judges, or of criminals; you will find they confirm my statement. You can also hear the same thing from women who have conceived without pleasure, who have been violated or abused when unconscious, only you must know how to put your questions, or better, how to win their confidence. It is only when people are convinced that the questioner has no thought of blame, but is seriously carrying out the commandment, "Judge not," that they will open a little the portals of their souls. Or listen to the dreams of these frigid sacrifices to man's lust: the dream is the speech of the unconscious, which allows something of itself to be read therein. The simplest test, however, is for you to take counsel with yourself, honestly, as your custom is. Will it not yet have happened to you that the man you love is at times unable to have union with you? If he is thinking of you, his manhood rises so powerfully as to give pleasure, yet when he is near you, his highness sinks exhausted. That is a remarkable phenomenon; and it means that the man may be fully potent even under unusual conditions, but that in no circumstances can he receive an erection while in contact with a woman who desires to prevent it. It is one of woman's most secret weapons, a weapon which she uses without hesitation when she wishes to humble a man, or rather, the woman's unconscious makes use of this weapon, as I think, for I would not willingly believe a woman to be capable of consciously perpetrating such villainy, and it seems to me more probable that unconscious processes in the organism of the woman are responsible for the diversion of the fluid which weakens the man. However that may be, it is in any case quite impossible for a man to take possession of a woman if she is not, in some way or other, consenting. In this connection you will be well advised to doubt the wife's frigidity, and to believe rather in her quest for revenge, and her unimaginably malicious intentions.

Have you never had the phantasy of being violated? You immediately say no, but I don't believe you. Perhaps you do not feel the terror experienced by so many women, more especially by those who feign coldness, of being alone in a wood or on a dark night; I said to you before that anxiety betokens a wish; whoever fears violation, desires it. Probably, if I know you aright, you also are not in the habit of searching under the beds and in the wardrobe; but how many women do this! Always with the fear and the wish to discover the man who is strong enough to have no terror of the law. You have heard before now the story of the lady, who, when she saw a man under her bed, broke out with the words, "At last! For twenty years I've been waiting for it." How significant it is, that this man is phantasied with a shining knife, a knife which is to be thrust into the body. Now you are superior to all this, but once upon a time you were younger; go back to that. You will discover a moment—do I say a moment? No, you will remember a whole series of moments when you went cold all over, because you thought you heard a step behind you; when you woke up suddenly in the night in a strange hotel wondering if you had locked the door. When you crept shivering under the bedclothes, shivering because you had to cool your inward heat lest you be scorched? Have you never put up a show of resistance to your husband, playing at a violation? No? Alas, what a little fool you are to deprive yourself of the joys of love, and what a little fool, to think that I believe you! I only believe in your poor memory, and your cowardly wilting before self-knowledge. For that a woman should not desire this highest proof, one might say this unique proof of love, is out of the question. To be so beautiful, so alluring, that the man forgets all else and simply loves, that is what every woman wants, and whoever denies it is in error, or willfully lying. And if I may presume to advise you, try to revive this phantasy within you! It is not good to play by oneself with hidden things? What will you wager? Shut your eyes and dream freely, without prejudice or forethought. In a few seconds you will be held by the fetters of phantasy, so transported that you hardly dare to go on thinking, to go on breathing. You hear the snap of the branches. There is a sudden spring and a clutch on your throat, you are thrown down, your clothes blindly torn, and then your mad terror! Is he tall or short, dark or fair, bearded or smooth-shaven? The wizard's name! Oh, I could see that you already know him! You saw him yesterday, or the day before, or many years ago, in the street, at the station, or hunting on horseback, or at a dance. And the name which flashed into your mind made you tremble, for you never would have believed that it would be just that man who roused your passion! You were indifferent to him? You shunned him? He was loathsome? Yet listen: your It is laughing at you! Now, don't get up, don't bother with your watch or your keys but dream and dream again. Of martyrdom, of disgrace, of the babe in your body, of the court, of meeting the criminal again in the presence of the stern judge, and of the torment of knowing all the time that you wanted him to do the deed for which he is now to pay the penalty. Terrible, inconceivable, but gripping you tight! Or another picture, how the child is born, how you work and stab your fingers with the needle, how the little one plays carelessly at your feet, and you do not know where to get it food—poverty, distress, destitution. And then comes the prince, the noble hero who loves you, whom you love and whom you renounce. Just hark, how the It makes merry over that fine gesture! Or another picture still: how the child grows in your body, and with it your terror, how it is born and you strangle it and throw it into a pond, and how you yourself are haled as a murderess before the threatening judge. Suddenly the scene changes, the scaffolding is erected, the child killer stands upon it, chained to a stake, and the flames lick round her feet. Hark again, the It is whispering the meaning of the stake and the tongues of fire, and is telling you whose feet those are which your deepest being brings to the flames. Is it not your mother? The unconscious is full of mysteries, and in the tracks between

31

flame, and shame, and name, lie sleeping the forces of heaven and hell.

And now for the people in an unconscious condition. If you get an opportunity of doing so, watch an attack of hysterical cramp. It will prove to you how many people by bringing about a loss of consciousness get voluptuous pleasure; certainly it is a stupid thing to do, but then all hypocrisy is stupid. Or go to a surgical clinic and watch a dozen people under chloroform; there you will be able both to see and to hear how much pleasure a man can feel even when he is unconscious. And I say it again, take notice of dreams: the dreams of men are marvelous interpreters of the soul.

To return then, I take it that one of the roots of mother love is to be found in the pleasure of conception. I will pass over, without thereby wishing to minimize their importance, a whole group of feelings connected with that, such for instance as the love for the husband, which is transferred to the child, and the gratification of success —and how strange it seems even to our far-seeing intellect that people should be at all vain about things which, like pregnancy, are controlled entirely by the It, and have as little to do with what we are accustomed to recognize as a noble deed, as have beauty and inherited riches and great gifts. I will not speak of how the admiration and envy of the neighbors encourages the growth of mother love, or how the feeling that she is exclusively responsible for another living being—for in that exclusive responsibility the mother likes to believe when all goes smoothly, though she accepts it unwillingly and only for very shame when things go wrong—how this feeling heightens her love towards the coming child, gives her a consciousness of greater importance which is fostered by herself as well as by others; or how the thought of protecting a helpless baby, of nourishing it with her own blood—a much loved phrase often used against the children later, in which the woman pretends to believe though she feels it to be false—how this thought gives the mother a kind of divinity and imbues her with pious sentiment towards the mother of the Heavenly Child.

I should like rather to direct your attention to something quite simple and apparently without significance, namely, that the feminine body contains a hollow empty space which in the course of pregnancy is filled up by the child. When you realize how disturbing is the sensation of emptiness, and how we are made "another man" by being filled, you will partly guess what, in this respect, pregnancy means to a woman. Partly, not entirely, for in the case of a woman's organism there is more than anything else the feeling of incompleteness which persists from childhood onwards, and which, in greater or less degree at different times lowers her self-respect. At one time or another, always quite early in life, whether through observation or in some other way, the little maiden learns that something is lacking in her which the boy and the man possess. And, apropos, is it not strange that no one knows when and how a child learns to recognize difference of sex, although this discovery might be said to be the most significant experience in man's life? This tiny mite, I say, notices that this portion of the human body is lacking to her, and takes it to be the fault of her own nature. Peculiar trains of thought arise from that, which we can take an opportunity some time of discussing, all of which bear the stamp of shame and of guilt. At first the hope that the defect will be made good as the child grows up in some measure counterbalances the feeling of inferiority, but this hope is unfulfilled, and there remain only the sense of guilt, the origin of which grows more and more obscure, and a vague yearning, both of which gain in emotional force what they lose in clarity. Through long years this constant pain afflicts the hidden life of woman, and then comes the moment of conception, the glory of fulfillment, the disappearance of a void, of consuming envy and of shame. And then hope springs anew, the hope that in her body there is growing a new portion of her being, the child, who will not have this defect, who will be a little boy. No proof is surely needed that the mother wishes to give birth to a boy. If anyone investigates a case where a girl is desired, he will certainly learn some of the secrets of this particular mother, but the general rule that the wife wishes to bring a son into the world will be confirmed. If I tell you nevertheless of a personal experience of my own, I do so because an illustration characteristically comes into my mind, which perhaps will succeed in reducing you to laughter, to that happy, godlike laughter with which we greet a great truth in comic form. One day I asked the childless girls and women of my acquaintance—naturally they were not very many, perhaps from fifteen to twenty in number—whether they would like to have a boy or a girl. They answered, one and all, a boy. But now came the strange thing. I asked further, how old they were imagining this boy to be, and what they pictured him as doing. All except three gave the same answer: he would be two years old, and would be lying on the baby's table, unconcernedly spouting a fountain out into the world. Of the three exceptions, the first gave him as taking his first step, the second as playing with a lamb, while the third said he was three years old, and was standing up, making "wee-wee."

Do you really understand that, my dear lady? There is an opportunity to peer into the depths of the soul, for one short moment in the midst of your laughter to discover what stirs mankind. Do not forget it, I beg. And consider whether there is not a possibility here of making further inquiry.

The conception of the child and its growth in bulk and weight within the mother's body are of importance to woman's mind in yet another way; they link themselves with strongly rooted habits, and, in order to bind the mother to her child, make use of the desires which from the deep-buried levels of the unconscious rule the hearts and destinies of men. You will have observed that a little child who is sitting on the chamber does not immediately release what the grownup—who finds little pleasure in the affair—at first with gentleness but with gradually ever-increasing urgency requires of him. If you are interested in following up this strange inclination to voluntary constipation, from which not seldom arises a lifelong habit, and truly that would be a curious sort of interest, I will bid you remember that in the abdomen, close to the rectum and the bladder, there run delicate and sensitive nerves whose excitation arouses agreeable feelings. Then you will also reflect how often children will fidget about on their chairs while they are at work or at play—perhaps you did it yourself in the days of your innocent childhood—sprawling and rocking up and down, until the significant order is heard from their mother: "Hans, or Liesel, go to the lavatory." Why is that? Is it really that the little one has lost himself in his playing, as mamma, with recollections of her own long-repressed inclinations, calls it, or that he is too absorbed in his school tasks? Ah no, it is the voluptuous pleasure brought about by the delay, a unique form of self-excitation practiced from childhood onwards until it finds complete fulfillment in constipation; only then, unfortunately, the organism no longer responds with the feeling of pleasure, but conscious of the guilt of masturbation it creates headaches or dizziness or body pains, or whatever else may be results of the habit of continuously maintaining pressure upon the genital nerves. Yes, and then you will recall other people who still make a practice of leaving the house before going to the lavatory; when they are out of doors they suddenly have urgent need and go through agonies, not knowing how sweet these are. But, struck by the frequency of this entirely unnecessary procedure, one gradually comes to the conclusion that in this case the unconscious is committing masturbation uncondemned. Now, most noble lady, pregnancy is another example of such guiltless masturbation, not merely guiltless indeed, for there the sin is sanctified; yet all the sanctification of motherhood does not prevent the pregnant womb from stimulating the nerves and producing sensuous pleasure.

You think there can be no pleasure without its conscious realization? That is false! I mean, of course, you can hold this opinion, but you must forgive me if it makes me smile.

And while we are occupied with the forbidden subject of sensuous pleasure, pleasure secret, unknown, never honestly named, may I take the opportunity of pointing out what the movements of the child mean for the mother? This experience too is glorified in romance, made roseate and delicately perfumed. In reality, however, if one removes the halo, the sensation is the same as was felt before, when something moved to and fro inside the body, only it is now devoid of any sense of shame, commended instead of blamed.

Are you not ashamed? you will ask. No, most gracious lady, I am not ashamed; so far am I from being ashamed that I will challenge you with the same question. Is there no shame in you, are you not overcome by sorrow and shame that human nature has so bemired the highest gift of life, the union of man and woman? Only ponder for a moment or two on what this mutual pleasure means to the world, how it has created marriage, the family, the state, how it has been the foundation of homes and of courts, how it has called forth knowledge, art, religion, out of the void; how it has created everything, absolutely everything that you revere, and then dare still to say that it is abominable to compare the act of begetting with the movements of the child within the womb.

But no, you are much too wise to resent my words, so horrifying to virtuous housemaids, once you have had time to reflect, and then you will readily follow me still further to a conclusion even more outrageous to sensitive and cultured minds, that more than anything else is the delivery itself an act of the very highest pleasure, the memory of which lives on as love for the child, as mother love.

Or does your willingness not extend so far as to credit me in that? It is contrary to all experience of all time? No, there is one experience which it does not contradict, and that I believe to be the fundamental fact from which one must proceed, the experience, namely, that new children are always and forever being born, that the sorrow and pain are outweighed by the pleasure, at least by some feeling of pleasure.

Have you ever yet watched a delivery? It is a remarkable thing. The mother groans and cries, but her face glows with feverish excitement, and her eyes have that wonderful light which no man ever forgets if he has once brought it into a woman's eyes. Here are the strange eyes, the strangely veiled eyes, which speak of bliss! And what is there wonderful, incredible, in the fact that pain can be the highest pleasure? It is only those who sneer at perversion and unnatural feeling, who do not know, or make out that they do not know, that great pleasure longs after pain. Shake yourself free of the impression you have gathered from the cries of the mother, or the stupid stories of envious old women, and try to be honest. The hen also cackles when she has laid an egg, but the cock shows no more concern about that than to pay his addresses anew to his little wife, whose dread of the pain of egg-laying reveals itself so strangely in that delightful dip before the lord of the fowl yard.

Woman's vagina is an insatiable Moloch. Where is to be found the vagina which would be content with a penis the size of a little finger when it could have one as big as a child's arm. The phantasy of woman is constantly preoccupied with the all-powerful penis. The larger the penis the greater the delight; however, the child works with his thick head during the birth through the passage of the vagina, the seat of feminine pleasure, in the same way that the man's penis works—here and there, up and down just as rhythmically hard and forceful. Certainly it is painful, this highest and therefore unforgettable repetition of coitus, but it is the peak of woman's joy.

But if giving birth is really a sensuous pleasure, why then have the pains of birth been misrepresented as never-to-be-forgotten woe? I cannot answer that question; you must ask it of women. I can only tell you that now and again I have met a mother who has said to me, "The birth of my child, in spite of all the pain, or rather because of it, was the most beautiful experience I have ever had." Perhaps one might say just one thing, that woman, being always forced to dissimulate, can never be quite sincere about her feelings, because it is her destiny through life to have to abominate sin. But how people came to connect sex-pleasure with sin will never be fully explained.

There are other lines of thought which might lead us through the maze of these difficult problems. Thus, it seems to me natural that anyone who has been taught all her life, even in the exercise of her religion, that birth-giving is horrible, painful and dangerous, believes it herself even against her own experience. It is clear to me that many of these alarming stories were invented in order to scare unmarried girls from unconsecrated sexuality. The envy of those who have not given birth, even more, the mother's envy of her own daughter, who now receives what she herself lost long ago, must also be reckoned with. The wish to frighten the husband, who must be made to realize what pain he gives to his dearest, what a sacrifice she is making for him, what a heroine she is, and the experience that he in fact allows himself to be so intimidated, and for the time being, at least, changes from a grumbling tyrant into a grateful father, these all urge in the same direction. And above all, that inner drive to see herself as the great and noble mother, forces her to exaggerate, to lie. And lying is a sin. Finally there rises from the gloom of the unconscious the mother imago; for every desire and every pleasure is drenched with the yearning to come once again into the mother's body, is fostered and poisoned by the desire for union with the mother. Incest,

37

blood, shame. Are they not enough to make one feel sinful?

But how do these mysterious motives concern us just now? I wanted to convince you that Nature did not trust herself to the noble feelings of the mother, that she does not believe that every woman, just because she is a mother, will become that self-sacrificing, beloved being whose like we shall never know again, who can never be restored to us, and whom it makes us happy even to name. I wanted to convince you that Nature does anything and everything to deprive the mother of all excuse for turning away from her child.

Have I been successful? That would indeed make me happy.

Your old friend,
PATRIK TROLL.

❋ LETTER V ❋

Then I did not deceive myself, my dear, when I thought that little by little you would get interested in the unconscious. You gibe at my weakness for exaggeration; that I am used to, but why do you specially take exception to my "labor-pleasures"? For there at least I am right!

You said recently that you approved of the little stories which I threw in here and there. "They give life to the argument," you said, "and one is almost tempted to believe you when you bring forward sheer fact." Now, you know, I might very well invent these, or at least embroider them; that is done in learned circles as well as outside. Good, you shall have your story.

Some years ago, after long waiting, a woman gave birth to a little girl. The birth was a breech presentation; the mother went to a nursing home and was skillfully delivered by a well-known *accoucheur*, with the help of two assistant physicians and two nurses. Two years later, she was again expecting a child, and since in the meantime

I had gained more influence with her, it was agreed that nothing should be done in connection with this birth without my knowledge. Unlike the first, this pregnancy ran its normal course without any difficulty. It was decided that the birth should take place at home, and that only one nurse should be called in. Shortly before the time, at the nurse's wish, I was summoned to the lady, who was living in a different town. "The child is lying in breech presentation, and what is now to be done?" When I arrived the child was in fact in that position; the labor pains had not yet started. The mother was extremely nervous, and wanted to be taken to a hospital. I set myself to inquire into her repressed complexes, of which I already knew a fair amount, and finally painted for her in glowing colors—I think you may judge if I was at all successful—the pleasure of giving birth. Frau X. was satisfied, and a peculiar look in her eyes showed that the spark was burning. Then I tried to find out why the child should have again come into this position. "The birth is easier so," she told me, "the little bottom is soft and stretches the channel more gently and accommodatingly than the hard, thick head." Then I told her, very much in the manner I recently wrote to you, about the thick and thin, the hard and flabby instrument in the vagina. That made an impression but still some little dissatisfaction remained. Finally she said that she would very much like to believe me, but that all the others had told her such dreadful things about the pains of labor, that she would still prefer to be under an anaesthetic; and if the child were in breech presentation she would receive an anaesthetic, that she knew from experience. So this was another reason for preferring that position. On that, I told her that if she were truly so silly as to want to miss the very highest pleasure of her life, there was nothing to stop her. I should have nothing against it if she arranged to have an anaesthetic when she could hold out no longer. For that, however, it was not necessary to have the wrong presentation. "You have my permission to have an anaesthetic even if the head shows first. You are to decide about it yourself, whether you shall have the anaesthetic or not." With that I left her, and on the very next day received news that half an hour after my departure, the child was lying with the head underneath. The birth then went forward smoothly. The mother sent me a pretty account of the event in a letter. "You are absolutely right, Herr Doktor, it really was a great pleasure. Since the ether bottle stood near me on the table and I had your permission to be given an anaesthetic, I hadn't the slightest anxiety, and could watch everything that happened and get its full value without worry. At one moment the pain which till then had been delightfully exciting, became too great and I shrieked, 'Ether!' but immediately got the reply, 'There is no longer any need; the child already cries.' If I have anything to regret, it is that my husband, whom I have for a year been tormenting with my stupid anxiety, can never experience the same wonderful delight."

If you are skeptical, it is open to you to say that this was a lucky suggestion of mine, and proves nothing. That seems to me immaterial. I am convinced that when you have another child, you also will be able to watch "without any worry," you will give up your preconceived idea, and you will learn something from which, up till now, stupidity has scared you away.

You show some cowardice, my dear, in the way you have taken up that never-to-be-mentioned topic of masturbation; you declare how much you despise secret lust, you give expression to your displeasure at my horrifying theory of the guiltless masturbation of a child sitting on the chamber, of constipated people, and of expectant mothers, and finally you think my views about the springs of mother love are cynical. "In this fashion one can carry everything back to masturbation," say you. Certainly, and you are not far wrong in supposing that, if not everything, at least I derive a very great deal from masturbation. The way in which I have been led to adopt this view is perhaps more interesting than the view itself, and so I will tell you something about it here.

I have often had the opportunity, both as a doctor and in other capacities, of being present when little children are given a bath, and from your own experience you will be able to confirm my statement that this proceeding is not always carried through without some howling. But probably you do not know—such trifling details in the behavior of little children are not worth the trouble of observing—that this howling starts at a particular stage in the ceremony and ceases at another. The child who was still shrieking while his face was being washed—if you want to know why he shrieks, get someone you are fond of to wash your own face with a cloth or a sponge, so big that it covers up at the same time mouth, nose and eyes—this child, I say, suddenly becomes quiet if the soft sponge is passed to and fro between his little legs. Yes, he even gets an almost ecstatic look on his face and stays absolutely quiet. And the mother, who shortly before was obliged to help the baby over this unpleasant business of washing by encouraging or consoling it, now at once has a tender, I might almost say an amorous tone in her voice; she too for the moment is lost in ecstasy, and her movements are different, more caressing. She does not know that she is giving the child sexual pleasure, that she is teaching it masturbation, but her It feels it and knows it. The erotic action brings forth that blissful expression in mother and child.

This is how it happens then. The mother herself gives the child instruction in masturbation, is obliged to do so, since nature has piled up the dirt which must be washed away just in the place where the organs of sensual pleasure are to be found. She is obliged to do so, and cannot do otherwise. And believe me, much that goes on in the name of cleanliness, the zealous use of the bidet, the cleansing after defecation, the douche, is nothing more than a repetition, directed by the unconscious, of this pleasurable lesson from the mother.

This trifling matter of observation, the accuracy of which you can verify whenever you like, at once disposes altogether of that dreadful bogey which men have made of masturbation. For how should one describe as a lust a habit which has been imposed by the mother? In teaching which, Nature has made use of the mother's hand? Or how may it be possible to cleanse a child without exciting pleasure? Is a necessity under which every man labors from his first breath, unnatural? By what justification is the term "secret lust" applied to a practice whose prototype is imprinted openly, without embarrassment, by the mother, several times a day, upon the child? And how can anyone dare to call masturbation shameful, when it is obvious and unavoidable in the life of mankind? Just as well could one call walking lustful, or eating unnatural, or hold that the man who blows his nose must inevitably die therefrom. That unavoidable "must" with which life compels man to masturbation, since it places the dirt

41

and the smell of urine and faeces in the region of sexual pleasure, proves that the Divine Purpose has, for definite ends, given this despised act of so-called lust to man as a part of his destiny. And if you would like me to do so, when opportunity offers, I will describe some of those ends to you, and show you that, in large measure, our human world, our culture, was certainly founded upon masturbation.

How has it then come about, you will ask, that this natural and necessary business has got the reputation of being an abominable vice, dangerous alike to body and to mind, a reputation that clings to it everywhere? You would do better to turn to more learned people for an answer, but something I can tell you. Firstly, it is not true that people are *universally* convinced of the sinfulness of masturbation. Of my own experience I have no acquaintance with exotic customs, but what I have read from time to time has given me the contrary opinion. And then it has sometimes happened on my walks that I have seen a peasant standing behind his plough, indulging himself in solitude and without shame; this also one can see with country wenches, if one has not been made blind and kept blind by the prohibition enforced in childhood. Under certain conditions such a prohibition operates for years, perhaps for a whole lifetime, and it is sometimes amusing to note everything that men miss seeing because mama forbade it. But you need not go first to peasants: your own memories will tell you enough. Or does masturbation lose its shamefulness because it is the beloved, the husband, who plays in those charming places? It is quite unnecessary to consider the thousand possibilities of hidden guiltless masturbation, of riding, swinging, dancing, retaining the stools; caresses whose deepest intention is masturbation, are also fairly common!

That is not masturbation, you say. Perhaps, perhaps not; it depends on how one looks at it. According to my view, it makes no great difference whether one's own hand or another's is tender, indeed, in the last resort no hand at all is needed; the thought itself suffices, and above all, the dream. There you have it again, this unwelcome revealer of hidden secrets. No, my dear, if you knew all that we physicians accounted as masturbation, you really would not speak of its shamefulness any more.

And have you ever yet known anyone who was injured

by it? By masturbation itself, not by anxiety as to the results, for that truly is harmful? And just because it is so harmful, a few people at least should try to free themselves from it. And how do you yourself think that the damage is done? Is it through the loss of a small amount of semen in the case of the man, or of the secretion with the woman? That you do not yourself believe, at least you would believe it no longer, if you opened one of the textbooks of physiology used in the universities and read it carefully. Nature has seen to it that the supply is rich, inexhaustible—and, besides, misusage is in its very nature impossible; with the man or the boy, a period of recovery is enforced by the cessation of erection and ejaculation; with the woman, there is also a lassitude which lasts several hours or days. It is with sex-appetite as with eating. Just as no one bursts his stomach by eating too much, so no one exhausts his potency by masturbation. By masturbation, be it understood: I am not speaking of masturbation-anxiety, which is something different, which undermines health; it is for that reason I want to make clear what criminals these people are, who talk of "secret vice," and drive men into anxiety. Since everyone, consciously or unconsciously, commits masturbation and feels even the unconscious pleasure as such, this is a crime against the whole human race, a gigantic crime. And an idiotic one too, just as much so as if one were to say there was something injurious to health in walking upright.

No, it is not the material loss, you say. Yes, but many people believe that it is, even now believe the secretion comes from the spine, that the spinal marrow is dried up by this famous "self-abuse," and that finally the brain dries up too, and so people become feeble-minded.

Even the adoption of the term onanism shows that it is the thought of the loss of semen that terrifies men. Do you know the story of Onan? Curiously enough it has nothing whatever to do with masturbation. Among the Jews there was a decree that a brother-in-law, if his brother died without issue, should have intercourse with the widow, and that the child so conceived should be the dead man's successor. Not altogether a stupid law, since it made for the maintenance of tradition and for the continuance of the family, even if the method by which it operated seems a little curious to us moderns. Our forefathers had a similar idea, and up to shortly before the Reformation, a like

43

decree held good in Verden. Well, then, Onan came into this situation through the death of his brother, but as he could not bear his sister-in-law he contrived that the seed should fall to the ground instead of impregnating her, and for this disobedience to the law he was struck dead by Jehovah. The unconscious of the masses has taken out of this story only the spilling of the seed upon the ground, and branded every similar act with the name of onanism, where the idea of death from masturbation found decisive confirmation.

Good, you do not believe that. But the phantasies of the sensual imagination, those are the essential evil things? Alas, dearest lady, have you then no sensual fancies whilst you are embraced? And not earlier, either? Perhaps you drive them away, you "repress" them, to use the technical expression; I shall be speaking of that idea of repression presently. But the phantasies are there still; they come, and must come, because you are a human being and cannot just get rid of the middle part of your body. There come to my mind those people who think they never have had voluptuous thoughts; they are always the sort who carry cleanliness so far that they not merely wash, but give themselves a rectal douche every day. Harmless little folk, are they not? They never remember that above the small portion of the bowel which they are able to cleanse, there are yards more of it, just as dirty. And to get to the point at once, they use their clysters unwittingly as an action symbolic of intercourse; the cult of cleanliness is but the screen by means of which the unconscious deceives the intellect, the lie which makes it possible to be nominally obedient to the mother's bidding. It is always thus when erotic phantasies are repressed. Pursue your inquiries, and the erotic is revealed in every shape and form.

Have you ever seen a gentle, ethereal, perfectly innocent girl become mentally deranged? No? That is a pity! For the rest of your life you would be cured of your belief in what people call "clean," and for this cleanliness and innocence you would find the honorable word, hypocrisy. Therein lies no reproach. The It has need of even hypocrisy for its own purposes, and indeed in this despised and yet so common practice its purpose is not far to seek.

Perhaps we shall come nearer to the reason why masturbation is condemned by parents, teachers, and other people whose position gives them authority, if we examine the history of this condemnation. I am not very well versed in that, but it would appear to have been towards the end of the 18th century that the cry against masturbation was first loosed. In the correspondence between Lavater and Goethe both of them speak of spiritual masturbation just as carelessly as they would talk about going for a walk. Now this was also the time when people began to develop an interest in madmen, and the mentally damaged, particularly imbeciles, are strongly addicted to onanism. It is quite conceivable that cause and effect were interchanged, and people believed that because the idiot masturbated, he therefore became an idiot through this act.

But in the last resort we must seek elsewhere yet another ground for this remarkable condemnation by mankind of something to which they have been guided by the mother from their earliest days of infancy. May I postpone the answer? I have already so much more left to say, and besides, this letter is quite long enough. But in all brevity I should like to call attention to a strange distortion of the facts of which even men otherwise sensible are found guilty. They call masturbation a substitute for the normal sexual act. Ah, what might not be written about that word "normal" sexual act! But here I am dealing only with the idea of "substitute." How may these people have arrived at such a stupidity? In one form or another onanism accompanies man throughout his life, while normal sex activity only begins at a particular age, and often ceases at a time when onanism takes on again the childish form of a conscious playing with the sexual organs. How can the one process be regarded as a substitute for another which only starts fifteen to twenty years later? It would be more profitable for once to make sure how often the normal sexual act is nothing but a conscious act of masturbation, the vagina or the penis of the partner merely replacing the hand or finger as the instrument of stimulation. On that subject I have been led to remarkable conclusions, and I do not doubt that the same will occur to you if you go into the matter.

Well, and mother love, what has it to do with all this? Something at any rate. I was saying a little while back that the mother is strangely altered while she is washing the child's sexual parts. She is herself not aware of that,

45

but it is just this common, mutual enjoyment which is the strongest of ties, and in giving any form of pleasure to a child the love of the adult is awakened. Even more truly than with lovers is it with mother and child more blessed sometimes to give than to receive.

I have still one other point to make about the influence of masturbation, and you will shake your head when I raise it. However, I cannot spare you, for it is important and gives you once again an opportunity to peer into the recesses of the unconscious. The It, the unconscious, thinks in symbols, and among others it has a symbol by which child and sex-part are identified, are used interchangeably. The clitoris is for the It the little thing, the girl, baby daughter or sister, little friend, while the penis is the boy-baby, the little brother or son. That sounds impossibly strange, but so it is. And now I must ask you once and for all to recognize clearly, without false shame or stupid prudery, what a high regard everyone has for his sex organ, and must have, because in the last resort he derives from it all pleasure and all life. And this regard which you cannot estimate too highly is transferred by the It to the child, for transference is also one of its properties; it exchanges, so to speak, sex organ and child. A goodly portion of mother love springs from the mother's love for her own organ, and from memories of masturbation.

Was that so very dreadful? I have for today only one little thing left to say, which will serve, perhaps, to explain partly why women are generally more fond of children than men. Do you remember what I said to you about the stimulation of the sexual parts in washing, and how I brought the pleasure arising therefrom into unconscious symbolization? Can you imagine that this stimulation during washing gives as much pleasure to the little boy as it does to the little girl? I cannot.

Ever your most obedient
PATRIK TROLL.

✳ LETTER VI ✳

It is your finding, O judge beloved but stern, that my letters betray overmuch the joy I feel in uttering my little erotic trifles. This is a just criticism. But I can do nothing to change it. I do rejoice, and I cannot hide that joy, or I should burst!

If you have shut yourself up for a long time in a stuffy, badly lighted room from sheer anxiety lest the people outside should scold or gibe at you, and if you then come out into the fresh air and see that no one bothers about you, or at most that someone looks at you for a moment and then goes quietly on, why, then you are nigh crazy with joy.

You know I was the youngest of my family, but you cannot guess what an amount of teasing and banter went on at home. It was enough to say just one stupid thing to have it served up every mealtime for days to come, and naturally, in a family fairly widely separated in age, the youngest would perpetrate stupidities most often. And so it came about that I early learned to keep my thoughts to myself; I repressed them.

Please take that expression literally. What is repressed does not vanish, it only loses its place. It is pushed into some corner or other where it has no right to be, where it is squeezed and hurt. Then it always stands on tiptoe, pressing from time to time with all its strength towards where it belongs, and as soon as it sees a gap in the wall in front of it, it tries to squeeze itself through. Perhaps it may succeed in so doing, but when it has got to the front it has used up all its strength, and the next good push from some masterful force hurls it back again. It is a most disagreeable situation, and when anything so repressed, crushed and battered, at length wins freedom you can imagine what leaps and bounds it will be taking. Only have patience! A few more letters in which to let itself go, and then this intoxicated being will settle down and behave as sedately as some properly constituted treatise by a psychological expert. Except, indeed, that its clothes are all soiled by the struggle, torn and crumpled, that the naked skin shows through everywhere and is not always clean, and that a peculiar smell clings round it of the crowds it has been squeezed among. Yet in that struggle it has learnt something which it can now pass on.

Before I let it speak, however, I should like to explain briefly the meaning of a couple of terms which I shall be using now and again. Don't be afraid, I have no wish to give you definitions; indeed, for my crushed spirit that would be impossible. But I will try to do the same with the words "symbol" and "association" as I have previously done with "repression."

I said to you sometime since that it was difficult to speak about the It. When used in that connection, all ideas and words seem to grow wavering, because the very nature of the subject implicates a number of symbols in every word and in every deed, and attaches to them ideas taken from quite different territories, "associates" them, so that something which may seem absolutely simple to the intellect is for the It extremely complicated. For the It there exist no watertight ideas, it deals with whole structures of ideas, with complexes, which are formed under the influence of symbolization and association.

Not to make you shy away from all this, I will show you by an example what I understand by the influence of symbolization and association. As a symbol of marriage you have the ring. Very few people have any clear idea why the wedding ring should stand for the idea of conjugal association. Alternative suggestions that the ring is a fetter, or that it signifies everlasting love without beginning or end, certainly allow of interpretations favorable to the mood or to the experience of the person using them, but they do not clear up the mystery, why a ring should be chosen through some unknown influence to denote marriage. If, however, one starts from the idea that marriage means sexual fidelity, then the symbol is easily read. The ring signifies the woman's sex organ, while the finger is that of the man. The ring is never to be put on any finger other than that of the plighted husband, and so this is equivalent to the vow that the "ring" of the wife shall never receive any member other than that of the bridegroom.

This parallel between ring and female, finger and male organ, is no casual invention, but is imposed by the It, and anyone can prove this at any time both for himself and for others if he watches how people play with a ring on the finger. Under the influence of certain emotions, easy to guess but as a rule not fully conscious, this game begins; up and down the ring is pulled, now twisted, now turned. The course of the conversation, the hearing or the utterance of particular words, a glance at a picture, at people or at objects, any and every possible sense impression may give rise to activities which at the same time expose to us the secret story of the soul, and also prove beyond doubt that the man does not know what he is doing, that something unknown compels him to reveal himself in symbols, and this symbolism does not arise from conscious thought, but from the unrecognized activity of the It. For who, consciously, under the eyes of another, would perform movements which betray sexual excitation, or which open to public view the secret, ever-hidden act of masturbation? And yet even those to whom the meaning of the symbol is clear go on playing with the ring; they cannot help but do it. Symbols are not invented, they are there, and belong to the inalienable estate of man; indeed, one might say that all conscious thought and action are the unavoidable consequence of unconscious symbolization, that mankind is animated by the symbol.

Just as the destiny of mankind is inevitably directed by the symbol, so also is it impelled by the force of association, which is fundamentally the same thing, inasmuch as it is always by association that the symbols are linked together. In the ring game referred to just now it is already clear that the unconscious symbolization of man and wife in ring and finger produces a striking representation of the conjugal act. If one follows up, in a single instance, those dim paths which lead from the half-conscious sense impression to the pulling up and down of the ring, one finds that certain ideas shoot like lightning through the mind, and these same ideas will be found in other people under other conditions. The associations follow a determined course. Even the symbolic bestowal of the ring as a sign of marriage has arisen from unconscious, predetermined associations. Intimate relations of the ring game with primitive religions, customs and ceremonies, as well as with complexes of importance to the individual, occur to one's mind, forcing one to abandon the illusion of the self-determined purpose, and to seek out the complicated and mysterious paths of association. Very quickly does one then realize that the apprehension of the ring as a fetter or as an eternal bond may be explained as the result of ill humor or of romantic excitement, which takes and is forced to take its expressions from man's common stock of symbols and associations.

We meet such examples of predetermined association everywhere, at every turn. One only needs to keep one's eyes and ears open. Rummage about in language a little; you have there love and lust, weal and woe. There, too, are fair and false, the cradle and the grave, life and death, here and there, up and down, laughing and crying, terror and torment, sun and moon, heaven and hell. The examples tumble over each other, and if you give your thoughts to it, it will seem as if a great temple of language suddenly rose up before your mind, as if pillars, façades, roofs, towers, doors, walls and windows formed themselves before your eyes, out of the mist. Your innermost being is shaken, the incomprehensible draws closer to you and almost overwhelms you.

Come away quickly, dear one, come! We may not linger. But keep just a few things in mind: How the force of association sometimes uses rhyme or rhythm, or emotional ties. How every language gives the despised sound "P" at the beginning of the word for the "begetter," while the "birth-giver" has the approved sound "M." And how this force works with contraries, a significant fact, since everything contains its opposite within itself, and that no one at any time must forget or he will really come to believe in the actual existence of eternal love, inviolable fidelity, unshakable esteem. Even associations will lie at times like these. But one cannot understand life if one does not know that phenomena are conditioned by their opposites.

It is not easy to find associations which are valid everywhere and in all circumstances, since life is varied, and the individual person and his immediate situation play a part in determining associations. It is, however, pretty sure that the perception of a draft, so soon as it becomes unpleasant, arouses the idea of shutting the window, while a stuffy room makes everyone want to open it, and that the sight of a loaf and a pat of butter makes one think of slices of bread-and-butter. And whoever sees someone else drinking, finds the thought slipping into his head, "Shouldn't I be drinking, too?" And now just stop a moment and try to realize what a tremendous part of human life, of human culture and development, is accounted for by the fact that on some ground or other, bridges of association were thrown, a hundred thousand times over, from the idea of urinating to that of the sea, until at last sea-voyaging was brought about, until the mast stood up in the boat as a symbol of male potency, while the oars moved rhythmically in love's exercise. Or seek out the path which leads from the bird to aviation, a path which proceeds from erection, the raising of a heavy weight, to the swaying sensation of highest excitement, to the stream of urine and semen shooting and spurting through the air, to the winged Eros and the Angel of Death, and this again to the belief in angels, and the invention of air machines. The It of man is truly marvelous!

But the ways of scientific thought are most marvelous of all. For long we have been speaking in medicine of the paths of association, and psychology zealously taught this and that about association, but when Freud and those who were and are around him, first made serious use of what they observed about people's associations, and connected these with man's instinctive nature, and proved that instinct and association were primitive phenomena in human life and the foundation stone of all thought and knowledge as well as of all science, a shriek of hatred went up through the land, and people behaved as if Freud wanted to tear down the whole structure of science, because he made clear the nature of the ground on which it was built up. Poor anxious souls! The foundations of science are more lasting than granite, and its walls and steps and chambers build themselves up again, even if here and there a bit of weak masonry falls down.

Would you like to come associating with me for once? Today I met a little girl with a red cap. She looked up at me as though astonished, not displeased, I think, but astonished, for I was wearing as a protection against the cold a black fur cap pulled well down over my ears. Something or other in the look of the child must have struck me. I suddenly saw myself at the age of six or seven, with a red fez. Red Ridinghood came into my mind, and then the line shot through my head, "There stands a little man in the wood all alone"; from that my thoughts passed to the dwarf and his capuche, and to the Capuchin, and finally I was aware that I had for some time been walking along the Kapuziner Strasse. The associations therefore ran in a circle, and returned to where they started from, but why did they do this, and how did they come in that order? I had to go through the Kapuziner Strasse, that was no matter of choice. The child I came across by accident, but that I took notice of her, and that the sight of her gave rise to this particular train of thought, how is that to be explained? As I was leaving the house, the hands of a woman drew my cap over my ears, and a woman's voice said, "There, Pat, now you won't be cold." With such words would my mother pull my fez over my head, many years ago. My mother also told me the tale of Red Ridinghood, and there she was before me, in the flesh. Red cap, which every boy will recognize. The little red head peeps out curiously from its cloak of skin every time he passes water, and if love comes, it stretches after the flowers in the meadows and stands up like a mushroom, just as the little man with the red cap stood on one leg in the wood; and the wolf which gobbles him up, and from whose body he is cut out nine months later, is a symbol of childish theories of conception and birth. You will remember that you yourself once believed in being cut out of the body, but certainly you will no longer remember that you were also once nearly convinced that everyone, even women, had this redcapped thing, but that it was taken away from you, and that somehow people must eat it for children to grow out of it. In creatures of association like ourselves, this theory is linked up with the castration complex of which you have still more to hear. From Red Ridinghood and the Humperdinckian mushroom one passes easily to the dwarf and his capuche, and from that again it is not far to the monk and Capuchin. In both ideas the castration complex is still echoing, for the aged dwarf with his long beard is wrinkled impotence, and the monk typifies the willingly unwilling renunciation. So far these associations are quite clear, but how came the castration idea into my head? The starting point of it all, do but remember, was an episode that recalled me to my mother, and the end was the Kapuziner Strasse. In that road many years ago I lay ill with nephritis, deadly ill, and I believe if I have rightly sounded the depths of my unconscious, that this edema was born of the specter of masturbation-anxiety, and this goes back originally to some injunction or other my mother would give me when she carefully took from out its covering my little dwarf, in order to let me urinate. This is conjecture only, I do not know it. But the mushroom standing alone in its red cap, the poisonous fly-fungus, points to masturbation, and the red fez to the incest wish.

Are you amazed at the tortuous paths I follow in seeking to make clear the meaning of association? But this is only the introduction, for now I am going to declare that the fairy tale comes into being through the force of association and symbolization, must so come, because the riddle of begetting, conception, birth and virginity torments the soul of man until it expresses in mythical form what is so incomprehensible. I venture to say also that the rhyme about the little man in the wood, through unconscious association, is derived in all its details from the appearance of pubic hair and erection; that the belief in dwarfs must have arisen in the same manner, through the association of wood and pubic hair, relaxation and wrinkled dwarf; and that the monastic life with the cowled cloak is the unconscious effect of a flight from incest with the mother. So far do I carry my belief in the power of symbolization and association—and further still.

May I give you another example of the force of association? It is significant because it makes some little use of the speech of the unconscious through the dream, a province of the It which solves many a problem for us physicians. It is a short dream, a dream of one single word, the word "house." The lady who dreamed this went from the word "house" to "dining room," from that to "a case of table silver," and then to "a case of operation instruments." Her husband was then awaiting a severe operation, Talma's operation on the liver, and she was anxious about him. From the name Talma she went on to Talmi (imitation silver), which she connected with her table silver; it was not silver but only imitation. Talmi also stood for her marriage, since her husband, who was to undergo the Talma operation, was at all times impotent. Talmi, she was false to me, the one who was treating her. From that it came out that she had lied to me, that she herself was really the "imitation silver."

In all this there is nothing exceptional; at the most, the desire to get rid of a husband who was only imitation silver, and to get another who would be of pure silver, is worthy of remark. But the telling of that story with its quick succession of associations had a notable result. For two days that woman had been tormented by a severe anxiety attack; her heart beat in rapid strokes and her abdomen had blown up with air. Scarcely twenty minutes had she needed to get the associations from the word "house." When she came to the last, her body was relaxed, her heart was beating quietly, and the anxiety had vanished.

What am I to conclude from this? Was her anxiety, her acute neurosis of the heart, the dilatation of her bowel (her "dining room") really anxiety about her sick husband, remorse for her death wish against him? Was it because she had repressed all this, not allowed it to enter her consciousness, or did she suffer all these woes because her It wanted to make her produce associations, because it sought to drag up a deep secret that had been hidden since the days of her childhood? All that may have been operating simultaneously, but for the purpose of my treatment, for the severe pain which had reduced her to a helpless cripple, with arthritic limbs, it seemed to me that this last possibility was the most important; the attempt of the It to reveal through the way of association a secret kept hidden since her childhood. For she reverted to this dream a year later, and then for the first time told me that the word Talmi certainly had some association with impotence, only not with that of her husband, but with her own, profoundly felt, and that the operation anxiety also had not to do with her husband but with her own masturbation conflict; which appeared to be the original cause of her childlessness and of her illness. After this explanation her recovery went on smoothly, and so far as one may use the term "health," this woman is now healthy.

So much for associations.

If, my dear, after all this talk I still have to add that I claim for myself, personally, the general human right to use ambiguous modes of expression, I think I have at least awakened you to a sense of the many difficulties to be encountered in speaking about the It. It seemed to me the only way to an understanding was to jump at once into the middle of things. Since I am dealing with definitions now,

I will also endeavor to explain the word "transference," which has appeared now and again in my writings.

You will remember what I said about my father's influence upon me, how I imitated him both consciously and unconsciously? Imitation requires an interest in what is imitated, as well as an interest in the person imitated. As a matter of fact I was extremely interested in my father, and still feel for him a great admiration which is quite emotional in character. My father died when I was eighteen, but the disposition to emotional admiration has remained with me ever since, for a thousand and one reasons which we can discuss another time. I have little inclination to make a cult of the dead, and bestowed the emotion which was then set free upon the new head of the family, my eldest brother; I transferred it to him. And this is the sort of thing one means by "transference." But it seems that his personality did not suffice for the needs of my youthful spirit, since there arose in me a few years later, without any diminution of regard for my brother, a similar intense admiration for my medical instructor, Schweninger. Some of the feeling which had been linked up with my father had remained up to this time at my free disposal, and was now transferred to Schweninger. That it really was at my disposal is proved by the fact that during the time between my father's death and my getting to know Schweninger, I went through similar attachments to many people, but they lasted only a short time and there were intervals between, in which my feelings of admiration were apparently without an object, or else were directed towards historical characters, books, works of art, in short, towards every possible thing.

I do not know whether I have yet succeeded in making clear to you the great significance I attach to the idea of the transference. I will therefore put the matter before you once again, only beginning from the other end. Do not forget that I am speaking about the It, that nothing therefore is so sharply defined as the words would seem to imply, that we are dealing with things which are closely interwoven and must be skillfully disentangled. You must think of any talk about the It as something like the division of the globe into degrees. One imagines lines running up and across, and one divides the earth's surface in accordance with these. But the surface itself takes no account of that; where water is 60 degrees east longitude, it is at the same time some degree or other west longitude. These are just means of orientation. And so far as the real nature of the earth is concerned these lines can only be used very conditionally for the purposes of inquiry.

With this proviso I would now say that man has within him a certain amount of emotional capacity—for the moment we cannot differentiate between capacity for attachment and that for repulsion. I am also ignorant as to whether this amount is always quite the same; no one knows that, and perhaps no one ever will find it out. But in virtue of my authority as a letter writer I propose to assume that the amount of emotion at a man's disposal is always the same.

Now there can be no doubt about one thing: the greatest part of this amount of emotion, nearly the whole of it, man bestows upon himself. Another part, relatively small yet extremely important in life, can be directed towards the outer world. Now this outside world is very varied. There are persons, objects, localities, dates, habits, phantasies, actions of every kind. In short, everything connected with life can be used by man as an object of affection or repulsion. The important point is, that he is able to change these objects of his feelings; or rather, on his own account he cannot do so, but his It forces him to change them. Still it looks as though he himself were doing it. Think of an infant; probably he has a liking for milk. After some years he is quite indifferent to milk, or even dislikes it, and prefers bouillon or coffee or rice broth or anything else you like. Or we need not consider so long an interval: even now he is all eagerness for drinking, but two minutes afterwards he is tired and desires to sleep, or wants to scream or to play. He withdraws his favor from one object, milk, and bestows it on another, sleep. In the same way a whole range of emotions will repeat themselves and he will find enjoyment in them, he will always be seeking anew to bring this or that emotion into being; certain desires are necessities of life to him and accompany him throughout his life. Among such are the love for bed, or light, or whatever else may occur to you. Now there is one, at least, among the human beings who surround a child, who looms largest in his emotional world, and this is his mother. Yes, one would almost certainly be right in maintaining that this love for the mother—which is always con-

ditioned by its opposite, repulsion—is just as unchange-
able as that for himself. In any case it must be acknowledged to be the first, since it is already formed within the
mother's body. Or are you among those peculiar people
who believe that unborn children have no capacity for
emotion? But I trust not!

Well then, on this one being, the mother, for a time at
any rate, the child heaps so much of its emotion that no
other person comes into his thoughts. But this love, like
every other, yes, perhaps more than any other, is full of
disappointments. You know the emotional world sees men
and things otherwise than as they really are, it makes a
picture of the object of affection and loves this picture, not
the real object. Such a picture—or imago, as it is called by
the people who first with great difficulty followed up
these things—is made of his mother at some time by the
child; it is probable that he makes many different pictures
of this kind. But because it is the easiest thing to do,
we will take just one picture, and because it is a useful expression, we will call it the mother imago. Man's emotional
life reaches after this mother imago as long as he lives,
reaches so longingly, that the yearning for sleep, for
rest, for protection, for death, may well be regarded as a
yearning for the mother imago, and I shall take this view in
my letters. This mother imago has therefore universal traits,
such for example as those mentioned just now. But also
there are quite personal qualities which are attached only
to the particular imago constructed by the one individual
child. Thus the imago has perhaps blonde hair, it bears
the name of Anna, it has a slightly reddened nose, or a
mole on the left arm, it is full-bosomed, has a particular
smell, stoops a little or has a habit of sneezing loudly, or
whatnot. For this imagined being of phantasy the It re-
serves a certain emotional value, keeps this in stock, so to
speak. Now supposing that sometime or other this man—
or this woman, it makes no difference—meets a person
whose name is Anna, who is a blonde and full-figured,
who sneezes loudly, have you not the possibility there that
the latent desire for the mother imago will be stirred up?
And if the circumstances are favorable—we shall come
to an understanding about that, too—this man will suddenly take all the feeling he has for the mother imago and
transfer it to this one Anna. His It compels him to, he is
forced to transfer it.

Have you grasped what I mean by the "transference"? Please ask, if not, for if I have not made myself sufficiently clear, it is useless to proceed. You must understand the significance of the transference; otherwise we cannot go on talking about the It.

Be so kind as to send an answer to these questions to your ever obedient

PATRIK TROLL.

✳ LETTER VII ✳

My poor dear, the last epistle was too dry for you? For me, too! But give up faultfinding. You will not taunt me into saying what you would like to hear. Make up your mind once for all not to search in my letters for the things your counscious "I" will value, but to read them as though they were travel books or detective stories. Life is already serious enough without making it worse by taking too seriously one's studies, or lectures, or work, or anything else at all.

You scold me, too, for lack of clarity. Neither transference nor repression has been made as real to you as you would wish. To you they are still mere empty words.

With that statement I cannot agree. May I point out something in your last letter which proves the contrary? You speak of your visit to the Gessners', which amusing experience, by the way, I envy you, and you tell of a young woman student who drew down upon herself the wrath of schoolmaster Gessner and all his family by contradicting the all-powerful head of the sixth form, and even doubting too emphatically the usefulness of teaching Greek at all. "I must acknowledge," you continue, "that she really behaved badly to the old gentleman, but I don't know how it was, everything about her pleased me. Perhaps it was because she reminded me of my dead sister; you know Susie died in the middle of taking her State examination. She could be sharp like that, too, and almost bite your head off, and when excited could be very wounding. Furthermore, just like my sister, this youngster at the Gessners' had a scar over her left eye." There you have a transference of the first water. Because someone or other resembles your sister, you like her, although you yourself feel there is some witchcraft in it. And the nicest thing about it is that, without knowing it, you give in your letter the information which shows how the transference has come about. Am I mistaken in my belief that the topaz ring of whose loss and refinding you recount, quite contrary to your custom, with such detail, came from your sister? Your thoughts were clearly occupied with Susie before you ever saw this girl, and you were ready for the transference.

And now for repression: after putting down in black and white that your unmannerly young friend had a scar over her left eye "just like my sister," you go on, "I don't know, by the way, whether Susie's scar was on the left or the right." Yes, but how is it that you don't know it, when she was someone so near to you, whom you saw every day for twenty years, and who even had you to thank for the scar? That is the same scar, is it not, that you yourself made with the scissors, "by accident," while you were playing? According to my view of the case it was not merely an accident. You remember that you acknowledged, when we were once talking about it, that there was some purpose to be served there; an aunt had praised Susie's fine eyes and had teasingly compared yours to the family cat's. That you do not remember whether Susie had that scar on the right or the left is the result of repression. The incident was unpleasant to you because of your mother's disgust and reproaches. You have tried to get rid of the memory, have repressed it, but have only been partially successful; it is only the memory of the position of the scar that you have driven out of consciousness. However, I can tell you that the scar really was on the left. And how do I know that? Because you have told me that since your sister's death you have suffered, just as she did, from a headache on the left side, starting from the eye, and because your left eye now and then deviates a little—it suits you, but it is true, just a little, from the right path, squinting outward as though seeking for help. By making use of the word "accident" at that time, you tried to turn wrong into right, to remove the wound in phantasy from the wicked left, to the good right side. But your It was not deceived. As a sign that you did evil it weakened the one eye mus-

59

cle and thereby warned you not to deflect again from the right. And when your sister died you inherited by way of punishment her left-sided headaches, which you had always so dreaded for her. You were not punished at the time as a child, probably because you trembled so in fear of the cane that your mother took pity on you. But the It means to have its punishment, and if it has been defrauded of the pleasure of suffering, it has its revenge some time or other, often very late; it has its revenge, and many a mysterious sickness gives up its secret when one makes inquiry of the It concerning the punishments escaped in childhood.

May I briefly give you yet another instance of repression from your letter? It is, if you like, unwarrantably dragged in by the hair, but I consider it is justifiable. I spoke in my last letter about three things, transference, repression, and the symbol. In your reply you mention the first two, but the symbol you leave alone. And this symbol was a ring. But lo! Instead of naming the symbol in your letter, you actually lost it in the form of your topaz ring. Isn't that funny? According to my reckoning—and your answer seems to me to confirm it—you received my letter describing the entertaining ring play on the very day you lost your sister's ring. Now do be good and tell the truth for once! Susie came next to you in age, and I believe it is almost certain that together you both came by sexual enlightenment, about whose beginnings no one knows or wants to know anything—would not Susie have something to do with the ring play, with learning to masturbate? I come to that because you gave such a short sharp answer to my remarks on masturbation. I believe it is simply from your own consciousness of guilt that you are unjust to this harmless human pleasure. Consider, then, that nature gives a child brothers and sisters and playmates, that he may learn from them of sexuality.

I should like to take up again the subject from which I broke away, of that remarkable human experience, the giving birth to a child. It surprised me that without remonstrance you accepted my opinion that pain heightens enjoyment. I remember a lively quarrel I once had with you over man's pleasure in inflicting and suffering pain. It was in the Leipziger Strasse in Berlin. A cab horse had fallen down and a crowd had collected; men, women, children, well-dressed people and others in workmen's garb;

all were watching with more or less noisy satisfaction the animal's vain efforts to get on its feet. You then called me a barbarian because I thought such accidents worth seeing and even went so far as to say that the interest which ladies show in murder trials, mining disasters, and terrible catastrophes, I found both understandable and natural.

We can, if you think well of it, take up that quarrel again. Perhaps this time we shall come to a settlement.

The two events important to the life of a woman, and indeed to every human being's life, since without them no one could exist, are connected with pain, the initial sexual act and childbirth. The parallel is so striking in this respect, that I cannot but try to find a meaning for it. As to the voluptuous enjoyment of labor pains, there may be some dispute by reason of the screaming, but there can certainly be none in regard to the pleasurable nature of the bridal night. Now it has come, what the young girls dream of, awake and asleep, what the boy and the man has pictured to himself a thousand times over. Some girls feel, or pretend to feel, anxiety about the pain. Search deeper and you will find other grounds for this anxiety, complexes, and long hidden childish ideas of the fight between the parents, the father's violence and the bleeding wounds of the mother. There are women who can only think with a shudder of that first night with their husbands. Inquire further and you will come upon the disillusionment, that everything failed to come up to those hopes that had been cherished, and in the darkest depths you will find the mother's prohibition against sexual indulgence, and the fear of being wounded by the man. There have been times, and indeed times of advanced civilization, as in the case of the Greeks, when the husband avoided initiating his wife in sexual intercourse, and left the duty to be performed by slaves, but all this has nothing to do with the desire—stirring man to his depths—for the first love-act. Provide the anxious maiden with a skillful lover who charms away her feelings of guilt, and knows how to rouse her to ecstasy, and she will exult in the pain. Give to the disillusioned wife a partner who understands how to excite her phantasy, so that she feels that she is experiencing the love-act for the first time, and she will thrill with enjoyment of the pain of which she was once defrauded, yes, she will even contrive to bleed, to complete her self-deception. Love-making is a curious art, which is only in part

61

a matter for learning, and, if ever anything is ruled by the It, it is that. Look at the intimate incidents of married life. You will be amazed how often even people who have long been married will go through the bridal night all over again, not only in phantasy but with all its joy and all its fear. And even the man who shrinks from the idea of causing his beloved pain will enjoy doing it, if the right partner knows how to allure him.

In other words, pain belongs to the highest moment of pleasure. And, without exception, everything that seems to disprove this is founded on anxiety and on man's consciousness of guilt which sleep in the depths of his being; the more intense these are, the more powerfully do they break out in the disguise of fear or pain in the moment when all wishes are fulfilled. In reality the fear is a need for punishment long overdue.

It is therefore not true that pain is an obstacle to pleasure. The truth is that on the contrary it is a condition of pleasure. What you have read and learned about sadism and masochism is also untrue. To brand as perversions these two inescapable human desires which are implanted in every human being without exception, and which belong to his nature just as much as his skin and hair, was the colossal stupidity of a learned man. That it was repeated is intelligible. For thousands of years man has been educated in hypocrisy, and it has become second nature to him. Everyone is a sadist, everyone a masochist; everyone by reason of his nature must wish to give and to suffer pain; to that he is compelled by Eros.

It is not true that one man wants to inflict pain, and another to endure it, that the one is a sadist and the other a masochist. Everyone is both. Do you want evidence for that?

It is very easy to speak of the roughness of man and the sensitivity of woman and all the mollycoddles of both sexes speak thus and are applauded by the timidly conventional, among whom in our many hours of hypocrisy we must reckon ourselves. But bring some woman into a state of maddened frenzy—but no, that is not necessary nor would it become her as a woman—give her merely the freedom and courage to love truly, to show her naked soul, and she will bite and scratch like an animal, she will cause pain and delight in doing so.

Do you still remember what your child looked like

when it was born? All swollen and squashed, a badly treated little worm? Have you ever said to yourself, "I did that"? Oh no, all mothers and women who desire to be mothers are content to make much of their own suffering, but that they are squeezing head-foremost through a narrow passage a wretched, helpless, tender little creature, pressing it down for hours at a time as if it hadn't a trace of feeling, that never comes into any mother's mind. They even have the effrontery to say that the child does not feel the pain! But if the father or anyone else takes up the child carelessly, they shriek out, "You're hurting the child," "Clumsy Peter!" and if the child comes into the world without breathing, the midwife slaps it on the back until it gives proof that it feels pain by screaming. It is not true that the woman has tender feelings and hates and despises roughness. She only reacts in that manner when other people are rough. Her own roughness she calls holy mother-love. Or do you believe that Caligula or any other "sadist" with like equanimity would have bethought himself of so horrible a torture as to squeeze anyone by the head through a narrow hole? I saw a child once who had stuck his head through the railings of an iron fence and could move it neither backwards nor forwards. I shall not soon forget his screams.

Cruelty, sadism if you prefer to call it, is not remote from the character of woman. One does not need to be an unnatural mother in order to torment one's own children. Surely it was not so long ago that you told me of a friend who dwelt with pleasure on the rueful astonishment on her child's face when she suddenly took the nipple out of his sucking mouth. Just a game, of course, quite understandable, and it is emulated by all of us in the form of teasing little children. But it is playing with torture and, yes, I must tell you first what it means, though you must fit it together for yourself when you remember the symbol. During the suckling the mother plays the part of the husband in giving, the child that of the wife in receiving. So there comes about a very intimate relationship between suckling and begetting, a symbolism that is used to serve and strengthen the bond between mother and child. The playing of your friend—I believe unconsciously for her—is tinged with erotism.

And as the woman, whose natural role is said to be suffering, voluptuously inflicts pain, so also does the violent man go out to find pain. Man's desire is for fatigue, for the torment of a task, the allurements of anger, of struggle, of war if you like. War as Heraclitus saw it ("War is the father of all things"), war with men, things and thoughts, and the enemy which gives him the greatest trouble, the task that almost crushes him, these he loves. And above all he loves the woman who wounds him a thousand times over. So do not wonder at the man who runs after a heartless coquette, but keep your wonder for the man who does not. And when you see a man ardently in love, you may quietly draw the conclusion that his lady is cruel at heart, cruel deep down, even when she seems kind, and wounds him in her play.

This all sounds paradoxical to you, pure drollery. But while you are still looking for contradictory evidence a thousand thoughts come into your mind which confirm what I am saying. Man is conceived in pain, for the true conception is that of the first night, and he is born in blood. Is that to have no significance?

Think it over, you are clever enough for that. Above all, accustom yourself to the idea that the newborn infant feels, that he probably feels more intensely than the adult. And when you have grasped that, consider again what goes on during birth. The child sees the light of the world, and this light mankind loves; he seeks it and creates it for himself in the darkness of the night. From a narrow prison the child comes out into freedom, and freedom man loves above all things. He tastes the pleasure of drawing for the first time the breath of life, and all his life long will he love to take deep breaths. Anguish, the fear of being suffocated, he feels during birth, and anguish stays with him all the days of his life as the companion of all his greatest joys, of all that his heart leaps for. Pain he feels in the pressing towards freedom; pain he gives to his mother with his thick head, and this pain he tries ever anew to repeat and repeat again. The first thing that greets his senses is the smell of blood, mixed with that curiously exciting exhalation from a woman's body. You already know that in the nose there is a certain point which is closely associated with the sexual zone. The infant has this point just as much as the adult, and you would never believe how cleverly nature makes use of the child's sense of smell. But the blood which man sheds in being born, whose essence he breathes in with his first breath, which is therefore something he will never forget, is the mother's blood. Should he not love this mother? Should he not also, though in a sense not usually used, be in blood relation to her? And deep hidden is something else lurking behind, which binds this child to his mother with ties unbreakable: guilt and death. For whoever sheds man's blood, so shall his blood also be shed.

Ah, dear one, human speech and human thought are but a poor tool when one is trying to give knowledge of the unconscious. But one grows thoughtful over the words, "Mother and child." The mother is the cradle and the grave, and gives life and death.

And unless I make a great effort to stop, this letter will never come to an end.

PATRIK TROLL.

✳ LETTER VIII ✳

My dear, I did not doubt that you would acknowledge I was right in much that I have said. Indeed, I am so bold as to think that presently you will come to agree with me, if not in every detail, at any rate in the main. But as yet you still scoff, and take the view that three-fourths of my ideas arise from contrariness of spirit, and that of the rest, at least half are to be put down to my sadistic nature. "If you are to be believed," you write, "we must abandon the accepted idea that there are unnatural lusts and adopt the view that what we are wont to call perversions, masturbation, homosexuality, sodomy, or whatever these things are named, are innate tendencies of man, the common property of everybody's nature."

Have we not already had a talk about that word "unnatural"? To me it seems an expression of man's self-glorification, that he likes to feel himself lord of creation. He divides the world into two parts; whatever pleases him at the time is for him natural; what he has an aversion to he calls unnatural. Have you ever yet seen anything at all that lay outside the realm of nature? For that is what is signified by the word unnatural. I and Nature, that is how man thinks, and never once is he troubled at the thought of his presumptuous self-deification. No, dear scoffer, whatever is, is natural, even if it seems to you to be contrary to rule, even if it goes against the law of Nature. Natural laws are the creation of men, one must never forget that, and if anything appears to be contrary to a natural law, that is only proof that the law is wrong. Strike the word "unnatural" out of your vocabulary, and there will be one stupidity the less in your speech.

And now for the perversions. An investigator whom I hold in high regard has pointed out that the child has every conceivable perverse inclination; he says the child is "multiple perverse"; go a step further and say that everyone is multiple perverse, everyone has within himself every perverse desire, and there you have my view. But it is unnecessary and impractical to go on using the word "perverse," since the impression is thereby given that these inclinations, which every man has as individual, inalienable, and lifelong possessions, are exceptional, strange, and surprising. If you must scold you should use the word "lusts" or "filth," or whatever other expression is at your disposal. But it would be a finer thing to do if you strove towards the position, "Nothing that is human is alien to me." This is truly an ideal which we never achieve but which nevertheless has been given authority and which we physicians are in duty bound to strain every nerve to attain. We shall have to speak a good deal about these inclinations which you call perverse, and which I attribute to every man, as well as the reason why men give themselves the lie in these matters.

You have granted me a real triumph on which I am pluming myself. Recently you rebuked me for being ruthless because I had spoken of the mother's hatred for her child. Today you tell me—and with noticeable satisfaction—of young Frau Dahlmann, who is bitterly distressed because already in the first month after her marriage she is missing her period. With what vivid intuition you are able to describe her plight. I saw it all to the life—the savage anger with which this little society dame laced up her corsets with all the strength she could muster so as to stifle the new life. It is certainly very sad, when one has looked forward with such pleasure through all the days of the engagement to the moment when, as the consort of the chief person present, one shall enter the ballroom on his distinguished arm and with the pleasing knowledge that the next day one will be described from top to toe under the title of "the charming Frau Dahlmann." It is indeed very sad to think that one cannot appear in public because of one's figure!

Do you find it very dreadful that human vanity and love of pleasure should loom so large? That the delights of dancing should lead to attempted murder? But suppose these two mighty instruments of culture be lacking, what then would become of you? In a short time you would be covered with vermin, tearing your meat with fingers and teeth, dragging turnips out of the ground to devour them raw. You would no longer wash your hands, and instead of a handkerchief you would make use of your fingers or your tongue. Believe me, my view that the whole world rests on the propensity to onanism—of which the desire for beauty and cleanliness are the handmaids— is not so foolish as you take it to be.

To me the aversion of the mother for her child is easily understandable. That it is not agreeable for a woman nowadays to be expecting a child I have recently had fresh occasion to observe. I was walking about twenty paces behind a middle-class woman in advanced pregnancy. Two schoolgirls, who might be twelve or thirteen years old, looked sharply at her, and were scarcely past before one said to the other, with a foolish schoolgirl giggle, "Did you notice that big stomach? She's going to have a baby." And the other replied, "Oh, don't talk of such beastliness; I don't want to know about it." The woman must have heard the words, for she turned around as if to say something, but went on again without speaking. A few minutes later a wagon came lumbering down the quiet street. The driver grinned and shouted after the woman, "You do well to parade yourself, to let the world know your husband still shares your bed." Things are not made easy for the pregnant woman, that is certain. There is no longer any glory in being fruitful to help the woman to support the burden of a large family. On the contrary, the maiden grows up with a dread of childbearing. Dispassionately observed, the education of our daughters consists in our seeking to protect them from two things, venereal infection and the bearing of illegitimate children, and we know no better way of achieving these ends than by representing sexual love as a sin and childbirth as a grave danger. There are people who in all seriousness compare the prospects of death in childbirth with those of death in battle. That is one of the delusive ideas of an age weighted down with terrors of conscience, an age which forever entangles itself in the guilt of hypocrisy, of hypocrisy in connection with the begetting of children, and because of this goes more and more quickly to its doom.

The wish of the maiden for a child originates in a passionate feeling which few people perceive, at an age when the difference between legal and illegal is not yet understood, when the half-uttered warnings of the elders against illegitimate births are understood to refer to all births—perhaps not so understood by the intellect but certainly by the unconscious which lies beneath. However, these are matters that admit of remedy, that certainly this or that race, in this or that age, has sought to remedy. But in woman's very being are rooted reasons for hating the child which are immutable. In the first place the child robs the mother of some of her beauty and that not only during pregnancy. Even after that is over a good deal of damage remains that can never be repaired. A scar on the face may throw into relief the beauty of the features, and I can well believe that at heart your sister was very grateful to you for that interesting wound over the eye. But pendulous breasts and a withered body are considered ugly and a civilization must be founded upon fertility if it is to be given value.

The child brings trouble, care, work. Above all, it demands the renunciation of many things that make life worth while. I know that the joy of motherhood can outweigh all the loss, but the counterweight is always there, and if one wants to realize the true circumstances one must not think of a balance in which the heavy scale rests on the bottom while the other hangs motionless in the air, but rather of one in constant motion, as the hand of life with heedless strength throws into the scale an invitation to a ball, an interesting friend, a journey to Rome, and so at times bears down the other side. Accordingly there is a continual fluctuation, and always a fresh sacrifice has to be made which inflicts its own weal and woe.

It may perhaps be possible to prepare oneself before-hand and to arm oneself against this renunciation, these troubles and cares. But there are emotions which mothers do not clearly recognize, which they feel but never allow to become voiced, whose poisonous talons they press deeper and deeper into their souls if only not to lose the dignity of their motherhood.

A little while since I took you with me to a birth. Do you remember it? *Accouchements* are not in my line but there were special reasons why the mother in this case particularly wished me to be her obstetrician. I did not mention these to you at the time, but now I want to repair the omission. I treated this woman throughout her term of pregnancy. First she suffered from vomiting, then fol-lowed fainting fits, bleeding, pains, swollen leg, and every other ill that can surprise one at such a time. What seemed to me now to be important was her horrible fear that she would bear a child with a crippled foot, and would die herself. You know that the child was born sound, and that the mother is still living, but for a long time she was pos-sessed by the idea that something would happen to the child's leg. She recalled the fact, apparently correctly, that for some weeks after birth her eldest child suffered from a mysterious suppuration of the bursa of the left knee, which became worse and had to be operated upon. This left a scar which slightly interfered with the use of the left knee joint. I must leave you to form your own opinion as to whether this suppuration had any connec-tion with what I am about to relate. For my part I think it had, although I am not able to show you how the mother—of course unconsciously—brought it about. The woman of whom I speak was the eldest of five children. With the two next younger she behaved well, but against the fourth child, of whom she was for a time placed in charge owing to her parents' limited means, she felt from the beginning a strong aversion which has always remained with her, even today. When the fifth child was on the way the girl's character changed; she now attached herself to her father, became hostile to her mother, tor-mented her youngest sister, and was, in short, a regular nuisance. One day, on being told to mind the baby, she went into a fit of temper, screamed and stamped her foot, and when her mother punished her and made her obey she sat herself down on the cradle, rocked it violently with her foot so that the child began crying, and called out, "Old witch, cursed old witch!" An hour later her mother was taken suddenly ill and sent her for the midwife. She then saw that her mother was bleeding copiously. A baby was born that same night, but for many months the mother was bedridden and never afterwards looked quite the same. The idea then came to the girl that it was her curse which brought on her mother's illness, and that she was to blame. Now that is an experience which is sufficiently important for the determination of the destiny, character, disposition to illness, and fear of death of the person concerned in it, but of itself it is not enough to explain the fear of a crippled leg for the baby that is to be born. The foot stamping, the naughty rocking of the cradle with the half-conscious purpose of throwing the baby sister out, give some grounds, it is true, but alone these are not sufficient. From another side came a heavier count of guilt. In the village where my patient grew up there lived an idiot with crippled legs who on fine days was put in a chair outside his parents' cottage, where in spite of his eighteen years he would play like a child with stones and twigs. The crutches he had by his side he could not use without assistance, and apparently he kept them nearby for the sole purpose of threatening the teasing village children, at the same time uttering hoarse, unintelligible cries. While she was going through this troublesome stage the little Frieda—that was the name of my patient—who at other times was a pattern of good behavior, joined the other children in their mockery until one day her mother came up behind her, gave her a severe scolding, and said to her: "God sees all things and He will punish you by giving you a crippled child like this poor lad." A few days later occurred the events of which I have already spoken.

Now the associations are clearly to be seen. On top of the original mood of resentment against the mother's pregnancy there came about two unhappy experiences, the threat of God's wrath at her mockery of another's misfortune, and the mother's illness which she believed was the result of her outburst. Both of these for the faithful—and Frieda was brought up as a strict Catholic—are grievous sins. They were pressed down into the depths of her soul, to reappear in the form of anxiety when her own pregnancy gave an objective association with the childish experiences. Both of these have in common that the foot plays some part, and this accessory circumstance, as so often happens, seized upon the sense of guilt and drove it into the foreground as the dread of a misshapen baby, while the accompanying fear of death remained below under repression, and was apparently the first to vanish during treatment. But only apparently, for some years later it re-emerged in a strangely interesting form, as fear of cancer, associated again with the cursing of the mother. But that is another story.

If I am to make you understand the motive I had in giving you this tale, and what it has to do with a mother's hatred of her child, I must refer to something I mentioned which probably escaped your notice. Frieda had not only turned against her mother during her pregnancy, but she had formed so surprising an attachment to her father that even now, after many years, she still dwells on it. There you have the Oedipus complex of which you must have heard already. To be on the safe side, however, I had better say a few words that will make it clear. By the Oedipus complex is understood the passion felt by the child for the parent of the opposite sex, the son for the mother and the daughter for the father, coupled with the death wish directed against the parent of the same sex, against the father by the son and against the mother by the daughter. With this Oedipus complex which is part of the inevitable heritage of mankind we shall have to concern ourselves further, but here I will merely point out the fact that mother and daughter are always and without exception rivals and therefore are endowed with the reciprocal hatred of rivals. The exclamation, "Cursed old witch," has a much deeper significance than a mere reference to the increasing family. The witch casts a spell over the beloved, so it is in fairy tales and in the maiden's unconscious. The origin of the witch idea is to be found in the Oedipus complex; the witch is the mother who binds the father to herself by her magical arts, although he properly belongs to the daughter. In other words, mother and witch are one and the same to the It of humankind, the creator of fairy tales.

You see, here we have some part of the child's surprising hatred against the mother, which is only in part counterbalanced by the belief in young and beautiful witches, red-haired, godless creatures, a belief which

71

springs from the hatred of the ageing mother for her vivid, freshly menstruating (and therefore "red-haired") daughter. This hate must indeed be strong to bring forth such fruit. In Frieda's curse was concentrated the torment of long years of jealousy. It is the measure of one side of her feelings towards her mother, feelings which were heightened into rage because of the coming of another child. For in order to have become pregnant her mother must have received the embraces of the father, and these the daughter demanded for herself. She had secured the child for herself by witchcraft, and had so defrauded the daughter.

Do you understand now why I told you Frieda's history? Her case is typical. Jealousy flares up in every daughter when the mother is pregnant. It is not always obvious but it is there. And whether it is expressed or remains deep-hidden, the power of the moral commandment, "Thou shalt honour thy father and thy mother that thy days shall be long upon the earth," pushes it down, represses it, sometimes in greater, sometimes in lesser degree, but always with the same result, that it gives rise to a sense of guilt.

What happens, then, with this sense of guilt? It demands punishment, and appropriate punishment. Frieda mocked at the cripple, therefore she must bring a cripple into the world. She cursed and railed at her mother, so will her own child do to her. She hated her mother; the child now in her womb will requite it. She wanted to rob her mother of the father's love; the same theft will be committed against her by the coming child. "An eye for an eye, and a tooth for a tooth."

Can you not understand why Frieda, who felt her life and happiness threatened by her child, should not always love that child; why, at times when the poison of those childish experiences is stirred from its depths by some event, she even hates the child, the young witch, beautiful and blossoming, to whom belongs the future?

The feeling of guilt which every daughter has in relation to her mother forces upon her this capacity to hate her own child; this is a truism.

Probably you again think that I am exaggerating, that I am drawing general conclusions from a single instance, as is my wont. But no, my dear, this time I have not exaggerated. I have not as yet named the most important cause of the guilt feeling, which extorts unfailing dread and repugnance, but recently I referred to it. It lies in the fact that at birth the child sheds the mother's blood in the act of being born. And whosoever sheds another's blood, shall his blood also be shed. The woman who awaits her child cannot help but fear that child, for it is the avenger of blood. And no one is so holy as always to be able to love an avenger.

I have written at great length because I very much wanted to give you an idea of the intricacies of all the ties between mother and child. It is to be hoped you have not fully understood, or else I shall think I have not shown you the darkest corners! But by degrees we shall come to an understanding, either through your rejecting everything—in that case we have at least had some correspondence—or through your growing, like me, cautious in your views about humanity, patient, and absolutely convinced that there are two sides to everything.

May I make another short reference to Frieda's experiences? I told you that, like all little girls, she claimed the mother's child for herself. Not only on this one occasion, but in some mysterious way does the wish to receive a child from the father persist in the unconscious throughout a woman's whole life. And to this incest wish is attached the word "idiot." You will find no woman to whom the thought has not at some time occurred, "Your child will be born an idiot, or will become feeble-minded." For the belief that from the union with the father must be born an imbecile child is rooted deep in the brain of mankind. The fact that the cripple was also an idiot worked in with this belief, so that the suppressed emotion of that time was poisoned by the dimly felt wish and dread of incest.

There is something still lacking to a complete presentment of the picture. I spoke to you before about the symbolism of the sexual organs. Now, the clearest symbol of the female organ, shown in the very word *Gebärmutter* (womb), is the mother. For the symbol-making It—and I told you that the It cannot help but symbolize—the female organ is the childbearer, the mother. If Frieda cursed her mother, then she also cursed the symbol, the sexual organ, her own childbearing, her life as wife and mother.

Did I not rightly say that in explaining the It one can but stammer? I had to say it, and must say it again, or in

the end you will still think me crazy. But even so you will
see there is method in my madness!

Affectionately yours,
PATRIK TROLL.

✳ LETTER IX ✳

No, you are wrong, my dear. The responsibility that life
is so complicated does not lie with me. If you want to
understand everything with care I must once again refer
you to the textbooks. There you will find things beauti-
fully arranged and clearly explained. There is no mist or
darkness to be found there, or if there are, the virtuous
textbook passes them by with the observation: "This is
obscure."

Academic science is like a fancywork shop. You find one
skein next to another, linen thread, silk, cotton, wool, of
every hue, and every skein is carefully wound; if you take
hold of one end of the thread, you can quickly and easily
unwind it. Yet I remember from my childhood what a
commotion there would be if we disturbed our mother
in her sewing or knitting, and tangled the yarn. It was
quite a business to sort the threads out again, once they
were all muddled and knotted. Sometimes the scissors
proved the sole means of salvation, cutting so easily
through the knots. But now picture to yourself the whole
world full of such jumbles of yarn. Given enough imagination and if you do not at once cry out, "No, never will
I believe such a thing!"—there you find the field of research work. It's at the back of the shop, out of sight. Unless he is obliged to, no one goes into this room, where
everyone holds some thread between his fingers and busily teases it out. Here are strife and envy, mutual help
and despair, and not one, not even one, ever finds an end.
Only now and then some ignorant little dandy comes to
the back of the shop, seeking a piece of red silk or of

black wool, because it pleases a lady customer—perhaps it is you—to knit something pretty. Then a tired man, who has just dropped his hands out of sheer exhaustion from the hopelessness of his task, points out the few yards of yarn which he has managed in years of laborious work to extract from the tangled mess. The shop assistant takes out his scissors, cuts off this smooth piece and twists it cleverly into a skein as he walks back into the shop. And you buy it with the smug belief that you understand something about mankind. Yes, you do!

Now the workshop in whose salesroom I am serving—for I am not one of those patient people who spend their lives in disentangling the yarn, I sell the skeins—well, this workshop is badly lighted and the yarn is roughly spun and already in a thousand places it is cut and mangled. They always give me infinitesimal pieces which I must knot together, and sometimes I must use the scissors myself, and later, when it has to be sold, the thread is full of knots, or different colors are put together, or cotton and silk—in short, it is not fit to be sold. That I am powerless to alter. But the odd thing is that there are always people to buy it, childish people obviously, who take pleasure in variegated colors and irregular skeins. And the oddest thing of all is that you yourself are one of these people who come to make a purchase.

Well, where shall we start today? With the baby, with the tiny baby that is still sleeping within its mother's body? Do not forget, it is phantasy-wool that I offer you. One thing has always seemed especially noteworthy to me in the life of the unborn child, namely, that it is alone, not only that it has a world to itself, but that it *is* a world in itself. We certainly have no reason to infer that the unborn child is without interest or understanding. On the contrary the anatomical and physiological conditions force us to assume that the child thinks even before it is born—and mothers confirm this from their perceptions of the child in the womb. If the unborn child has an interest, in essence it can only be an interest in itself. It thinks only of itself; all its feelings are directed towards its own microcosmos. Can we wonder that a habit practiced from the very beginning, and forced upon every man, should persist throughout his life? For whoever is honest knows that at all times one refers everything to oneself, that it is a more or less attractive mistake to believe that one lives for anything or anybody else. That we never do, not for an instant, never. And He whom they invoke to champion the noble but false and artificial ideals of self-sacrifice, self-denial, and altruism, Christ, He knew this, for as the highest ideal, as an unattainable ideal, He gave forth the commandment: "Thou shalt love thy neighbour as thyself." Not "more than thyself," be it understood, but just "as thyself." He said this commandment was like unto the other: "Thou shalt love thy God with all thy heart and with all thy strength." It is a question whether this is not, in quite a different sense, like the other commandment, whether it is not in some manner identical with it, as I indeed believe. On that we can exchange our ideas at some future time. But in any case He made clear His conviction that man gives most of his love to himself, and the prattle of good people He called pharisaical and hypocritical, which indeed it is. The psychology of today gives to this instinct of self-love, this instinct of exclusiveness which is rooted in the solitude of the child within the womb, the name of narcissism. You know Narcissus was beloved by himself, and was drowned in the stream which mirrored his image—an astonishing representation of the instinct of self-gratification.

You may remember my statement that the object of man's love was first and foremost—and almost exclusively—himself. The nine months' communion with himself to which nature forces man in the time preceding birth, is a notable means of achieving this object.

Have you ever tried to get inside the thoughts of an unborn child? Try it once. Make yourself very, very tiny, and creep back into the womb from which you issued. This is not at all such a crazy challenge as you think, and the smile with which you dismiss my suggestion is childishly kind, a proof that the thought is familiar to you. As a matter of fact, without our being aware of it, our whole life is guided by this desire to get back to the mother. "I should like to creep into you"—how often one hears it said! Let us assume that you are able to return into the womb. I think myself it must be the same sort of feeling as if someone goes to bed after a checkered day, full of agreeable and disagreeable thoughts and events, full of sorrows and cares, of work and pleasure and danger, and then gradually gets drowsy and with the delightful sensation of being safe and undisturbed, goes off to sleep. Only a thousand times finer, deeper, more peaceful must this feeling be, perhaps like that which we sometimes hear described by a sensitive person in speaking of a swoon, or that which one attributes so gladly to a dying friend who slips peacefully into death as into slumber.

Need I expressly make the point that the bed is a symbol of the womb, of the mother herself? Yes, I go further still. You remember what I wrote you about man's symbolic thinking and action, how he is at the mercy of the symbol and must obediently fulfill the demands of this destiny, how he invents just what is forced upon him by this symbolization. Truly, in order to preserve the semblance of our divinity we prize our inventions as the work of our conscious thought, of our genius, and forget altogether that in its web the spider has invented a tool no less ingenious than the net we use to catch fish, and that birds build nests which are as intricate as the work of any human architect. It is wholly a mistake to prize man's conscious intelligence and to ascribe to it the merit of everything that occurs; an understandable error, since it rests on man's feeling of omnipotence. In reality we are the tools of the It; it does with us what it will, and it is worth our while to pause and observe its power. To put it shortly, I believe that man had to invent the bed because he could not extricate himself from his yearning to return to the womb. I do not believe that he has contrived it for himself in order to lie more comfortably, or to indulge his laziness the more, but because he loves his mother. Yes, it seems more probable to me that a man's sloth, his pleasure in being in bed and his lying there far into broad daylight, is proof of his great love for the mother, and that lazy people, who delight in sleep, are the best children. And if you remember that the more a child loves his mother the greater must be his struggle to free himself from her, you will be able to understand people like Bismarck and Frederick the Great, whose tremendous activity is in curious contrast to their great laziness. Their unremitting labors are a revolt from the dragging chains of childish love.

This revolt can be understood, for the happier a child has felt within its mother's body, the deeper must be its horror of being born. The more intensely it loved the womb in which it rested, the stronger must be the dread of leaving this paradise of sloth, from which it can once more be driven out. Dearest of friends, I hereby solemnly warn you against continuing this correspondence with me. I will lead you, if you will listen, so far away from everything taught by rational people that it will afterwards be difficult for you to find again the correct and healthful way of thinking. Many a learned man well versed in history has examined the mentality of Bismarck at every point, and has come to the conclusion that he did not take much account of his mother. He scarcely mentions her, and where he does there is a sound of grumbling in his words. And now I come along and maintain that his mother was the center of his life, that she was the being he loved best. And my sole proof is the fact that he always longed for rest and yet fled from inactivity, that he hated work and yet was always working, that he enjoyed sleeping and yet was a bad sleeper. But before you utter the word "absurd," permit me to cite two or three more facts about Bismarck. First there is that curious phenomenon which scientific observers never fail to mention. He talked—and that was strange in a man of his massive build—in a high-pitched voice. For one of our coterie, this signifies that something in this man had remained a child, and stood in relation to the world as does a child to its mother—an opinion which can easily find support in some of the characteristics of the "Iron Chancellor," who had in fact the nerves of a boy. But one does not need to examine the individual character-habits of the possessor of this high-pitched voice, to say: "This man is childlike and a mother's boy."

Do you still remember—ah, how long ago it was!—how we went together to the German Theatre to see Joseph Kainz as Romeo? We were amazed that the pitch of his voice was so high in the love scenes, and at the strangely boyish tone with which he pronounced the word "love." I have often pondered on it since, for there are many people who always, however manly they may otherwise be, pronounce the word "love" in a treble tone. Why? Because at this word is suddenly awakened that first, deepest, never-dying love which they felt when children for the mother, because they want to show, they have to show without wanting to, "I love thee as I loved my mother, and all the love I have to give is a reflection of my love for her." No man can easily cast off this mother-being; right to his grave she rocks him in her arms.

In yet another matter does the "mother's boy" come to the surface in Bismarck; he was a great smoker. Now why do you at once think it funny that I should quote smoking as a proof of filial love and of dependence upon the mother? Has it never occurred to you what a similarity there is between smoking and sucking at the breast? You have eyes and see not. Take heed then of these everyday things; they will reveal to you many a secret, not merely the one that the smoker is a mother's boy.

For me there is no doubt—and I could go on with more chatter about it—that this strong man was ruled in the depths by his mother imago. You are already acquainted with his *Thoughts and Memories*. Did it not surprise you that a person so matter of fact as he thought it necessary to relate a dream of how he was scattering with a switch a rock that blocked his path? It is not the dream that is remarkable, for to everyone who busies himself at all with dreams it is clear that the incest wish, the Oedipus complex, is concealed here. But that Bismarck should have told it, it is that which deserves attention. When close to death he was still so greatly under the influence of his mother that he had to interpolate this secret of his life in the midst of the story of his great deeds.

You see, my dear, with a little investigation there can be found in everyone's life the workings of the mother imago. Whether what I think is correct you may decide in accordance with your own judgment. But I am not concerned with being right. My aim is rather to implant a little maxim in your memory, because I find it useful in dealing with myself and others: "Where one scolds, one loves."

Pay attention to the things people reprove, what they despise, what they loathe. Behind the reproof, the scorn, the disgust, the revulsion, there is always hidden, without exception, a stern and still raging conflict. You will never go wrong in concluding that a man has once loved deeply whatever he hates, and loves it yet, that he once admired and still admires what he scorns, that he once greedily desired what now disgusts him. Whoever abominates lying is certainly a liar against himself, whoever is disgusted by dirt, for him dirt was once an enticing snare, and whoever despises another, admires him and envies him. And it has a deep significance that women—and men also—are frightened by snakes, for there is a snake which rules the world and womankind. In other words, the depths of the soul in which rest the repressed complexes, reveal themselves in resistances. Whoever is concerned with the It must pay heed to two things, transference and resistance. And whoever wants to treat the sick, whether he be surgeon or *accoucheur* or general practitioner, can only be of help in so far as he succeeds in making use of the transferences of the patient, and freeing the resistances.

I shall raise no objection if you apply this rule in judging and condemning your ever faithful

PATRIK TROLL.

✳ LETTER X ✳

Many thanks for your reminder, my dear. Yes, I *will* try to get my feet on solid earth—only not today.

I must tell you something. In pleasant lonely hours there sometimes comes to me a daydream of curious import. I imagine myself pursued by an enemy, fleeing towards an abyss whose rocky edge, like a broad-eaved roof, juts out over the precipice. Loosely slung round a tree stump a long rope hangs down into the gulf below. Down this rope I glide, and swing to and fro, ever wider and wider, now against the rocky wall, now away from it. To and fro, to and fro, I sway above the abyss, carefully keeping my body from being crushed by fending myself away from the rock with my legs. There is a seductive charm in this swinging, and my phantasy draws it out at length. But at last I achieve my goal. There in front of me lies a natural cave; it is hidden from all eyes, I alone know of it, and in a long gentle swing I flee inside and am saved. My enemy gazes down from the rocky heights above into the fathomless depths, and then goes on his way with the certain conviction that I lie shattered beneath.

I have often thought that you would envy me if you knew how sweet was the joy of this phantasy. May I interpret it to you? This cave, whose entrance is known to me alone, is the mother's body. The enemy who pursues me, and whose hatred is satisfied when he believes me to be destroyed, is the father, the husband of this mother, who thinks he is her master and yet does not know this untrodden, unattainable kingdom of her womb. Reduced to its simplest form, this waking dream says nothing more than just what I used to answer as a child, if anyone asked me, "Whom would you like to marry?" It never entered my head that I could ever marry any woman but my mother. And it is due simply to the inconsolable loneliness of my school days that this intense desire of my being was repressed into a hardly recognizable symbolic phantasy. Only the inexpressible sense of bliss in the swinging still betrays the ardor of that emotion. And the fact that I remember as good as nothing of those years between twelve and seventeen, except that I had to pass them away from my mother, shows what conflicts I went through. Such detachments from the mother have often very strange results, and I can certainly say that fate dealt gently with me.

Today that has been made clear to me once again. I have had a hard struggle with a young man who certainly wishes to be treated by me, but who trembles with fear and can scarcely utter a word, so soon as he sees me. He has come to identify me with his father, and however I begin, he holds to the belief—or perhaps his It holds to it—that I have a knife hidden somewhere, and that I will seize him and cut off the sign of his masculinity. And all that because he loved his mother, who is long since dead, too intensely! In this man there once existed—perhaps through years, or only for a few moments, perhaps there still exists—the raging desire to take his mother as a lover, to possess himself of her body. And out of this desire, this lust for incest, grew the dread of the father's revenge, that he would sever the wanton member with his murderous knife.

That a patient should see his father in his doctor is explicable. The transference of the feeling for father or mother to the person of the doctor takes place in every treatment: it is prognostic of the measure of its success, and according to whether the patient's emotional life centered upon the father or upon the mother, so will he prefer the forceful or the gentle physician. We physicians would do well to keep this fact in mind, for three-fourths of our success, if not more, rests upon the accident which gave to us some sort of resemblance to the parents of our patients. And the majority of our failures are also to be traced to such transferences, a fact which in some measure may console us for the blow to our vanity given by the recognition of the transference as the real physician. "Not all my worth nor all my pride"—these words of Luther must remain in the hearts of all who wish to live at peace with themselves.

There is nothing remarkable, then, in the fact that my patient sees the father in me; but that he, a man so bound to the mother imago, should choose for himself a father physician is surprising, and permits the inference that, without having realized it, he is equally dependent upon the father as upon the mother. That would give a favorable prognosis. Or it may be that his It drove him to me because he wants to show, through an unsuccessful course of treatment such and such a number of times by such and such a number of instructors and physicians, that the father is a poor, wretched creature. Then there is little chance of my being the one to help him. I should do better to explain the circumstances of his case to him and send him to look for a physician of the mother type. But I am an incorrigible optimist, and believe that in his innermost soul, in spite of his dread, he honestly believes in my ascendancy, and loves it, even if he likes to make the treatment a little troublesome. Patients who play such tiresome tricks are not at all rare. In this case conditions are somewhat doubtful, and it is only at the close of the treatment that I shall learn what induced the patient to come to me in particular.

I know one means of bringing to light the hidden feelings a man has against me, just as they are at the moment, and since you are a clever little dear and have sufficient sense of humor to try it without risk of wounded feelings, I will reveal it to you. If you want to discover anyone's regard for you, ask him to name some slighting term. And if he says "goose," as we might anticipate, then you must infer, and without vexation accept the fact that you chatter too much for him. But don't forget that roast goose tastes very nice, and that it can just as well be a compliment as a slight.

Now I took a favorable opportunity to ask my patient for some term of abuse, and there came pat, just as I had expected, the word "ox." That settled the question; my patient considers me stupid, bovine. But that may only be a momentary feeling with him, which we hope will pass away. It is something else that interests me in the word, which, like a glimmering in the midst of gloom, illuminates for a moment the darkness of his disease. The ox is castrated. If I overlook, as beseems a decent physician, the malicious gibe which degrades me to the condition of a eunuch, I find in the word "ox" a fresh explanation of my patient's dread, yes, it brings me so much the nearer to the general solution of an extremely important difficulty, which in our queer medical-German is termed the castration complex. And if once I master this castration complex in sum and in detail, I shall call myself Doctor Know-All, and shall graciously present you with one of the many millions that will flow into my coffers. The word "ox" shows me, that is to say, that my patient had at one time the wish and the intention to castrate his own father, to make the steer into an ox, and that on account of this malicious design he is anxious about his own member, in accordance with the decree, An eye for an eye, a tooth for a tooth, a tail for a tail. What may have brought him to this wish?

You are swift with the answer at hand, my dear, and I envy you that quick decisiveness. "If this man," you say, "is overpowered by the desire to possess his mother as a lover, he cannot suffer that another, the father, should possess her, and so he must either kill his father, as Oedipus did Laius, or he must castrate him and so make him the harmless slave of the harem." Unfortunately, in life things are not so simple, and you must now arm yourself with patience to listen to a long explanation.

My patient is one of those people who are double-sexed, who have emotional ties with men just as they have with women. He is, to use my beloved medical language again, at once heterosexual and homosexual. You know that with children this condition is normal. From my own personal knowledge I can add that its occurrence in adults argues a persistence of the childish It, a trait of some importance. My patient's case is still further complicated by the fact that towards people of either sex his feelings can be those of a man or of a woman, and he has therefore the most varied possibilities of emotion. It may very well be, then, that he only wants to castrate his father so as to transform him into a loved woman, or on the other hand, that his dread of having his sexual parts cut off by his father is a suppressed wish to be a wife to him.

But I am quite forgetting that you cannot in the least understand what I mean when I say that by cutting off the male genitalia a man is made into a woman. Let me ask you to come with me into the nursery. There sits Greta in her three-year-old nakedness, waiting for the nursemaid who is fetching hot water for the evening toilet. In front of her stands little Hans, looking inquisitively between her straddling legs. He puts his finger gently to his little sister's open gap, and asks, "Was it cut off?" "No, it's always been like that."

If I did not so much dislike to quote—in our family it was the accepted opinion, and my mother as well as my brothers tormented my vanity a thousand times over because they could all quote better than I, the poor Benjamin; moreover, occasions were not lacking when I brought humiliation on myself by a false quotation—and if it did not seem to me so stupid, I would now tell you something of the deep significance of children's games. Instead, I want to speak in all soberness of what this business of cutting off signifies. At some time or other—and it is remarkable that scarcely anyone can remember when this happens—and still more remarkable is it that in thinking and writing so many of my sentences are interrupted like this—you may judge accordingly how difficult it is becoming for me to discuss these matters, and I leave you to draw your conclusions, therefore, as to my own personal castration complex.

Well, then, at some time or other the small boy observes the difference between the two sexes. With himself and his father and his brothers, he sees an appendage which is quite specially jolly to look at and play with. With his mother and sisters he sees in its stead an opening out of which shows raw flesh like that of a wound. He concludes from that, in vague, indefinite fashion as it comes to his childish brain, that with part of mankind the little tail they were born with has been removed, torn out, pushed inwards, crushed, or cut away, so that there shall also be women and girls, since the good God needs them for childbearing. And then again at some time, in his strange bewilderment at these unheard-of things, he makes out for himself that the little tail is cut away, since now and again mama makes blood in the chamber instead of the clear yellow "wee-wee." Therefore every now and again the wee-wee maker, the little turncock from which the water spurts, must be cut off, and this, indeed, papa must do at night. And from this moment on the little boy conceives a sort of contempt for the female sex, of anxiety for his own masculinity, and a sympathetic longing to fill up mama's opening and then the wounds of other girls and women with his own little turncock and so to lie with them.

Ah, my dear, do not imagine that I have found in this the key to the eternal mystery of love. The veil is still there; I only try to lift one tiny corner and what I see behind is dim. But at least it is an attempt. And do not imagine that this infantile sexual theory—don't be horrified at this learned phrase—comes clearly into the child's thoughts. But he dare not think it out clearly because five minutes later he will replace it with another theory, only in its turn to be rejected; in short, because he never once brings these things up into his consciousness but lets them sink into the depths of the unconscious, just because of that, they have such an immeasurable effect upon him. For what shapes our lives and natures is not simply the content of our conscious mind, but in much greater degree that of our unconscious. Between the two is a sieve, and above, in the consciousness, only the coarse material is kept back; the sand for the mortar of life falls into the depths of the It; above remains only the chaff, down below the good flour for the bread of life collects, down there in the unconscious.

With every good wish,

PATRIK TROLL.

✳ LETTER XI ✳

It is a refreshing change, my dear, to write to you. When I tell other persons about the castration fear they lose their tempers, abuse me, and altogether behave as if I were responsible for man's heritage of sin and punishment. But you point out immediately the parallel in the legend of the Creation, and for you, Adam's rib, out of which Eve was created, is the sexual organ of the man. You are right, and it delights me.

May I call your attention to some further points in regard to this? First, a rib is hard and stiff. It is therefore not merely the penis, from which woman is created, but the hardened, bony, stiff, erect phallus of sexual pleasure. Voluptuousness is accounted wicked by the human mind, and deserving of punishment; it is accordingly punished by castration. Voluptuous pleasure, then, transforms a man into a woman.

Pause a little in your reading, my pupil, and dream over what it has meant and still means for human sexuality and its development, that our most powerful instinct is felt to be a sin, an instinct which is untameable and can only be repressed, never be destroyed, by the power of will; and that an inescapable natural process like an erection is covered with guilt and shame. Out of the repression, out of the compulsion to repress this or that, grew the world in which we live.

Shall I help you a little? What is repressed is forced out of its place, pressed and changed into another form, to reappear in the shape of a symbol. Thus extravagance is changed to diarrhoea; parsimony into constipation; the desire to give birth into body pains. The sexual act appears in dancing, melody, drama, or builds itself up, for all men to see, in a church with a projecting male tower and the mysterious womb of the vault, or shows itself in the tender of an engine or the rhythmic stamping of the road paver, or the swing of the woodcutter's axe. Listen to the sound of voices, to the up and down in modulation, to the beauty of the tone; how secret is this influence, and how, gently and unperceived, it stimulates everything. Then look within the depths of your own heart, and dare to deny that everything that is good is a symbol of human bodies palpitating in the heaven of love! And everything that is evil, too! But what has come out of the repression of the erection, this striving upwards which is threatened with the curse of castration? Up towards heaven man stretches himself, raises his head, plants his feet firmly, rears himself up and lets his searching eyes wander over the world, takes everything in with his thinking brain, develops, gets bigger and stands upright! Just think, dear, he became human, having achieved his lordship through the repression and the symbol. Isn't that fine? And why to our ears do *schlecht* (base) and *geschlecht* (sex) sound so much alike?

Confronted by the nature and the secret thoughts of the It, one may feel fear, or bewildered admiration, or one may smile. The important thing is to combine these three feelings. Whoever can bring them into harmony, we shall love, for he is worthy of love.

But how comes it that man looks upon the fact of erection as sinful, that he vaguely feels within himself, "Now you will be a woman, now a hole will be cut in your body"? Every physician knows something of the human soul, and will tell part of what he knows, but there is much that will never be thought out even with moderate clearness. Two things, however, I can tell you. One is something that we experienced together, and that made us glad and merry. We had had a beautiful day, the sun had been warm, the wood was green, the birds sang and the lime trees buzzed with bees. Filled with the freshness of the world, we returned to your home just as your little boy was to be put to bed. "Whom are you going to marry some day?" you asked. He flung his arms around your neck, kissed you, and said, "Mama, only mama!" Neither before nor since have I heard love avowed in such a tone as that. And your eyes suddenly filled with the tears of that happiness which lies in perfect acquiescence. So it is with every boy; he loves his mother, not with filial piety, innocent and pure, but ardently, with a passion saturated with the full force of voluptuous love. For what is the sensuality of an adult in comparison with the emotion and desire of a child? This glowing ardor of love, founded through years of physical pleasure shared by mother and child, diminishes under the influence of law and custom, under the shadow of the mother's conscious shamefacedness, her lying and hypocrisy, under the sense of guilt and anxiety. And behind the desire there glitters the knife which shall cut away the boy's weapon of love. Here we have the Oedipus situation.

There are races which allow marriage between brother and sister, and others whose custom it is to give the marriageable daughter to be sexually initiated by her father before the husband is allowed to possess her. But never, since the beginning of the world and so long as it shall stand, is a son permitted to lie with his mother. Incest with the mother ranks as the vilest of crimes, worse even than matricide. It is the sin of sins, in a class apart. Why should this be so? Tell me. Perhaps woman can throw more light on this than man. One fact remains: because every erection is desire for the mother, every erection, without exception, following the law of transference, is accompanied by the dread of castration. Wherever the sin, there shall be the punishment: for the woman in cancer of the breast and the womb, because it was in her breasts and her womb that she committed sin; for the man in wounds and blood and madness, because he dealt wounds and thought evil, and for every man the specter of castration.

My second instance is an actual experience: every erection is succeeded by relaxation. And does not this unman one? This relaxation is the natural castration, and a symbolic source of the anxiety.

Is it not remarkable that people always talk of sensuality as "dissipation"? And has nature, then, made of this symbolic warning of relaxation an insurmountable barrier against excess? Or is this way of talking nothing but anxiety arising from the Oedipus complex or from the specter of onanism, or any other peculiarity of the human soul, or is it perhaps only envy—the envy of the impotent, of the needy, the envy every father feels for his son, every mother for her daughter, the elder for the younger?

I have wandered far afield, but what I wanted to write

about was the fashioning of woman out of Adam's rib. Notice, if you please, Adam was originally alone. But if a hard rib is to be made out of the soft flesh, of which he has more than is given later to woman, then his desire, which produces the erection, must have arisen from himself, and must be narcissistic. Adam experiences pleasure and satisfaction in his own person; by himself he brings about the change from flesh to rib. And the creation of woman, the cutting out of the rib from which arises the wound in the woman's body, this castration is, in essence, the punishment of onanism. How was man, when he first had the idea, "Onanism is to be punished," to choose any other form of punishment with which to frighten himself than the castration, since the symbolic castration—relaxation—must follow unconditionally, upon every single act of onanism?

So far the matter is more or less clear, but now remains the question, Why does man see a sin in onanism? It is easy to suggest a partial answer at least. Think of a tiny infant, a boy. At first he has to learn to know himself, to catch hold of everything within his reach, and play with everything that belongs to him, with his ear, his nose, his fingers, his toes. Will some inborn sense of morality make him neglect in his experiments and games the little tassel plaything that hangs below his tiny body? Surely not. But what happens now, when he plays? His delighted mother coaxes him to touch his ear, his nose, his mouth, fingers and toes, and encourages him in every way. But so soon as the baby plays with his tassel there comes a great hand —a hand that man's mythologizing powers will change into the hand of God—that removes the tiny baby hand. Perhaps, almost certainly, there comes into the face of this being who owns the hand, of the mother, therefore, a grave look, anxious and ashamed. How great must be the terror of the child, how deep the impression made, if always and only with this particular action there comes the hand of God to stop him. But all this belongs to a stage when the child cannot yet talk, yes, when he has not yet been able to understand a word. The command is buried deep in the lowest depths of the soul, deeper than speaking, walking, chewing, deeper than the picture of sun and moon, of round and angular, of father and mother: "Thou shalt not play with thy sexual organ," and at once is joined to it the thought, "All pleasure is wicked." And perhaps experience adds to this: "If thou dost play with thy sexual organ, something shall be taken away from thee." And then follows necessarily the further idea, "Not only thy hand, but the organ itself shall also be removed." We really know nothing about the child, we do not know how far it already has developed a sense of personality, whether it is born with the feeling that hand and leg belong to it, or whether it must first acquire this. Has it already from the beginning onwards the sense of being "I," of being separate from its environment? We don't know; we only know this one thing, that it is not until later, beginning first around the age of three, that the child uses the word "I." Is it therefore overdaring to believe that, to begin with, he thinks of himself as a stranger, as someone else, since the little Hans does not say, "I want a drink," but "Hans wants a drink"? We humans are foolish folk who lack the courage to pose such questions, simply because our parents once upon a time forbade us to ask so many questions.

There still remains one difficulty in the legend of Creation, to which I should like to refer briefly. We both interpret the fashioning of Eve from Adam's rib as the transformation of a man into a woman through castration. Then our logical mode of thinking objects to the two Adams, one who remains Adam and one who becomes Eve. But that is only a stupid rationalization, for when has legend ever balked at making two people out of one, or one out of two? The very existence of drama depends on the power of the dramatist to cleave himself into two, nay, into twenty different characters. The dream does the same, and every human being also, for to every man only such things are true in the world as exist within himself; he is continually projecting himself into his environment. That is life, and so it must be; the It drives us that way.

But forgive me, you do not like this philosophizing. And perhaps you are right. Let us return to the realm of so-called fact.

"Man was not made to live alone, I will give to him a helpmate," says the Lord God, and He makes a creature which has an opening in the place where man has a projection, and where he is flat He rounds out two breasts. In that there lies the essence of woman's helpfulness. It is the same idea as the child's: in order to be born, an Eve has to be made by taking out Adam's rib. Is it not worthy of remark that there should be such consonance between the mind of the child and that of the race? If it would please you, we will ourselves do some research into the myths and legends, the modes of architecture and the technical achievement of different races; perhaps we shall find the child-mind on every side. That would not be unimportant; it would make us tolerant towards little children, of whom Christ said, "Of such is the Kingdom of Heaven." Yes, perchance we should also rediscover our long lost wonderment, the child's power of adoration, and that would indeed be something in our Malthusian age.

But give heed to that word "helpmate." It does not contain the slightest hint that man is transformed in the whole of his nature or his strivings; in spite of the castration he remains what he was, a being who is centered upon himself, who loves himself, who seeks and finds his own pleasure. Only now someone has come who helps him in this, who makes it possible for him to find part of his pleasure elsewhere than in his own body. The urge to seek self-gratification remains; the penis is not destroyed, it is still there; Adam is not changed, he is still subject, exactly as before, to the compulsion to secure pleasure for himself. That is a curious thing.

How so? May it not be that the verdict of wise and foolish alike, that masturbation is a substitute for sexual intercourse, arising from the lack of an object, because the man's desire finds no woman available, and therefore takes refuge in what can be done by himself—may not all this be mistaken? Consider the facts. The little child, the infant, is driven to masturbate. The growing child, at puberty, repeats the act, and—strange to say—the old man and the old woman take to it anew. And between childhood and old age there is a period when masturbation frequently vanishes and intercourse with someone else makes its appearance. Is it not rather that sexual intercourse is a substitute for masturbation? And is it really so, as the Bible puts it, that this intercourse is only a help?

Yes, my best of friends, so it is. It is really true that masturbation goes quietly on, in spite of love and marriage, in close connection with love and marriage. It does not cease, it is always there and lasts till death. Consult your own memories, you will find the proof in many a day and many a night, in your love-play with your husband and in your own phantasy life. And when you have found it, your eyes will be opened to a thousand phenomena that show, clearly or obscurely, their connection with, indeed, their absolute dependence upon, onanism. And you will be cautious in the future about calling this an unnatural vice, even if you cannot make yourself regard it as the creator of what is good. For to get to that point you must vanquish the hand of God, the mother's hand, which once interrupted your own game of pleasure, must vanquish it within your own soul. And that is in no one's power.

Affectionately,
PATRIK TROLL.

✳ LETTER XII ✳

I really can't understand what imp has possessed you, my dear! A little while ago you wrote delightedly of your conviction that the castration ideas were more and more obvious in human affairs, and today you bring forward objections. But after all, why am I surprised? All men suppress these things into the depths of their souls; how much more, therefore, do you, who are, and always were, so proud? The thought of castration in itself imposes a heavier burden upon woman than upon man. With him there is always the compensating fact that he is still a man, wearing upon his body the scepter of manhood, of lordship, to counterbalance in some measure the weight of the castration complex. He has wishes and fears, but he sees with his own eyes that he still possesses the member for whose sake he suffers anxiety. But the maiden says, at the sight of her emptiness, "I am already castrated; my only hope is that the wound will heal, and this lordly organ grow out anew." To renounce this hope, to come to terms with the feeling of one's own inferiority, still more, to convert this feeling, as you have done, into an honest recognition of one's womanhood, with pride and love for one's womanhood, demands fiercer struggles to effect successful repressions. Everything must be sunk deeper and thrust away, and the slightest agitation of the repressive mass causes revulsions of feeling which we men never know. That can be seen, and you yourself can feel it, at the time of the period. The monthly bleeding, the woman's brand of Cain, stirs up the castration complex, brings the repressed poisons up out of the dregs of the unconscious, and in conjunction with many other things, clouds the serene naïveté of human kind.

Is it not strange that Europeans immediately think of bleeding at the mention of the period? Even this interest in blood, narrow as it is, is linked up in our crude thinking only with dirt and smell, secret shame, pain and child-bearing. And yet there is a wealth of interest in the phenomenon of this rhythmic flow!

For this is the essential characteristic: the intoxication, the ardor, the sexual passion of woman is greatly intensified during the days of bleeding, and, like the animals, who are by no means lower than mankind, she attracts the man to herself in some way or other during this period; and intercourse during menstruation is most passionate and joyful, or rather, it would be so were it not banned by custom. As evidence that this is really so, there is the curious fact that three-fourths of all cases of rape take place during the period. In other words, a mysterious something in the menstruating woman throws the man into a madness in which he no longer fears to commit the crime. Eve tempts Adam; so it was, and is, and ever shall be. She must tempt him, because she is ardent in bleeding, because she herself feels desire. Mothers teach their daughters that the period is there for the sake of the babies. That is a strange error, a fateful deception. For the attempt to refer all erotic phenomena to the instinct of reproduction is one of the greatest stupidities of our time. Every bough of apple blossom, every flower and every work of man is evidence against so narrow an interpretation of the purposes of Nature. Of the twenty thousand ova capable of being fertilized which are born with the girl-child, only a few hundred are left by the time she has reached puberty, and of these, to take a high figure, a dozen come to fruition; and of the many millions of the man's spermatozoa, countless troops perish without even reaching a woman's body. People babble a great deal of nonsense, and I may include myself in their number.

Don't you see the crazy associations, the tangled threads, that run from one complex to another? In the center of the love life one finds blood and the delight in blood. In contemplating the life and thought of mankind what is man to do? Is one to laugh, to scorn, to scold? Perhaps it is better to remain aware of one's own foolishness, to pray, with the publican, "God be merciful to me, a sinner." But I should like to say that it is untrue that cruelty is perverse. Every year Christendom celebrates Good Friday, the day of joy. Humanity created for itself a God who suffered, because it felt that pain was a way to heaven, because sorrow and bloody torment it esteems divine. Were your lips never made to bleed by kissing? Was your skin never reddened by the ardent sucking of the mouth? Did you never bite into an encircling arm, and did it not seem good to you to be bruised? And then you come to me with the foolishness that children should not be punished? Ah, most dear lady, but the child wants to be punished, he yearns for it, he pants for a beating, as my father used to say. And he uses a thousand tricks to attract punishment. The mother soothes the child on her arm with gentle pats, and the child smiles; she washes it and kisses it on its rosy little bottom, which only just now was so full of dirt, and as the last and greatest treat she gives the dancing babe a slap which sets it crowing with joy.

Have you never quarreled with your darling? Then reflect: What was your purpose and how did it all turn out? A prick from this one, an injurious word from the other, and then things got warmer, sharper, with scorn, anger, rage. What were you after, in wantonly getting your husband to take up arms? Did you desire what really happened, that he should clap on his hat, take up his stick, and bang the door to? Ah, no; he ought to have opened the door which led into the chamber of your body, let his little man enter, put onto it the hat of the mother's womb, crowned it with the wreaths and coronets of your virginity. Nature gave him a stick that he might use it for you, beat you with it, and love you with cruelty. For in every language the sign of manhood is called the rod. Cruelty is indissolubly linked with love, and red blood is the deepest enchantment of red love.

94

Without the period there would be no love of woman, at least none that would justify the words that woman was created to be the helpmate of man. And that is the heart of the matter. For to your amazement and your uplifting you will find that much, if not everything, in human life arises out of love, and the fact that Eve was given to Adam not for childbearing but to be a helpmate, gives one the power to say a word at least in opposition to the clamor of the crowd who do not know their Bible.

Well, then, this is what appears to me to be the case. I take the woman's period, and especially the bleeding, to be the means of attracting the man. And that view is supported by a trifling observation I have made from time to time. Many women who have been parted from their husbands for a long time start their period on the day they are united. They think the long separation may have perhaps brought about an estrangement, and to counteract this they prepare the magic love philter which shall bring the husband to their arms.

You know I like turning things inside out, and I hope I have succeeded in doing so here, but to be fair I will tell you of two other motives which prompt the It to take this curious step, and which will meet with less opposition from you. If a woman is having her period, she cannot be pregnant. Through her bleeding the It gives obvious and eloquent proof to the husband that his wife is faithful. "See," she says, "if I now have a baby it must be from you, for I was menstruating when you came." Now, if I were naughty, and wanted to arouse the menfolk—but anyhow, it is understood that these letters are for your eyes alone, so I can say my little wickedness to you without making mischief among the husbands. A strong emphasis upon innocence always gives rise to the suspicion that it conceals the consciousness of guilt. And, indeed, in cases of this kind which I have investigated I have discovered the disloyalty which had to be concealed by the red blood, though certainly not actual infidelity with another man. That I never remember to have met with, but only the thought of infidelity, the half-repressed sin, whose hidden mischief is all the greater because it falls short of action and stays clogged in the morasses of the soul. You would never believe what secret humor is to be derived from these matters. Life offers unique contrasts. It knows right well how to protest innocence and confess guilt in one and the same phrase. In exactly the same way does the second purpose of the It, which I spoke of, play a double game. "Entice the man," it says to the woman, "entice him with the blood of your love." The woman listens to this voice, but irresolutely asks, "And if it fails?" "Tush!" says the It, with a laugh, "then you will have the best of excuses to offer your offended vanity, for how could a man wish to have contact with a woman who is unclean?" In actual fact, why should he wish it, since it has been forbidden for thousands of years? If then the embrace is tempestuous, all is well, the more so because the prohibition of custom was defied, and if it is not, then that is because custom forbids.

With such reassurances the It plays busily and with success. Thus it implants near the loving mouth which is yearning for kisses, a disfiguring eczema; if in spite of that I am kissed, then indeed I shall be happy, but if the kiss is not forthcoming, then it is not because I am unloved but because of the revolting eczema. That is one of the reasons why the adolescent boy has pimples on his forehead, and the girl, going to a ball, finds on her bare shoulder or bosom little spots which succeed in attracting the eye to these parts; why the hand becomes cold and moist if it is stretched out to meet a lover; why the mouth which desires kisses has an evil smell; why a flux starts in the sexual parts; why women suddenly grow ugly and capricious, and men tactless and childishly embarrassed. And with that I come very close to the great riddle, why human custom—so far as I know, at all times and in every country—has forbidden sexual intercourse during the period.

This is now the third time that I have dealt with a prohibition in these letters: first against onanism, then against incest with the mother, and now against sexual relations during the period. If, therefore, strong barriers are raised against our mightiest instinct, self-love, against incest with the mother, and now against sexual intercourse itself, one may expect something big in the way of results. As a matter of fact, these three prohibitions have produced results the influence of which can scarcely be estimated. With your permission I will divert myself a little with these.

First there is the oldest prohibition, that against onanism, which first affects the life of the individual. Pleasure, once enjoyed, longs after fresh pleasure, and since the way to self-pleasure is barred, the instinct abandons itself even more fully to similar enjoyments which will be continued by the hand of another, by the mother's hand in washing and bathing, in urinating, and in every other way which necessity and the all-covering sanctity of mother love makes possible and free. The erotic ties with the mother are strengthened through the prohibition of masturbation, the passion for the mother is all the greater. And the stronger that is, the stronger also will be the resistance against this purely sexual, physical love, until finally it reaches its limit in the express command against incest with the mother. A new outlet is now sought, which leads by way of the symbolic resemblance, *Mutter, Gebärmutter* (mother, womb), to the impulse to have intercourse with some other woman. The right time for this intercourse is when the womb is ardent, during the period. But precisely at this time there breaks in between the wish and its fulfillment a "No," which has the force of law in the Hebraic civilization, as well as in many others. Obviously nature (*Gottnatur*) makes use of such prohibitions, which are framed in such or such a manner, as need arises. Our own age, for example, instead of forbidding intercourse during the period, has chosen the form of excluding, under legal penalties, from every sexual act except masturbation, certain years, and those are the very years of puberty when passion is hottest. Perhaps it would interest you to think out the consequences of such a prohibition.

For one thing is clear: the prohibition can indeed repress the wish, can drive it out of its path, but it does not destroy it. It merely forces it to seek out other means of fulfillment. These it finds in a multitude of ways, in every activity of life that you can think of; in the invention of chimneys or of steamships, in the use of spade and plough, in poem and in reflection, in the love of God and of nature, in crime and heroism, in good deeds and in evil, in religion and in blasphemy, in the staining of the tablecloth and the breaking of the glass, in heartbeats, or in sweating, in hunger and thirst, in fatigue and in energy, in drug taking or in temperance, in marital infidelity or in vows of chastity, in walking, standing, lying down, in pain and in joy, in happiness and discontent. And—now at last I am going to show that I am a physician—the repressed wish is to be seen in every sickness, whether it be organic or functional, whether it is called pneumonia or melancholia. But that is a long chapter, too long to follow up today. Still I will cast you just a tiny bait, at which I hope you will nibble.

What arises from the wish of the man to have intercourse with a woman during her period? What excites him is the blood. The tendency to cruelty, which is with him from the beginning, now flares up. He invents weapons, devises operations, goes to war, builds slaughter houses, climbs mountains, goes exploring over the sea, seeks the North Pole or secret Tibet, hunts, fishes, beats his children and thunders at his wife. And what comes from the woman's wish? She fixes a bandage between her thighs, unconsciously commits onanism under the universally approved excuse of cleanliness. And if she is dainty she will do this a day in advance to be on the safe side, and for the same reason wear it a day longer. And if that does not suit her, she will make the flow last longer or come on more frequently The urge to self-love has freer sway, and through the desire of woman builds the foundation of our civilization, cleanliness, and from that, water supply, baths, and canalization, hygiene and soap, and then comes the value attached to purity of mind, nobility of soul, the inner harmony of aspiring humanity, while man as the blood worshiper presses into the mysterious bowels of the earth and untiringly goes on working upon life.

There are strange courses in life, some of which look like circles. But in the last resort there remains to us mortals one thing alone—wonder!

Your affectionate,
PATRIK TROLL.

❋ LETTER XIII ❋

I am grateful to you, my dear, for eschewing technical expressions and definitions. One can get on without them and I shall at least be in no danger of bringing disgrace upon myself. For in strictest confidence I will confess to you that often I myself do not understand definitions, either my own or other people's!

Instead of giving definitions, I will do as you wish and tell you something more about the influence of the prohibition of sexual intercourse during the period, and since fate has destined me to be a physician, it shall be something medical. During the last hundred years or so, since the very masculine symbol of the angel was converted into a feminine figure, it has been the fashion to credit woman with a noble soul, which is revealed in her horror of everything erotic, for this indeed is looked upon as dirty, and which treats in particular the woman's "unclean" time, the period, as a shameful secret. And this madness—for how else is one to describe a mode of thinking which disallows sensuality in women, as though nature were so stupid as to bestow upon that half of humanity which must bear the burden of pregnancy less desire than upon the other half. This madness is carried so far that the textbooks you rate so highly speak in all seriousness of the existence of frigid women, publish statistics thereon, based on the hypocrisy forced on women by custom, and so drive them, learnedly ignorant as they are, deeper and deeper into deception and fraud. For, thinks that poor anxious creature whom we call a young lady, why should I not behave as if I really had nothing between my head and my feet, since my mother certainly desires it, my father regards it as self-evident, and my lover adores my purity? She plays her enforced role with skill; indeed, she really strives to live as if this behavior were natural to her, and she is only defeated by the madness of the fourth week. Then she needs a help, a ribbon, so to speak, to tie on her mask more firmly, and this help she finds in falling ill, first and foremost with pains in the os sacrum. The woman's activity during intercourse consists in the moving backwards and forwards of the sacrum: pain in the bone prevents this movement, and strengthens the prohibition of intercourse.

You must not think, my dear, that by making these little observations I imagine I am solving any problem whatsoever. I only want to make you understand what so often seems incomprehensible to you, why I am forever asking of my patients the purpose of their illness. I don't know whether the illness has a purpose, and I don't care, but

99

sucn an inquiry has often proved its value by somehow stirring up the patient's It, and not seldom it has led to the disappearance of a symptom. The procedure is a little crude, suggestive of charlatanism, if you like, and I am quite aware that every spectacled wiseacre will sniff at it. But you have asked me about it and I give you my answer.

Sometime or other in the course of the treatment I am accustomed to call my patient's attention to the fact that from the human semen and ovum there is born, not a dog, nor a cat, but a human being, that there is some force within the germ which is able to fashion a nose, a finger, a brain, that accordingly this force, which carries out such marvelous processes, might well produce a headache or diarrhoea or an inflamed throat, that indeed I do not consider it unreasonable to suppose that it can even manufacture pneumonia or gout or cancer. I dare to go so far with my patients as to maintain that the force really does such things, that according to its pleasure it makes people ill for specific ends, that according to its pleasure it selects for such ends the place, the time, and the nature of the illness. And with all this I never worry myself in the least as to whether I believe what I am saying or not; I simply say it. And then I ask the patient, Why have you a nose? To smell with, he replies. So I say, Your It has given you a cold in order that you shall not smell something or other. Find out what it is you are not to smell. And now and again the patient will actually find out some smell which he wants to escape, and you need not believe it, but I do —when he has found it, the cold disappears.

I am of the opinion that the pains in the sacrum facilitate the woman's resistance against her desire during the period. But it does not necessarily follow that this is the only purpose served by pains of this sort. You must remember that the whole mystery of Christianity lies in this word *Kreuz* (cross), that the *Kreuz*-bone, os sacrum, holy bone, conceals the problem of the mother. Upon that and upon another question I do not wish to say more at this point, but would rather go on a little further. At times the pains in the sacrum are not sufficient; then are added, as a warning, cramps and recurrent abdominal pains, and if these fall short of their purpose, the It seizes upon headache, in order to deaden thought, migraine, indigestion, and vomiting. Here you are surrounded by strange symbols, for indigestion, vomiting, the sensation of a bursting head, are all birth images in the form of sickness.

You understand that where everything is so complicated it is impossible to give clear explanations. But one thing I am able to say: the more severe the inner conflict, so much the more severe are people's illnesses, which indeed symbolically represent the conflict; and vice versa, the more serious the disease, so much the greater must be the desire and the resistance to that desire. This holds for all sicknesses, not only for those of the period. If a slighter degree of ill health does not suffice to solve or to suppress the conflict, the It has recourse to more serious forms, to fever, which keeps the man indoors, to pneumonia or a broken leg, which fling him into bed, so that the circumstances are narrowed that might heighten his desire, to fainting, which excludes every impression, to chronic disease, paralysis, cancer and consumption, which slowly bury the conflict, and finally to death. For he alone will die who wishes to die, to whom life is intolerable.

May I repeat what I am saying? Illness has a purpose; it has to resolve the conflict, to repress it, or to prevent what is already repressed from entering consciousness; it has to punish a sin against a commandment, and in doing that it goes so far that one can draw conclusions as to the time, the place, and the nature of the sin that is to be punished, by considering the time, the place, and the nature of the illness. Whoever breaks an arm has either sinned or wished to commit a sin with that arm, perhaps murder, perhaps theft or masturbation; whoever grows blind, desires no more to see, has sinned with his eyes or wishes to sin with them; whoever gets hoarse has a secret and dares not tell it aloud. But the sickness is also a symbol, a representation of something going on within, a drama staged by the It, by means of which it announces what it could not say with the tongue. In other words, sickness, every sickness, whether it be called organic or "nervous," and death, too, are just as purposeful as playing the piano, striking a match, or crossing one's legs. They are a declaration from the It, clearer, more effective than speech could be, yes, more than the whole of the conscious life can give. *Tat vam asi.*

And how strangely the It amuses itself! Just now I mentioned consumption (*Schwindsucht*), the pining to die away (*Sucht zum Schwinden*). The desire must die away, then, the desire for the in and out, the up and down of erotic love, which is symbolized in breathing. And with the desire the lungs die away, the representatives of symbolic conception and birth; the body dies away, the phallus symbol, it *must* die away, because desire increases during the illness, because the guilt of the ever-repeated symbolic dissipation of semen in the sputum is continually growing greater, because the longing for death is forever being renewed by the suppression of these symbols as they strive to reach the conscious level, because the It allows pulmonary disease to bring beauty to the eyes and cheek, alluring poisons! And the cruel, murderous play of the It is all the madder because it is founded on error, for *Sucht* (disease, passion) has nothing to do with *Sehnsucht* (longing), but is derived from *siech* (sick). But the It appears to know nothing of etymology; it attends to the sounds of words, like the unlearned Greek, and makes use of their sounds to bring about disease, and to increase it.

It would not be at all a bad thing if the elite of the medical world would be a little less clever, and would adopt a more primitive method of thinking, and reason more as children do. Perhaps something better would come of that than of the building of sanatoria and public clinics.

Am I right in thinking you could bear to hear a few emphatic words about cancer, too? With the help of our assiduous obedience to the dictates of anatomy, physiology, bacteriology, and statistics we have gradually made such progress that no one knows any longer what is to be called cancer and what is not. The consequence is that the word cancer, like the word syphilis, is spoken and is printed a hundred times a day, for what do men love to hear better than ghost stories? And since one can no longer believe in ghosts, these two names, still indefinable in spite or by reason of so much scientific knowledge, which call up so much that is grotesque and horrible in their associations, provide a good substitute for grizzly specters. Now there is a phenomenon in the life of the It, anxiety, to wit, which, because it arises in times preceding memory, takes possession of these two words in order to play tricks on the lofty intellect and to provide it with an explanation of the appearance of anxiety. If you count in masturbation-anxiety you have a great mass of associated anxiety, and anxiety is half of life. But I wanted to tell you something of my cancer lore, and I see that anger has lured me from my path. Pay a call upon your friend next door, and bring the conversation round to the subject of cancer; she will jump at it, for she has the dread of cancer like every other woman, and then ask her what comes to her mind at the sound of the word *krebs* (cancer and crab). She will tell you at once, "The crab walks backwards," and after some delay, "It has shears." And if you have torn at the veil of scientific mystery as impudently as I, you will conclude from that that the superficial complex which feeds the dread of cancer has something to do with a backwards movement, and deeper down is something connected with the idea of cutting. That is quite easy to explain since a patient who has cancer goes backwards in strength and courage, and the doctor cuts if he sees the illness "at an early stage." But if you go further into the question you will find that the backwards movement stands in an enforced relationship to childish observations, which, after undergoing early repression, have been operating ever since. The little angel of a girl-child is certainly not innocent, as people like to suppose, certainly not pure, as superior people maintain, any more than is the dove which is displayed to us as the symbol of innocence and purity, though the Greeks made it the companion of the goddess of love; this little angel sees the curious movements of hound and bitch, of cock and hen, and since she is not stupid and guesses from the foolish behavior of mother and teacher that she is standing before the secret of sex-love, she makes a mental comparison between this and that other, to her far more important, secret of the parental bedroom.

In other words, the child comes to the idea that intercourse takes place from behind, and buries this idea in the depths of her mind until one day it rises again in the form of anxiety by the path of association via "backwards" and "crab." But the shears—I need hardly say—lead directly and indirectly to the great anxiety problem of castration, of the transformation of the woman supposed to be originally a man, into a female woman, through the cutting off of the penis, which leaves between the legs a hole

103

which bleeds from time to time. This idea itself is supported by experience, one of the first experiences of life, the cutting of the umbilical cord.

Of all the theories put forward in connection with cancer, only one has in my opinion survived the passage of time, namely, that cancer leads through definite stages to death. I mean by that that what is not fatal is not cancer. From that you may conclude that I hold out no hope of a new method of curing cancer. But in all the many cases of so-called cancer it is worth just once questioning the It of the patient.

Ever yours,
PATRIK TROLL.

✳ LETTER XIV ✳

My dear, you have understood aright: the life of man is governed by the Oedipus complex. But I don't quite know in what way I am to fulfill your desire to hear more about it. The legend itself, how Oedipus, the guiltily innocent, slays his father and begets unhallowed children by incestuous intercourse with his mother, you know already, or you will easily find it in any book of legends. That its content—the passionate desire of the son for the mother, and his murderous hatred against the father—is typical, and is valid for all men of all times, and that in this story a deep secret of man's being is half disclosed, I have already told you. And its application to your own life, to mine, or to anybody's else, you must make for yourself. At most I can tell you a few tales, from which you can pick out a little for yourself. But you must not lose patience; the life of the unconscious is hard to decipher and you know I make nothing of a few mistakes.

More than twenty years ago—I was then still a young doctor, with a foolhardy confidence in my own powers—a boy was brought to me suffering from a curious skin complaint called scleroderma. The wide extent of the trouble, which spread over the greater part of his abdomen, breast, arms and legs, had led the authorities to give up his case as hopeless. I boldly undertook to treat him in accordance with the principles I had learned from Schweninger, and as the sickness came to an end after perhaps a year, I felt no presumption in posing as a god, and ascribing to my own—yes, my own—hard work the recovery, or what is called a recovery, for we doctors are very optimistic on that point when estimating our own results. At the end there remained much to be desired, as, for instance, the scars which the process of healing left behind, the size of which you can scarcely imagine, elbow joints so contracted that the arms could not be fully outstretched and a leg that was, and that remained, as thin as a lath. The excessive irritability of the heart, too, which showed in the occasional racing speed of its beats and in anxiety states, together with an almost continuous headache and a whole series of neurotic symptoms could not be got rid of. Still, the boy lived, passed through the Gymnasium, was for some years an army officer, and then changed to one of the learned professions. From time to time he returned to me for a few weeks' freshening. Between whiles he was treated by one doctor or another for the many troubles he had, and finally he stayed under the charge of a well-known Berlin physician, whose name you and I both respect. For some years I heard no more of him, then came the war, and a few months later he came again to me.

This time the illness took a curious form. Shortly after the outbreak of war Herr D., as we will call him, had been taken ill with severe rigors, and a temperature as high as 104° F. This had lasted some time without the doctor being able to discover the cause. At last the case seemed to declare itself. The temperature sank in the morning below 97° F., to rise again at night to 102°-104° F. The blood was examined for malaria, once, twice, a dozen, twenty times over, to no purpose, and even quinine and arsenic which were given as a precautionary measure proved ineffectual. In the meantime a test for tuberculosis produced no result, and an old diagnosis of syphilis was revived on account of which some years before he had received antiluetic treatment (how fine that sounds!). The famous Wassermann test—you know what that is— gave doubtful results and in the end everybody was just as wise as before. Suddenly the fever disappeared, the completely prostrated body began to recover, his uniforms were put ready to use, and all seemed well. Herr D. went out again, made a formal request to his ministry, which had declared him "indispensable," to be allowed to go as a volunteer to the front. He received permission, and on the same day was taken ill with fever and throat pains. The doctors who were summoned examined his mouth and found sores on the tonsils, and palate. But since after the fever disappeared the sores increased, a suspicious breaking-out appeared, and some of the glands were so obliging as to be swollen, they pronounced it a recurrence of the earlier attack of alleged syphilis, for which I cannot blame them. The Wassermann test was certainly negative, it remained so, but—in short, mercury and salvarsan were given. The result was terribly disappointing. Instead of his improving, the mysterious fever returned, sometimes accompanied by complete loss of consciousness, the patient got weaker and weaker, and finally with the last remnants of his strength he was brought to me.

At that time I was not so certain as I am now of the dependence of organic disease upon the It, and moreover, misled by some wickedness in my unconscious, I thought that if I were to change my method of treatment I should forfeit the confidence of a patient whom I had treated for fifteen years by another method. In brief, I gave him the treatment which he was accustomed to have from me, very hot baths locally, massage, careful diet, and so forth. This did not exclude my attempt to influence his mind, only the attempt was made in the old way, to help the patient by authoritative suggestion. First I declared with complete conviction and sufficient emphasis to allow of no opposition, that there could be no question of syphilis; and then I showed him that his illness had some connection with his wish to go to the front. He resisted this suggestion for a time, but finally conceded that it might possibly be so, and told me a few details of the past which confirmed my view.

The case seemed to go on well. Herr D.'s strength returned, he began to take walks in the country round about, and spoke again of announcing his readiness to take military service. This was a serious business for him; he came of an old military family and had thrown himself into his duties as an officer with zest. One day the fever returned again in its old fashion with a low morning temperature and a steep evening rise, and at the same time there appeared again the remarkable symptoms which suggested syphilis. There came a sore on one elbow joint; then, when this was healed, one below the thigh, and finally another on the penis. In between there appeared an eruption resembling roseola; in short all sorts of things happened which made me waver as to whether it was syphilis or not. The Wassermann tests carried out at the university clinic gave varying results; sometimes the verdict was definitely negative, sometimes it was uncertain. Thus three months went by. Suddenly, and without my being able to discover any sort of reason, the whole illness cleared up. Herr D. began to flourish. He gained in strength and weight every day, and all was well. I gave him the prescribed injections against smallpox, cholera and typhus, and he put his knapsack on his back and took leave of me, intending to report to the local command immediately after a three-days' walking tour in the Black Forest. On the third day of his tour the fever broke out again and he came back to me for some days, but then went on to Berlin to see what could be done there for his health by another medical adviser.

In the summer of 1916, nearly sixteen months afterwards, he returned. He had been treated for a long time in Berlin, had then been sent to Aix to try the waters, to Sylt, in the hills, to Nerndorf, and finally, had been dangerously ill for weeks and months in Berlin. His condition was as before, frequent attacks of raging fever, sores, fainting fits, heart trouble, and so on. I was surprised to find that his old illness of scleroderma had broken out again in certain parts, and that the neurotic symptoms had increased.

In the meantime I myself had changed very much. During my stay at the war hospital I had often seen the results of psychoanalytic treatment of the wounded and of men with organic diseases; my private practice had given me a good deal of experience; I had elaborated a special technique of my own; in short, I took on the treatment of Herr D. with the firm determination not to bother myself about a diagnosis or about physiological or medical therapy but to analyze him. Success followed; one symptom after another disappeared, and after six months Herr D. went to the front as an infantry officer, to fall on the field of battle two months later. Whether his cure would have been permanent I cannot decide, for death has intervened. So far as my present knowledge goes, I think that the time allowed for treatment was too short, and that the patient would probably have relapsed if he had survived. I am, however, convinced that a permanent cure was possible in his case. The matter is really unimportant. I tell you these histories not because of their results, but to give you an idea of the workings of the Oedipus complex.

Concerning the treatment I will only say that it was far from easy. Fresh resistances on the part of the patient were always coming up. My Christian name would be connected with that of a false Irishman. Sometimes they took my rubber shoes or my carelessly knotted tie as an excuse. The cravat was for Herr D. a long, flabby testicle, such as he had once seen on his old father; the rubber shoes revived old childish vexations. Then again he would entrench himself behind my second name, George, which reminded him of a fictitious character in *Robert the Cabin Boy,* of a seducer and thief; with that emerged a whole crowd of Georges, all of them blackguards, until at length one special criminal came into view in the shape of a teacher who without listening to any explanation, had boxed D.'s ears whilst he was at the Gymnasium. We took longest over getting the significance of one of my habitual phrases at that time; now and again I would use the words, "To be frank," or even, "I must frankly confess to you." D. concluded from that that I was lying, which was not at all stupid of him.

The resistance of the patient to the doctor is the objective of every treatment. The It from the beginning certainly does not wish to become healthy, however much the illness afflicts the patient. On the contrary, the very existence of the disease proves, in the face of all the assurances, complaints and endeavors of the conscious man, that this man wishes to be ill. This is important, dear. A sick man wishes to be sick, and he struggles against the healing, much as a spoiled little girl who in her heart would like to go to the ball will nevertheless do everything she can to put obstacles in the way of going. It is always worth while to look carefully at the objections put forwards by such resistances against the doctor; they expose many things in the patient himself. So it was in D. The flabby testicles and the rubber shoes of the weakling excited opposition in him, because he himself had a very strong sense of impotence. The lie, as he understood it, in "Patrik" and "to be frank," he abominated like all honorable people, but like all honorable people he deceived himself, and therefore others, without ceasing. He was so irritated by my Christian name because he hated his own name, Henry. He got his intimate friends to call him Harry instead, because one of his heroic ancestors had borne this name. And in that he felt the lie, for some vague feeling from the It warned him that he was no hero, that his disease was the creation of his fear-ridden unconscious. "George" finally was intolerable to him, because, like the thief in *Robert the Cabin Boy*—this memory emerged during severe illness and fever—he had once stolen two medals from his father. But "medal" led him to the word "medallion." His father wore a medallion with the portrait of his mother, and this medallion was really the object of his theft. He wanted to steal his mother away from his father. Oedipus!

Still another curious thing remains to be mentioned. D. carried about with him a lot of far-reaching complexes, which were all, in the last analysis, connected with the Oedipus complex and the idea of impotence. If, during the treatment, the Oedipus complex was touched in a sensitive spot, the fever returned. If one came too close to the impotency idea, then the syphilitic symptoms reappeared. For that D. gave me the following explanation: "In the course of time I have become quite indifferent to my mother. I am ashamed of that and, whenever I am compelled to think of her, I try once again to rekindle the old flame. And because my mind fails me in that, the fever starts in my body. To my father, who was old, in my opinion too old, when I was born, I ascribe all the blame of my impotence. And because I cannot punish him personally, since he is long dead, I punish him in his image, in the begetter, in that which begets, in my own sex organ. This has the advantage that at the same time I punish myself for my lie; for not my father, but I myself am to blame for my impotence. And finally, a syphilitic ought to be impotent; it is well for him and for women." You see, D. had something of the Troll in him; that made me like him.

And now the Oedipus complex. In the foreground stands the passion for the mother. I omit a mass of detail:

I gave you, as an example, the theft of the medal, which signified the symbolic theft of the mother. Instead of small clues I will pick out some which will show you the deeper workings of the It. First, there is D.'s persistent susceptibility which from time to time degenerated into severe and tedious illnesses. The sick man needs nursing, he forces matters so that he gets nursed. Every illness is a repetition of the infantile situation and arises from the longing for the mother. Every sick man is a child and everyone who takes care of the sick man becomes for him the mother. The susceptibility, the frequency and the duration of the illnesses, are a proof of the extent to which the man is still bound to the mother imago. You can go further in your conclusions without much danger. If anyone gets ill, it is probable that in some way or other, in close proximity to the time of the outbreak of his illness, he was forcibly reminded of the mother imago, of the imago of his earliest weeks of infancy. Yes, I am not afraid to use the word "always" in this connection. It is always so. And there is scarcely a stronger proof to be found of anyone's passion for the mother, of his subjection to the Oedipus complex, than lasting delicacy.

This passion, in D.'s case, brought about yet another result which is often to be noticed. The master, the possessor of the mother, is the father. Does the son wish to be the master, the possessor, the lover of his mother? Then he must become like his father. That happened with D. Originally—I have seen portraits of him as a child—there wasn't a trace of resemblance to his father, and, according to the mother, they had nothing in common in their natures. In the twenty years during which I knew my patient, I was able to observe from year to year, in gestures, bearing, habits, in face and stature, in thought and in character, how a gradual approach was made to the father. Not that the It changed, but on top of it, so that the real essential man only now and again appeared, there was built up a superficial It, if you like to call it so, and this new It—that is what proves my case—disappeared during the process of cure. The true D. reappeared. D. showed his growing resemblance to his father most clearly in his premature ageing. Already, when thirty years old, his hair was perfectly white. I have seen several cases where the hair turned grey in imitation of the father, and even where it changed back again later. How it would have been with D., I do not know. He died too early.

A third sign of his devotion to his mother imago was his impotence. The first question to be asked of any man lacking virility is always, how does he stand in regard to his mother? D. had the characteristic form of impotence, as described by Freud: he classified women as ladies and prostitutes. With the lady, that is with the mother, he was impotent; with the prostitute he was able to have intercourse. But his mother's image worked mightily in him, and so his It, to protect him absolutely from every sort of incest, even from that in the person of the harlot, invented the syphilitic infection. That anyone, under the pressure of the Oedipus complex, can become infected by any woman whatever, I have often seen. But that this infection should be invented by the It, and dramatically acted for years with the symptoms of syphilis or gonorrhea, seems to be rare. Up till now I have seen only two definite instances, in D., and in a woman.

Further, the beginning of the illness—the early symptoms are always worth observing for they reveal a great deal concerning the designs of the It—was the scleroderma in the left leg, which then went on to the right arm. What is going on in the left leg tells me in its own foolish speech which I have interpreted for myself, "This man wants to go the wrong way, the wicked left way, but his It prevents him from doing so." If the right arm gets ill in any way, then it signifies, "This right arm wants to do something at which the It takes offense, and therefore has been lamed in its action." Shortly before the onset of the trouble in the leg there occurred a significant event. D.'s mother became pregnant. He was fifteen years old at that time, but says he noticed nothing of her condition; that is a sure sign that deep disturbances of his being were forcing him to repress. This struggle to repress came in the middle of the boy's adolescence and so was mixed up with a second conflict of repression connected with sex. For, just as D. maintained that he was absolutely astonished at the birth of his little brother, so did he also assert that at that time he had no knowledge whatever of sexual intercourse. Both things are impossible. The second because at that very time the boy was keeping pet rabbits, and for hours at a time would watch the sex-play of these

111

animals; and the first because he himself very soon found out that already, during the period of pregnancy, he had the murderous thoughts of which he immediately began to tell me. From the idea of getting rid of this late arrival was derived in part the attack of scleroderma on his right arm. The idea of killing off people who are a nuisance accompanies us all through our lives, and in disagreeable circumstances the wish to kill and the horror of killing grow so powerful that the It resolves to lame the human instrument of murder, the right arm. I think I have already told you why these murder thoughts are so general, but for your use and profit I will say it again. The child makes acquaintance with the idea of death through its play. It shoots and stabs a grownup, who falls down and shams dead, only to wake up again very soon. Is it not strange, that the It knows how to represent our hardest problem in a frivolous form, as a joke, to the child-mind; that it understands how to make a game of dying, to the child? And is it any wonder that he stores away in his mind this pleasant idea of death with a speedy reawakening, which he has learned through the happy experiences of his childhood, and that he keeps it ready for convenient use later on? In fine, the illness of leg and arm arose from sexual conflict in the sphere of mother-child erotism.

I come now to the strange feature of this strange illness, to the way in which the syphilis idea sprang out of the mother complex, and by reason of this origin grew so powerful that it was able to produce fresh symptoms over and over again, and to produce them in such a manner as to deceive all the physicians, including myself, who treated the case. I asked D. whether he then knew who it was who had infected him. "I don't even know whether I was infected," he said. "I *suppose* I was." "And why do you suppose so?" "Because I once had intercourse with a girl who wore a veil." When he saw the doubt in my face, he added, "All street prostitutes who wear a veil are syphilitic." That was a new idea to me, but, as I considered it reasonable, I inquired further. "Then you think it was this girl who infected you?" "Yes," he said, then immediately added, "but I don't know, I absolutely don't know whether I was infected. Certainly not after that, for I never again had intercourse with a woman. The morning afterward I was frightened and went to a doctor to be examined. He sent me away, telling me to come back again in a few days. I did so, and was again asked to come back, and so it went on for some time, until one day he told me, half laughing and half angry, that I was quite sound, and there was no question of syphilis. Since then I have been examined by numbers of doctors. Not one has found anything." "But," said I, "before your wartime sickness began, you had had antiluetic treatment?" "Yes, at my own request. I thought that my headaches, my sore leg, my arm, everything must have come from syphilis. I had read everything that was written about scleroderma, and some people connect it with syphilis." "But you were only fifteen when that started." "With hereditary syphilis," he broke in. "I have never really seriously believed in the infection, but I thought my father was syphilitic." He was silent for a time, and then said, "If I remember rightly, the girl I spoke to you about didn't wear a veil at all. On the contrary, I know for certain that she had not the tiniest spot on the whole of her body. I had the electric light burning all night, looked at her naked before the mirror, read her health card; in short it is quite impossible for her to have been diseased. The fact is, I had a horrible dread of being an hereditary syphilitic. It was on that account I went to the doctor, and I told him the lying tale about the girl being veiled, because I did not want to reveal my suspicion about my father, and I have since then repeated it so often that finally I have come to believe it myself. But now, with all this analysis, I know definitely that I never thought the girl was syphilitic, and that she didn't wear a veil."

All of this seemed to me just as strange as it does to you, no doubt. I wanted and I hoped to get light upon it, so I asked Herr D. what he associated with the word "veil." Instead of one answer, he immediately gave me two: "The widow's veil, and the Raphael Madonna with the veil." From these two associations there issued a long train of others which took up weeks of our time, but of these I will give you only a short summary.

The widow's veil led at once to the death of the father, and the mother's mourning. From this it presently became clear that in the course of his struggles for the repression of the incest wish, D. had identified his mother with the prostitute, that he had fictitiously assigned to her the black veil and had made her a syphilitic in his phantasy, because his unconscious believed that in this way it would be easier to bring the incest wish to an end. The mother must and should be excluded from his erotic life; whoever has syphilis must be outside man's desire; therefore the mother must be made syphilitic. But that did not succeed —we shall soon see why—and so a proxy had to be found. This was managed with the help of the veil association, and in order to strengthen the barrier the idea was elaborated that the father had been syphilitic.

That the patient did not believe in the idea of the mother's syphilis will readily be understood, but Herr D. linked up with that another idea, which showed itself in the association of the Madonna with the veil. In this way D. made his mother unapproachable, immaculate, thus completely shutting out his father, and this had the further advantage that he could thereby regard himself as of divine origin, born of a virgin. The unconscious makes use of dreadful devices. In order to repress the incest wish, he deified his mother and, in the same breath, degraded her to the position of a syphilitic prostitute.

You have here, if you like to accept it, the confirmation of what I have so often tried to get you to believe, that we all arrogate a divine origin for ourselves, that for us the father is really God the Father, and the mother, the Mother of God. It cannot be otherwise; mankind is made that way, once and for all. We must at times believe that, and if today the whole Catholic faith disappeared, together with the Virgin Mary and the Christ Child, and not a single memory of them anywhere remained, tomorrow a new myth would be there, with the same conjunction of God and Man, and the same birth of the Son of God. Religions are the creation of the It, and the child can neither tolerate the thought of the love embraces of father and mother, nor is it able to renounce, in the struggle against the incest wish, the weapon it finds in the canonization of the mother. Nor, finally, can it abstain from the thought of being like God, since, as Ferenczi has shown us, it learned in the mother's womb to feel itself omnipotent.

Religions are creations of the It. Look upon the cross, with its outspread arms, and you will agree with me. The Son of God hangs and dies upon it. The *Kreuz* (cross, os sacrum) is the mother and upon the mother we all of us must die. Oedipus! Oedipus! But notice, too, if the cross is the mother, then the nails which fasten the son to her,

114

enter also into her flesh; she feels the same pain, the same sorrow as he, and with her strong maternal arms she carries his suffering and his death, she shares them with him. Mother and Son, in them is concentrated all the sorrow of the world, all its tears and lamentations. And the thanks the mother reaps is that harsh retort, "Woman, what have I to do with thee?" That is human destiny, and she is no true mother who is angry because her son waves her away. It has to be.

A still deeper conflict, common to all human beings, which through one of its roots draws sustenance from the Oedipus complex, is to be found in the story of D.'s illness, namely, the problem of homosexuality. When he was drunk, he told me, he would wander through the streets of Berlin in order to seek out pederasts, and whoever he might be, and wherever he might find him, he would beat him half dead. That was one statement. *In vino veritas:* it can only be understood when taken in conjunction with the second, which followed several weeks later. I found the patient one day in a high fever, and he told me that the previous evening he had been walking through the wood when the idea suddenly struck him that he would be knocked over by marauders who, having bound him, would abuse him through the anus, and would then leave him bound to a tree. This phantasy, he said, came frequently to him, and was always followed by fever. Anxiety is a wish, of that there is no doubt. The hatred with which D. in his drunkenness pursued the pederasts, was suppressed homosexuality; the fear phantasy is the same, and the extent of the fever measures the fierceness of the homosexual wish. I shall return another time to the question of homosexuality. At this moment I want to say only one thing, that among the different causes that may lead to homosexuality there is one which should never be overlooked, namely, the repression of the longing for incest with the mother. Man fights a hard battle to free himself from the mother's erotism, and one cannot wonder if in this struggle all conscious inclinations toward the female sex are at the same time forced into repression, so that finally, in a case here and there, all sexual connection with women is thenceforth barred. In Herr D., who had the dread of falling a prey to homosexual violence, still another cause of homosexual love was clearly revealed in his affection for his father, which he had repressed. For only from that cause could this anxiety have sprung, that D. at any time had the ardent wish to be a woman, to be his father's wife. Remember, my dear, the origin of perverse lusts, and you will judge them less severely.

With this, I come to the other aspect of the Oedipus complex, D.'s position in regard to his father. I must first of all call attention to something that is characteristic of many people. D. was firmly convinced that for him no one was more lofty, no one more honored, no one more loved, than his father, while he blamed his mother for anything and everything, and could no longer endure to be more than a few hours in her company. Truly, his father was dead, while his mother still lived, and it is convenient to deify the dead. Be that as it may, D. believed that he loved his father with all his heart, and had repressed his hatred for his father all his life. It is not to be denied that in very truth he had an ardent love for his father, his homosexual complex and his growing likeness to his father show that too clearly. But just as fiercely did he hate him, and more important than anything else at the outbreak of his illness was this active conflict between affection and repulsion.

From the memories of that time, which were released from repression during the analysis, I will pick out two. During his mother's pregnancy previously referred to D. had been in the habit of lying in wait for hours at a time, near the outlet of a drain, in order to shoot the rats as they emerged. Boyish sport, you say. Certainly, but why do boys so much enjoy shooting and why did D. shoot rats coming out of a drain? Shooting, I need scarcely say, is the predominant sexual urge of puberty, which finds vent in symbolic action. But the rat at which D. shoots is the sex organ of his father whom he punishes with death in the moment that he emerges from the drain, the mother's body. No, that is not *my* interpretation. It comes from D. I merely concur. And with the second of D.'s suggestions also I agree. According to this, the drain is once more the mother's vagina, but the rat is the child she is expecting. Next to the wish to castrate the father—for that is the meaning of the slaughter of the rats—is shown the wish to murder the coming child, both ideas being converted into symbolic form by the force of repression. And into the midst of these subterranean struggles, severe, but only vaguely realized, steps fate, and lets the newborn brother die after a few weeks. Now the guilt feeling, the gloomy companion of mankind, has an object, fratricide. You cannot imagine, my dear, how useful it is for the repressive forces to discover such a serious crime. Everything can be hidden behind that and, as a matter of fact, everything does get hidden behind it. D. had made valiant use of this absurd story of a brother's murder as an aid to self-deception. And because it is in man's nature to punish another for his own guilt, from the time his brother died D. shot no more at rats, but at cats, symbols of his mother. The It chooses strange paths.

D. had not been able to completely cover up the castration wish against his father by the idea of his brother's murder, as a secret memory shows. I told you that he kept tame rabbits during the time this conflict was going on. Among these animals was a snow-white buck, with which D. performed a strange drama. All the other buck rabbits he allowed to mate with the does, and enjoyed watching them; only the white rabbit was not allowed to mate. If he did so, D. seized him by the ears, trussed him up, hung him from a beam and beat him with a riding whip till his arm was tired. It was the right arm, the arm that first got bad, and it got bad just at this time. This memory came out after the very greatest resistance. Over and over again the patient evaded it and brought on a variety of severe organic symptoms. One of these was particularly significant; the sclerodermic patches on the right elbow grew worse. From the day on which this memory came up from the unconscious, these got well again and healed so completely that the patient from now on was able to bend and stretch his elbow joint to its full extent, a thing he had not been able to do for twenty years in spite of all the treatment. And he did it without pain.

The most important thing of all I had nearly forgotten. The white-haired rabbit which was kept from sexual pleasure and was whipped if he was incontinent, represented his father. Had you guessed that already?

Are you tired? Patience—a few more lines and the sketch is finished. Still another characteristic may be attributed to the hatred of the father, one of which you have already heard from Freud, and D.'s story has much in common with Freud's story of the rat-man. D. was a religious man, one might almost call him a Fundamentalist, but he concerned himself more with God the Father

117

than with God the Son, and prayed daily in his own fashion to the divinity he had himself created out of the father imago. But in the midst of his praying there broke forth words of abuse, curses, horrible blasphemies. His hatred against his father burst its bonds. You must look that up in Freud. I can add nothing new to what he has said, and should only spoil it by any would-be wise word of my own.

There is something else I must add to the rabbit story. D. had given the white rabbit the name Hans (Harry); as you know, that is the name by which he himself wished to be called. If he was striking the father in the person of the white-haired animal he was striking himself at the same time, or rather his generator, his Hans, the Hans he had hanging below his body. Or did you not know that the name Hans is so popular with young and old alike, because it rhymes with *Schwanz* (tail), and because Hans is connected with Johannes der Taufer (John the Baptist). I do not know if it is true, but an Englishman told me that in his country the member is referred to as John the Baptist, and the French have a similar habit. But that does not affect my story. In any case D. was thinking of his member when he christened the rabbit Hans, and the beating represented for him a punishment for masturbation. Yes, for masturbation. That is a little strange!

I come to an end, which means there is nothing more to say that matters, and if, as you will have noticed, I have left out the most important thing of all, the early memories of childhood, that is because I have only the very slightest knowledge of them. That is why I said just now that D. would probably have become ill again if he had survived. The analysis was nowhere near completion.

In conclusion I will give you at least one reason why D. dreaded going to the war, although he longed to go. He imagined that he would be shot through the eyes. That proved to me—I arrived at this conclusion through my experiences with other soldiers—that he had seen his mother naked at a time when he was conscious of the sin he was committing. There is a saying, Whoever sees his mother naked will go blind. And Oedipus tore out his eyes.

I send you my greetings, dear, and am always your

PATRIK TROLL.

118

✳ LETTER XV ✳

Assuredly, my dear, I could tell you any number of stories like Herr D.'s, about the workings of the Oedipus complex, and have even promised you to do so. But to what end? If you do not allow this one story to have any effect on you, then nothing would be gained by giving you several more. Besides, you will find a wealth of them in the literature of psychoanalysis. I prefer to try to meet your objections, otherwise your prejudices will take root and our correspondence become meaningless.

You fail to understand, you say, how it is that physical changes can take place in a man through such causes as I have described, how he can become organically diseased thereby, and still less do you understand how he can get well again by discovering these associations. All these things, my dear, I, too, fail to understand, but I see them, I experience them. Naturally I have all sorts of ideas about them, but these are difficult to communicate. One thing, however, I should like to ask of you, namely, to abandon the distinction between "mental" and "organic" in corresponding with me. These are only verbalisms, useful in getting a clear understanding of some of life's peculiarities, but in essence both mean the same, both are subject to the same laws of life, both take their root in the same life. Certainly a wine glass is something other than a tumbler, or than a lamp chimney, but it is nevertheless glass, and all this glassware was placed here by a human being. A wooden house is different from a house of stone, but you yourself do not doubt that it is simply a question of purpose and not of ability whether a builder puts up a stone house or a wooden one. It is just the same with organic, functional, or mental diseases. The It in its own lordly fashion chooses the illness it will produce, and is not guided by our terms. I think that we understand each other at last, or at least that you understand me and my unequivocal assertion that for the It there is no distinction between organic and mental, and consequently that if the It can be influenced by analysis, even organic diseases can, and in certain circumstances must, be treated psychoanalytically.

Physical, mental. What power lies in a word! People used to think—perhaps some still do—that the human body is like a house for the soul to dwell in. But even if one accepts that belief, it cannot be the body which becomes ill, for without a soul it is dead. A dead thing cannot become ill, at the most it can be damaged. Only the living can be ill, and since no one doubts that only he can be called alive who has both body and soul—but forgive me, this is all stupid talk. We will not quibble about words. It is only necessary for me to say what I mean in intelligible fashion, since you want to hear it. And I have told you plainly what I mean: for me the It is all that counts. If I use the terms body and mind, I understand by them phenomena of the It, or if you like, functions of the It. For me the two ideas are not mutually independent, and certainly are not antithetical. Let us drop this stale theme of an agelong muddle. There are other things to talk about.

You raise objection to the importance I attach to the workings of repression; you point out that there are also abortions and embryonic diseases, and you want me to recognize that there are other forces at work as well. As to that I can only reply that I find the term "repression" convenient. Whether it is sufficient for everything does not interest me. Up till now it has proved sufficient for me, even for my superficial acquaintance with embryonic life. I have therefore no motive for adding anything new to it, or for discarding it.

Perhaps it may be useful to phantasy a little, so that you may get some idea of the extent of such a repression. Suppose two children, a boy and a girl, are alone in the dining room. The mother is asleep or busy over something or other in another room; in short the children feel safe, so safe that the older child seizes the opportunity to inform both himself and the younger one, by actual inspection, of the differences between the sexes, and of the pleasure attaching to such interests. Suddenly the door opens, the children only just have time to spring apart,

120

but their guilty feeling cannot be hidden. And since the mother, who is convinced of the childish innocence of her offspring, sees them both in the neighborhood of the sugar bowl, she concludes that they have been pilfering, scolds them for it and threatens them with a beating if it should ever happen again. Perhaps the children defend themselves against the charge, perhaps not. In either case it can hardly be supposed that they confess their real sin, which they consider far more serious. They keep silent about that, repress it. At teatime the mother's exhortation is repeated, the child with the greater sense of guilt blushes, and so announces that he thinks he was the tempter. He again represses what he would gladly confess. After a few days—the mother has long since forgiven them, but enjoys teasing the children—there comes some joking word about it to an aunt. "The youngster knows where to find the sugar bowl," or something like that. And then this aunt will also make some allusion to it, later. And there you have a whole chain of repressions, such as all too frequently may come about. Now children respond differently: one takes his sin lightly, another seriously, while for a third it is almost unbearable to have committed a sin, and above all, not to have confessed. What remains for him to do? He presses and presses the thought down, drives it out of consciousness, stuffs it into the unconscious. There it stops, at first near the surface, but gradually is thrust deeper and deeper, until the memory has vanished from consciousness. To prevent it from ever reappearing, covering memories are put on top, in particular that the mother was unfair in accusing the child wrongfully of eating the sugar, and threatening to beat him. Now the way is open, or at least it may be so. There is built up a complex which is irritable if touched, which by and by gets so bad that even an approach to the complex is already felt as frightful. Now please look at this complex. On the surface are the covering memories: the sugar, the nibbling, the false accusation, the threat of a beating, the silence and deception, the blushing; further back are the sugar bowl, the dinner table and chairs, the dining room with a brown wallpaper, furniture of all sorts and pottery, the mother's green dress, Gretchen, the five-year-old girl, in a plaid frock, and so on. Deeper still lies the sphere of sexuality. In the circumstances the work of repression is already becoming difficult, but this work is sometimes increased to an almost incredible extent. Take the word "sugar": it belongs to the complex and must therefore be avoided as far as possible. Should it be burdened with guilt from any other source, perhaps through actual pilfering, then the desire for repression is so much the greater. But then it carries along other ideas with it; sweet, perhaps white, or square; next perhaps it seizes on other forms of sugar, the sugar hat (cone), from that to a hat itself, or to the blue wrapping paper. You can at pleasure prolong this to infinity, and, you may depend upon it, the unconscious, by means of association, does only too often prolong the work of repression into infinity. Out of the flight from sweet sugar there may arise a bitterness of soul, or a sickly sentimentality may be the substitute; an exaggerated carefulness never to claim the property of another connects itself with the word "pilfering" or a childish pleasure in a harmless deception is established, coupled with a pharisaical love of justice; the words blow, beating, battle, rod, Gertrude, Ruth, punishment, birch, broom, join in the complex; disgraced and yet alluring, for the unconfessed sin longs for punishment, even decades afterwards it clamors for punishment. Brown wallpaper becomes intolerable, green and plaid dresses too, the name Gretchen is revolting, and so it goes on. And besides all that there is the immense sphere of sexuality.

Perhaps you are thinking that I exaggerate, or that I am reading an unusual page dropped from the life story of an hysteric. Ah no, we all trail such complexes around with us. Only seek within your own soul, you will find several there; some inexplicable repulsion, some mental upset altogether disproportionate to its apparent cause, some irritability, anxiety or ill humor, which can only be understood when you take into consideration the complex from which it arises. How you will open your eyes when you have learned to build the bridges between the present day and childhood, when you understand that we are children and remain so, and that we repress, everlastingly repress. And that just because we repress without destroying, we are compelled to bring up, ever and anew, certain phenomena of life, to repeat again and again. Believe me, it is queer how often the wish repeats itself. Within it sits an elf who forces repetition upon it.

I should tell you more about this compulsion to repeat, but I am dealing with repression, and I owe you an explanation of how I came to regard the working of repression as the cause of organic illness. That it can give rise to mental difficulties of every kind, you will understand without my help. I am now going to give you phantasy-talk again. You can take it seriously or you can laugh at it, whichever you please—it doesn't matter to me. For me the question how organic diseases arise is insoluble. I am a physician and in that capacity I am interested solely in the fact that improvement sets in with the release of the repression.

Let me ask you to try a little experiment before going on to my explanations. Please think of something or other that is interesting you, perhaps whether you should buy a new hat or not. And now, suddenly try to repress the thought of the hat. If you have imagined a really attractive hat, and are thinking how it will suit you and how much you want it, then you will not find it possible to repress the thought of it without drawing together the abdominal muscles. Perhaps other groups of muscles will help to strengthen the repressive forces, the upper abdominal group will certainly do so; they are brought in with every exertion, even the smallest. The inevitable result of this is disturbance of the circulation, however slight, and with the help of the sympathetic nerves this disturbance is communicated to other parts of the organism, first to those which are directly adjacent, the bowel, stomach, liver, heart, and respiratory organs. You can think of this fluctuation being as small as you like, still it is there. And because it is there, and because it is affecting all sorts of organs, chemical processes are immediately set up of which even the most learned of men understand nothing at all. They only know that the processes do go on, and the more they have concerned themselves with psychology, the better they know this. Now just imagine this apparently unimportant incident repeated ten times a day. That already gathers significance. But if you meet it twenty times an hour, then you will have an unholy mixture of mechanical and chemical processes which you will find very far from beautiful. And strengthen the intensity and the duration of the effort. Suppose such an effort to be prolonged through hours, through days, so that only for short momentary intervals the abdomen is relaxed. Does it then seem very hard for you to fancy a connection between repression and organic disease?

Probably you have not yet seen many people's naked bodies, but it often falls to my lot to do so. And something curious is often to be found. Like a line drawn diagonally across the upper half of the abdomen there is a fold, a long drawn wrinkle. This comes from repression. Or there will be red streaks, or the abdomen is swollen, or something else still. Only reflect: for years, for decades of years, a man is going about who has a dread of stairs. A staircase is a sexual symbol, and there are countless people who are haunted by the fear of falling on the stairs. Or imagine someone who vaguely feels that a hat is a sexual symbol, or a button, or writing. Such people must forever, almost unceasingly, be repressing, be forever affecting abdomen, breast, arms, kidneys, heart and brain with disturbances of the circulation, with unexpected chemical products, with chemical poisons. No, dear, I do not find it in the very least astonishing that repression or any other psychical event should bring about organic disease. On the contrary, I find it surprising that such diseases are comparatively rare. And I am filled with amazement, with reverent amazement, at the power of the It to direct all that happens for the best.

Take an eye. If it sees, then various processes go on in it. But if it is forbidden to see, and yet does see but dares not communicate to the brain its impressions, what may then take place? Is it not conceivable, if it is compelled to overlook what it sees a thousand times every day, that finally it has had enough of the business and says, "I can manage this more conveniently. If I am not to see, I will be short-sighted, I will lengthen the axis, and if that is not enough, I will let blood flow into the retina and become blind." We know so little of the eye, so let me have the fun of phantasying.

Have you been able to follow what I have written? But you must read it indulgently, not on any account critically. On the contrary, you should sit down and build up two or three dozen such phantasies for yourself. What I gave was only a specimen, the invention of an audacious mood. Pay no heed to the form, nor even to the idea. What matters to me is your manner of thinking, that you should put aside the intellect and let yourself go with enthusiasm.

Since I have spoken of the onset of illness I must also say a word or two about treatment. Years ago, when I had so far got the better of my vanity that it permitted me to

124

write for the first time to Freud, he replied somewhat as follows: "If you have understood what transference and resistance are, you can undertake to give psychoanalytic treatment to the sick without any fear." Transference and resistance, then, are the points of attack in the treatment. I think I have already expressed fairly clearly what I understand by transference. To a certain extent the doctor is able to call it forth, or at least can and ought to try to maintain and direct the transference once it has arisen. But the essential thing, the transference itself, is a reaction process in the patient, and for the most part it lies outside the doctor's influence. So in the end there remains as the principal task of treatment the displacement and overcoming of the resistance. Freud once compared the conscious mind of man to a drawing room in which various types of people are received. In the anteroom behind the locked door in the unconscious a repressed mass of mental entities are packed together, and by the door stands a sentry, who only admits into the consciousness what is fit for the drawing room. According to this, resistances can start from three points, from the drawing room, *i.e.*, the conscious mind, which will not tolerate the presence of certain people; from the sentry, largely dependent on the consciousness but having a will of its own too, and now and again denying entrance purely out of caprice, even though permission has been given by the consciousness; and from the unconscious itself, which does not enjoy the ever-boring environment of a drawing room. And so one may conclude that all three types of resistance should be watched for in the treatment. And in all three one must be prepared to find all sorts of curious whims, and to meet every sort of surprise. But as, in my opinion, both conscious mind and sentry are in the last resort the unresisting tools of the It, this distinction has only a slight importance.

I took the opportunity offered by Herr D.'s story to give you a few examples of the forms taken by the resistance. As a matter of fact there are hundreds and thousands of such forms. One never finishes learning them, and little as I would claim to be the advocate of distrust, yet I am firmly convinced that as a doctor one must ever and always reckon with the patient's resistance. Behind every form and expression of life is entrenched the resistance; every word, every gesture, can conceal it or betray it.

How is the resistance to be got rid of? That is hard to say, dear. I believe that the essential thing is that one should begin with oneself, that one should first look into one's own nooks and corners, one's own cellars and dining rooms; that one should first have courage to see oneself, one's own vileness, or as I prefer to say, one's own human nature. Whoever does not know that he himself has stood behind every hedge and every door, and whoever cannot say what sort of muck heaps lie behind such a hedge, and how many heaps he has himself put there, such an one will not get far. The first requirement then is honesty, honesty to oneself. In one's own nature can one best learn to know the resistances. And one learns to know oneself best if one analyzes others. We physicians are happily placed, and I could not say what other calling would attract me. Then I think that every physician needs two things: watchfulness and patience. Patience more than anything, and yet again, patience. But this can be acquired.

To analyze oneself, then, is essential. Easy it certainly is not, but it shows us our individual resistances and before we have long been at it we meet phenomena which show that there are also resistances of whole classes of people, of whole nations, indeed of mankind collectively, resistances common to many people, yes, to everybody. Today again I met a form of resistance which I often find, namely, that we are shy of using particular childish expressions, expressions which were familiar to us in childhood. In talking to children, and even more remarkably, in lovers' talk, we use them without thinking, and we calmly speak of "wee-wee" and "popo," of "gee-gee," "bow-wow" and "pussy-cat," but amongst grownups we prefer to be ourselves grown up, we forswear our child-nature. Swagger, nothing else.

In conclusion I must say one more word about the way the treatment works. Only unfortunately I know little about it. I have a vague idea that the setting free from repression of repressed material has a certain significance in this, but whether it is directly the cause of the cure, I doubt. Perhaps, through the entrance into consciousness of something which has been repressed, there comes about a certain activity in the unconscious, and this activity brings cure or no cure. If so, it would not be at all necessary that the repressed thoughts which gave the urge to illness should make their appearance. They could

126

stop quietly in the unconscious, provided room could be found for them there. So far as my present knowledge of these things goes, and I said just now it was very little, it would seem to me that it is often sufficient to get the door-keeper to shout some name or other into the room of the unconscious, perhaps the name "Wüllner." If there is no one called Wüllner among those who are standing nearest, they pass the name further back, and if this precise name does not press its way to its rightful owner, perhaps a Müller will be there, who intentionally or unintentionally misunderstands the summons, forces his way forwards and enters consciousness.

My letter is long, and there will be no end to this babble. Farewell, dearest, it is bedtime. I am a really tired

PATRIK TROLL.

✳ LETTER XVI ✳

It all strikes you as being very complicated? So it does me, but it can't be helped. The It is always in eruption, and never for a second is there any peace. It bubbles and boils, and casts up now this bit of experience, now that. Just when I should have started this letter to you, I tried to make out what was going on within myself. Although I did not get down to the deepest levels, here is what I found.

In my right hand I hold a pen; with my left I am fondling my watch chain. I am looking at the wall opposite on which is hung a Dutch etching, a reproduction of Rembrandt's *Circumcision of Jesus*. My feet rest on the floor but my right heel is tapping the rhythm of a march which the Kurhaus orchestra is playing below. Simultaneously I hear the cry of an owl, the horn of a motorcar, and the rattle of a tram. I have no definite impression of smell but I feel that my right nostril is a little stuffy. My leg itches near the right shin, and I am conscious that to the right of my upper lip, perhaps a quarter of an inch from the corner of my mouth, there is a round red spot. My mood is uneasy and I have cold fingertips.

Let me begin, my dear, at the end. My fingertips are cold; that makes writing very difficult, and therefore means: "Be careful, or you'll write nonsense." And so with the uneasiness, too. It strengthens the warning to proceed with caution. My It is of the opinion that I ought to be doing something else. What this is, I do not yet know. Meanwhile I will assume that in conjunction with the vessels of my fingertips and the disquietude of my mood, it expresses the feeling: "Your correspondent will not understand what you are telling her. You would do better to make some methodical preparation." A fig for that! I will take the leap.

That I am playing with my watch chain will provoke a smile from you. You know this habit, and have often teased me about it, without knowing yourself what it meant. It is a masturbation symbol, like the playing with the ring, of which I recently spoke. But the chain has its own peculiar properties. The ring is a woman symbol, and the watch too, like every machine. The chain, to my idea, is not: rather it symbolizes what comes before the actual sex-act, i.e., before the play with the watch. My left hand betrays to you that I find more joy in the preliminaries to the actual union of man and woman—in the things that a boy loves; and indeed you've long known that I am a boy, at least on my left side, the love side, the side that carries the heart. What is to the left is love; what is to the left is forbidden and blamed by grownups: it is not to the right, it is wrong. There you have a new motive for the uneasiness that bothers me, for the cold fingertips. The right hand, the hand that produces, the hand of authority, of the right and good, has stopped its serious work of writing, to threaten the left, pleasure-loving child's hand, and from right and left come a wavering and an unrest which disturb the centers of blood control, and make my fingers chilly. "But leave the child alone," one voice from the It hushes the unwilling right, which represents my grownupness, "You see he is playing with the chain, not with the watch." By this it means that the watch represents the heart, as in Löwe's ballad. This voice deems it wrong to play with hearts. In spite of its reassurance I am still ill at ease, and the It of my right hand at once tells me how objectionable are the doings of my left.

"You need only play with a little extra force, and you drag out the watch, let it fall, and a heart is broken."

All sorts of memories flash through my mind in the shape of girls' names, Anna, Marianne, Liese and others. Of the bearers of all these names, once upon a time, I thought that through my playing I had wounded their hearts. But suddenly I grow calm. Since I have gone into the depths of maidens' souls, I have known that such play was pretty in itself, and only became painful to them because I took the adventure seriously, because I myself had a bad conscience and they divined it. Because the man makes the girl think she must be ashamed, she really is ashamed; not because the thing is evil, no, but because a moral purity is expected from her that she does not possess. Thank God she doesn't. But there is nothing more injurious than being supposed to be nobler than one is.

In spite of this self-defense in the matter of playing with hearts, the fact remains that I do not set the pen into action, and I try to understand why not. There come to me memories, if they can properly be called so. People with writer's cramp whom I have treated have, without knowing about each other, given me the following explanation as regards writing: "The pen is the male organ, the paper the woman who receives, the ink the semen which flows out in the quick up and down movement of the pen. In other words, writing is a symbolic sex-act. But at the same time it is a symbol for masturbation, for the phantasied sex-act." That this interpretation is correct appears to me to follow from the fact that these patients lost their cramp so soon as they had discovered the associations. May I play with a few ideas on this subject? The German script is more difficult than the Latin for people with writer's cramp, because the up and down strokes are much clearer, more strongly marked, more distinct from each other. A thick penholder is easier to use than a slender one, which more easily symbolizes the finger or the too-weak penis, than does the thick. The pencil has the advantage of avoiding the loss of semen; with the typewriter, although the erotic up and down motion on the keyboard is retained, the hand does not directly grasp the penis. All this accords with what happens in the case of writer's cramp, when the sufferer is led first to abandon his customary pen for a pencil, to adopt the Latin script, then to take to typing and finally to dictating.

So far I have not mentioned the part played by the inkwell, concerning which the symptoms of disease are so obliging as to give me information. The inkwell, with its gaping throat which leads down into black darkness is a mother symbol; it represents the womb. Suddenly the Oedipus complex appears, the command against incest. And now we get "a certain liveliness" among the little writing demons, who climb up out of the inkwell, the black womb of hell, and warn us of the close relationship between the thought of the mother and the kingdom of evil. You would never believe, dear one, what funny leaps the It will take when it is so inclined; how it will unite earth and heaven and hell with the urine and the pen-holder of the sick man, and how finally it makes a poor wretched doctor-brain so crazy that it seriously believes that inkwell, womb and hell are close connections.

There is more to the story. From the pen flows out the ink which fertilizes the paper. When it is covered with writing, I fold it up, put it in an envelope, and send it to the post. You open the letter, I hope with a kindly smile, and then you guess, shaking your head dubiously, that what you are about to read deals with pregnancy and birth. And then you think of the many people who are scolded for writing so little, and you understand why they find it so hard to write. All these people have in their souls the unconscious power of reading symbols, and all of them suffer under the terror of childbirth. In a happy moment there comes to you the recollection of our mutual friend, Rallot, who used to carry every one of his letters from the house to the letterbox and back again a dozen times before he sent them off, and you will be able to understand how it was I succeeded in freeing him, in half an hour's conversation, from this symptom of his disease, though not from the disease itself. Knowledge is a good thing, and you will become as God, knowing good and evil.

If I were not afraid of tiring you I should now like to venture on the question of handwriting, and to say one or two things about the letters of the alphabet. I cannot promise you that I shall not take an opportunity to come back to that subject again, but now I prefer to ask you to recall that, as children, we had for an hour at a time to draw *a*'s and *o*'s and *u*'s, and in order to make that bearable, we must have invested these signs with all sorts of forms and symbols. Try to be a child again, and perhaps you will get all kinds of ideas about the origin of the writing of characters, and you will wonder whether they are any more stupid than those of our learned pundits. With learning alone no one will get on terms with the It, and, yes, I have little opinion of science!

A few incidents come to my mind which have to do with the masturbation complex. I once had an argument with a good friend of mine—you do not know her, but she is no fool—because she did not want to believe my contention that illnesses were creations of the It, that they were desired and brought on by the It. "Nervous conditions, hysteria, I grant you," said she, "but organic diseases too?" "Organic diseases too," I replied, and then before I could bring out my favorite argument, that in the distinction between organic and hysteric the doctors are accusing themselves, are wanting to say, "We know little about the chemical, physical and biological processes in nervous conditions; the only thing we know is that such processes go on but they cannot be detected in our examinations; we therefore use the expression 'nervous' to inform the public of our ignorance, and to get rid of such an unpleasant proof of our incapacity"—before I could say all this, she asked again, "And accidents as well?" "Yes, accidents as well." "I am curious to hear," she then said, "what purpose my It had in making me break my right arm." "Do you still remember the circumstances of the accident?" "Certainly. I was in Berlin, in the Leipziger Strasse. I wanted to go into the Colonial Products shop, when I slipped and broke my arm." "Do you remember what you may have been looking at, at the time?" "Yes, in front of the shop was a basket of asparagus." Suddenly my antagonist became reflective. "Perhaps you are right," she said, and then she told me a story which I will not broadcast, but which turned on the similarity of asparagus and the penis, and a wish felt by the victim of the accident. A repressed masturbation-phantasy, no more. The breaking of the arm was a successful attempt to bolster up morality. If one has a broken arm, desire vanishes.

A second incident at first seems far enough removed from the masturbation complex. A woman slips on the smooth frozen street and breaks her right arm. She states that in the moment before slipping she had a vision. Suddenly, right before her eyes, she saw the form of a lady, dressed as she had often seen her for the street, only under her hat was not a living face but a skull. It was not difficult to guess that this vision contained a wish. The lady had once been her most intimate friend, but the friendship turned into bitterest hate, which in the very hour of the accident had received fresh stimulus. The belief that here we had to deal with a self-inflicted punishment for a murder wish was at once confirmed, the patient telling me that once before she had had a similar vision of another woman, who in that very moment had died. There seemed, then, sufficient motive for the broken arm, sufficient even for such a searcher of souls as I. But the sequel taught me better. The fracture healed smoothly, but for three years afterwards, from time to time, pains set in which were attributed to the change in weather, or to overexertion. By degrees there came to light a well-marked masturbation complex, into whose territory the murder phantasies had been drawn, and which was so objectionable to the patient that she preferred to conjure up the vision of murder and so win a certain freedom from her desire to masturbate, without ever letting this become conscious.

And with this I come to a point worth noting. On my watch chain hangs a little skull, the gift of a dear friend. I have often thought that I was done with the masturbation complex, that at least so far as my own person was concerned I was rid of it. Such a little incident as that of today, however, when I am hindered in writing by the playing with my watch chain, proves to me how deeply I am still involved in it. Onanism is threatened with death: that is given in its curious derivation from the name connected with an entirely different occurrence, which is remembered only because of the sudden death of the man concerned. The skull on my watch chain warns me, it repeats urgently to me the many warnings of the masturbation idiots, that one gets ill, goes mad, dies, if one allows this instinct free play.

The anxiety connected with masturbation eats deeply into the heart of man. I have already told you why, because, before the child knows anything at all of the world, before even it can distinguish between man and woman, before it knows the meaning of near and far, while it still grasps at the moon, and thinks its faeces are to play with, the threatening mother-hand interrupts that voluptuous playing with its sex organ.

But there is yet another connection between death and sensual pleasure, more important than the anxiety, and this shows with some impressiveness the symbolizing property of the It.

For the harmless man who has not yet grown pale with thought, death appears as the flight of the soul out of the body, as a giving up of himself, a separation from the world. Now this dying, this stepping out of the world, this giving up of the "I," occurs at moments during life; it comes when man has let himself go in sexual pleasure, when he becomes senseless, unconscious in ecstasy, when he, as the traditional phrase has it, dies in another. In other words, love and death are alike. You know the Greeks gave Eros the same features as death, but put in the hand of one the uplifted, erect, flaming torch, while the hand of the other is drooping, loose, extinct—a sign that they recognized the symbolic resemblance, the resemblance felt by the It. And we all know it, even as they. For us, too, the erection is life; the life-expending effusion of semen is the dying into sleep, and the sleeping is death. And according to the direction of our feelings concerning the idea of death in the woman, so there will arise in us a belief in an ascension to a heaven of the blest, or a sinking into the pit of hell, for heaven and hell are derived from man's death during the embrace, from the giving out of his soul to the woman, either in the hope of resurrection in the child after three times three months, or in dread of the everlasting fires of desire.

Love and death are one, of that there is no doubt. But whether anyone has come to actual death by giving himself up, the man to the woman, the woman to the man, I do not know. In the dead level of our own stage of civilization I think this is extremely unlikely. In any case the event is so rare that I can say nothing about it. Perhaps the people whose imagination pictures the coming of death during the embrace are nearest the possibility of this symbolic death, and since there have actually been cases of death at the climax of enjoyment, one might well suppose that in such cases the symbolic love-death was also lived through. The yearning for it expressed in music, poetry and oratory is widespread, and gives us starting points for the tracing of the paths between death and love, cradle and grave, mother and son, cross and resurrection.

Those people come close to this symbolic death who have an attack of hysterical cramp, which indeed, to all appearances, is a masturbation phantasy.

But I have wandered far. It is to be hoped you will read this through, and that you will be patient and let me, next time, return again to my subject. I attach importance to your learning, for once, everything I am conjecturing whilst my writing is delayed.

Affectionately yours,

PATRIK TROLL.

❋ LETTER XVII ❋

I do not wonder, my dear, at your disputing my views. I asked you a little while ago to read my letters like a traveler's guidebook; but I did not want you to attribute to this travel book any greater value than to the statements of the Englishman who, after a stay of two hours in Calais, maintained that all Frenchmen were red-haired and freckled, because, as it happened, the waiter who served him was like that. You are amused at my ascribing to the It a purposefulness which is able to bring about a fall and the breaking of a limb. I arrived at this conjecture—it is no more than that—through finding that it works. For me there are two kinds of opinions, those that one holds for one's own pleasure, luxury views therefore, and those that one uses as a means to an end, working hypotheses. Whether they are right or wrong is a matter of secondary importance to me. I take my stand by the answer Christ gave to Pilate's question, "What is truth?" as it is recorded in one of the Apocryphal Gospels. "Truth is neither in Heaven nor on the earth, neither is it between the heavens and the earth."

In the course of my soul-searchings I have had to occupy myself now and again with giddiness, and in that way I have been led to believe that every attack of dizziness is a warning from the It: "Take heed or you fall." If you want to inquire into the matter yourself, you must be so good as to bear in mind that there are two sorts of fall, a bodily fall and a moral fall, the nature of which is indicated in the story of the Fall of Man. The It does not seem to be in a position to distinguish sharply between these two kinds of fall, or as I would rather express it, the one fall makes it at once think of the other. Dizziness therefore always signifies a warning from both sides, is used both in the real and in the symbolic sense. And if the It believes that a simple giddiness, a false step, a stumble, a knock against a lamppost, the pain in a corn, or the treading on a sharp stone does not convey a sufficiently sharp admonition, it throws the man to the ground, makes a hole in his thick skull, injures his eye or breaks one of his limbs, the limb with which he wants to sin. Perhaps it even sends him a disease, gout, for instance; I shall soon return to that.

But first I should like to make clear that it is not I who regard as sinful a murderous thought, a wish to break the marriage vow, an imagined theft, a masturbation phantasy, but the It of the person concerned. I am neither priest nor judge, but physician. Good and evil are none of my business, I have not to give a verdict, but merely to state that the It of this or that person considers this or that to be a sin, judges thus or so. So far as my part goes, I endeavor to obey the edict, "Judge not, that ye be not judged." And I carry the sense of those words so far that I now try to refrain from acting as a judge towards myself, and induce my patients likewise to give up judging themselves. That sounds either very pious or very frivolous according to what one wants to make of it, but fundamentally, it is only a technical medical trick. That any harm could come of it I have no fear. If I say to people, and I do say it, "You must so change that in broad daylight you could crouch down in the middle of the street without embarrassment, undo your trousers, and evacuate," then the emphasis is on the word "could." To keep the patient from ever doing it there is the safeguard of the police, of custom, of the anxiety bred in him for centuries before. In this matter I feel quite unperturbed even when you call me Satan, or Destroyer of Morals. In other words, one may go to any amount of trouble to cease judging: one never succeeds. Ever and always the man gives a verdict as to worth, it is part of him like his eyes and his nose, yes, just because he has eyes and a nose he has always to say: That is bad. This he requires because he must worship himself, even the humblest must, even Christ Himself did on the Cross in uttering the words, "My God, my God, why hast thou forsaken me?" and in the others, "It is finished." To be pharisaical and always to say, "Oh God, I thank thee I am not as other men," is human. But equally human is the "God be merciful to me, a sinner." Like everything else, man has two sides. Sometimes he shows one, sometimes another, but both are always there. Because man is obliged to believe in free will, and to take credit to himself for certain parts of his nature, therefore must he also find guilt, in himself, in others, in God.

I am now going to tell you a story which you won't believe. But it amuses me, and because a good deal is compressed in it which I have not yet, or have not sufficiently clearly, explained, you are to listen.

Some years ago a lady came to me for treatment who suffered from chronic inflammation of the joints. The first beginnings of the illness lay eighteen years back, during adolescence. At that time the right leg began to be painful and swell. When I first saw her the joints of her hands, fingers and elbows were almost useless, so that she had to be fed; the thighs could only be slightly moved apart and both legs were perfectly stiff, she could not turn nor bend her head, one could not get a finger between her teeth because the joints of the jaw were diseased, and she was unable to raise her arm to the level of her shoulder. In short, as she said, with a turn of wry humor, if the Kaiser came riding by she could not wave to him and call "Hurrah" as she had done as a child. She had been bedridden for two years and had to be fed; altogether, her condition was discouraging. And even if the diagnosis of consumption in the joints, which had for years been made to her, did not turn out to be right, still one had every reason for describing it as arthritis deformans of the worst type. The patient is now able to walk again, she can feed herself, she can dig in her garden, can go upstairs, she bends her legs sufficiently, turns and bends her head in whatever way she wants, can spread out her legs as far as she likes, and if the Kaiser were actually to come she would be able to shout "Hurrah!" In other words, she is cured, if one can call full capacity for action a cure. One surprising thing is that even now she walks in a curious way, with her buttocks pushed out behind as though she wanted them to be smacked. And all those torments she endured because her father was called Friedrich Wilhelm, and because she had been told in a joke that she was not her mother's child but had been found behind a hedge!

This brings me to the subject of what my Freudian friends call the "family romance." You will recall times in your childhood when you took a lively interest in playing or phantasying that you had been stolen by gypsies from your real parents, who were people of high degree, and that the father and mother with whom you lived were only foster parents. Every child indulges in these or similar fancies. At bottom they are repressed wishes. So long as, from the cradle, we can lord it over the household, we are pleased with our relatives, but when training comes with its legitimate and illegitimate claims to interfere with our favorite habits, we find at times that our parents are quite unworthy to have such a superior child. We want to preserve the illusion of our own importance, in spite of our childish weakness and dependence, so we degrade them to the position of stepparents and witches, while we ourselves appear as the tormented prince. All of that you can read for yourself in the legends and fairy tales, or if you wish to get it with less trouble, you can find it in the valuable books of the Freudian school. And you will also read in them how, to begin with, we all look upon the father as the strongest, best, most highly placed of men, but that gradually we see, as he looks subdued before this person or that, that he is by no means the absolute master we had thought him. But because we want at all costs to keep to the idea that we are children of great parents—for respect is just as hard to renounce as vanity —we phantasy for ourselves the kidnapping and the substitution, our fairy-tale life. And in order to be able to continue to tell ourselves that, since even the king at last is not sublime enough to satisfy our restless craving for greatness, we decree that we are the children of God, and produce the idea of God the Father.

Such a family romance lived—unknown to herself—in the mind of a patient of whom I want to tell you. Her It made use of two names for this purpose, that of her father, Friedrich Wilhelm, and her own, Augusta. Finally it had drawn in also the childish story that a girl is made out of a boy through castration. The train of ideas was as follows: I am the child of Friedrich Wilhelm, at that time Crown Prince, and later Kaiser Friedrich; I am really a boy, the rightful heir to the throne and now by rights the Kaiser, with the name Wilhelm. Immediately after my birth I was stolen away and a witch-child was laid in the royal cradle in my place; he has now grown up and seized the Imperial throne for himself as Wilhelm II, wrongfully and to my hurt. I myself was put behind a hedge and, so that every hope might be lost to me, I was made into a girl by the cutting off of my sex organ. As the sole sign of my position I was given the name Augusta, the lofty one.

One can date the beginnings of the unconscious phantasies pretty definitely. At latest they must have started in the year 1888, and therefore at a time when the patient was not yet four years old. For this idea of belonging to the Hohenzollern family was grounded on the name Friedrich Wilhelm, which the phantasied father only bore as Crown Prince. The discussion over his being ill with cancer, concerning which the four-year-old would scarcely grasp anything except that the word crab (cancer) linked up with the idea of shears, of cutting, of castration, is of some importance here. It is connected with personal experiences of the cutting of nails and hair, the association of which with the castration complex is strengthened still further by hearing *Struwwelpeter* read aloud, and being shown the pictures: there is still to be found in this immortal book the story of Konrad the thumb-sucker, a story which arouses the old yearning for the mother's breast and the painful memories of the weaning, that unavoidable castration by the mother.

I briefly indicate all this, so that you may think it out a little for yourself. For only through your own reflection can you be convinced of this, that just in that age between three and four the ground is prepared for a phantasy that has so tremendous a result as this in my patient. Give ear only to this: the It of this woman is convinced, or rather it wishes to convince itself, that it is the It of a rightful Kaiser. The wearer of a crown looks neither to the right nor to the left, he judges without side glances, he bows his head before no earthly power. "Therefore," the It commands the body and blood of this person it has bewitched, "carry your head firmly to hold the crown. Close up the jaws so that they cannot shout 'Hurrah.' They did that once, they hailed and acclaimed the usurper, the witch's changeling. Lame the shoulders, so that never again with upraised arm can they do homage to the false Kaiser; your legs must grow stiff, for never should a mighty Kaiser kneel before anyone whatsoever. Press together the thighs, that a man shall never be able to lie between them, for that would mean the success of this most devilish device. If this body, which vulgar hatred and pitiless envy have transformed from a male to a female, were made to bear a child, it would be the frustration of every hope. Hold yourself so that the body is drawn backwards, that no one may find the entrance; be careful to arch the body, force it to stand and walk with the sacrum pressed backwards. There is still no reason to suppose that the secretly stolen proof of manhood may not grow again, that this Kaiser may not actually become a man. Show to this castrated being, O body and blood, that it is possible to make lax members stiff, by making it impossible for the legs to relax, to kneel; teach him to show in the symbol that he is a man."

I can imagine, honored lady, how indignantly you exclaim, "What nonsense!" And then you come to the idea that I am really recounting to you the delusions of a lunatic. That you must not think. The patient is as sane as yourself; what I was telling you are some of the ideas—very far from all—which can bring an It to the point of producing gout, of laming a person. If what I have said led you to ponder on the onset of mental disease, it would become clear to you that the lunatic, considered without prejudice, is by no means so mad as at first sight he seems to be, that his fixed ideas are such as we all have, and must have, since they are the foundations of human life. But why the It builds out of such ideas, for one the religion of God the Father, for another, rheumatism, for a third, madness, why in yet another it produces the founding of a kingdom, scepter and crown, for brides the bridal wreath, for us all the striving after perfection, ambition and heroism, these are questions with which in hours of boredom you might occupy yourself.

You must not believe that I found this royal romance in the mind of my patient as smoothly as I have presented it to you. It was torn into a thousand tatters, which were hidden away in the fingers, the nose, the bowels and the abdomen. We have between us patched them together, and have intentionally left out many, while still more have been stupidly forgotten or never traced. Indeed I must confess, in conclusion, that I have put aside everything that was not clear—and that was certainly the most essential part. For in the last resort—and you must never again forget what I say now—everything one thinks one knows about the It is only conditionally right, is only right in that moment that it is expressed by the It in word, gesture or symptom. Even in the next minute truth has flown away and can no more be found, neither in Heaven, nor on the earth, neither is it between the heavens and the earth.

PATRIK TROLL.

✳ LETTER XVIII ✳

As an earnest pupil, my dear, you desire to be informed why, instead of continuing to give you my ideas about the play with the watch chain, I tell you stories that have nothing whatever to do with it! I can give you an amusing explanation. Recently, when I began this little bit of self-analysis, I wrote to you: "In my right hand I hold a pen; with my left I am fondling my watch chain," and then I worked it out that both were masturbation complexes. The next words were: "I am looking at the wall opposite on which is hung a Dutch etching, a reproduction of Rembrandt's *Circumcision of Jesus.*" That is quite wrong; the etching reproduces a picture of the *Presentation of Jesus in the Temple*, among a crowd of people. I must have known this, in fact I did know it, for many times have I contemplated this etching with interest. And yet my It forced me to forget this knowledge and to convert the Presentation into a Circumcision. Why? Because I was entangled in the masturbation complex, because masturbation is punishable, because it is punished with castration, and because circumcision is a symbolic castration. My unconscious, in reacting from the masturbation idea, grasped the castration idea; on that account it rejected altogether the idea that the Infant Jesus should be presented in the Temple before the eyes of all men; for this baby boy, like every other, is a symbol of the male organ, while the Temple is the symbol of the mother. Had the subject of the etching succeeded in reaching my consciousness, it would, in close association with the penholder and the play with the watch chain, have signified, "You are carrying on the play with your member in front of everybody, and you are showing them that in its final meaning this masturbation play is concerned with the mother imago, as Rembrandt has symbolized it, in the form of the Temple in his mysterious chiaroscuro." That was unbearable to the unconscious because of the double prohibition of masturbation and incest, and it preferred at once to put forward the symbolic punishment.

That the rite of circumcision really has some connection with castration I am inclined to believe, since its inception is associated with the name of Abraham. In Abraham's life we read the strange story of the sacrifice of Isaac, how the Lord commands him to slay his son, how he is willing to obey but at the last moment is prevented by an angel; in Isaac's place a ram is sacrificed. With a little good will, you can see in this story that the sacrifice of the son signifies the cutting off of the penis, which is indeed represented symbolically by the son. In this way the story would mean that instead of the self-castration of God's servant, which has its fulfillment in the Catholic priests' vow of chastity, at some time or other there has been substituted the sacrifice of an animal; the ram is especially appropriate to this solution of the symbol, since at all times castration has been customary in sheep breeding. If one understands it so, the story of the covenant of circumcision between Jehovah and Abraham is only a repetition of the symbolic legend in another form, such a duplication as one frequently meets with elsewhere in the Bible. Circumcision accordingly would be the symbolic remnant of the religious castration. But, however that may be, so far as my own unconscious is concerned— and that is the only thing in question in this conversion of presentation into circumcision—castration and circumcision are very nearly related, indeed identical, for to me, as to so many others, the fact first became clear comparatively late, that a castrated man, a eunuch, is something distinct from a circumcised man.

For the rest, these associations between circumcision and castration have a special significance in the Freudian teaching, and I must advise you to read Freud's book, *Totem and Taboo*. For my part I only want to give you at most a little phantasy from racial psychology, out of which you can make what you like. It seems to me that in times when marriages were still consummated at an early age, the eldest son must have been a pretty unwelcome inhabitant of the father's house; the differences of age were so slight that the first born was in everything the natural rival of his father, and must have been specially dangerous for the mother who was not so much older than himself. Even now, indeed, father and son are natural rivals and enemies, and again in relation to the mother, whom the one possesses as wife and the other desires with his most ardent love. But at those times when the superiority of the elders was not yet so clearly acknowledged, when instincts and emotions were still more violent and uncontrolled, the father felt a conscious desire to kill the inconvenient son, a thought which has now been long repressed, but which is still operating frequently and markedly in manifold relationships of life and symptoms of disease. For father love, looked at closely, seems no less curious than mother love. It would then appear that it was a primitive custom to slay the eldest son, and, because man is an actor and a pharisee, the crime has been converted into a religious rite, and the son has been offered up as a sacrifice. This had, in addition to the ennoblement of the action, the further advantage that one could eat the sacrifice after the murder, and so might carry out the childish idea of the unconscious, that pregnancy arises from the eating of the penis, the symbolic son. With the gradual repression of the hate instinct other methods were adopted, and with the growing need for labor, simple murder was wasteful. A man then got rid of his rival in love by castrating him; he need fear him no longer and without trouble he had obtained a slave. If the population grew too dense, then man adopted the means of driving the eldest into exile, a procedure which was still recognized in historic times as the *ver sacrum*. And finally, when the needs of agriculture and the foundations of nations through the joining together of tribes required the preservation of all sons for the sake of labor and defense, man symbolized the murder and invented circumcision.

If you now want to close up this circle of phantasy, you must take the son's point of view, who certainly had no less hatred against his father than the father had against his son. The murder wish against the father is turned the other way round in the castration idea as we meet it in the myth of Zeus and Cronos, and there comes out of that the religious castration of the priest, for as the penis is symbolically the son, so is it actually the begetter, the father, and its castration is the murder of the father in symbolic form.

I fear to tire you, but I must again return to my watch chain. By the side of the skull which is attached to it, hangs also a tiny globe. As my thoughts skip about, it occurs to me that the earth is a symbol of the mother, and that accordingly my playing with this represents symbolic incest. And since the skull is threatening near by, the explanation of my halting pen is that it did not want to be at the disposition of the two sins, onanism and incest.

And now whither lead those sound perceptions of which I wrote to you, the march music, the owl's cry, the motor and the electric tram? For the march we get beat and rhythm, and from the word rhythm my thoughts pass on to reflect that every activity is easier if carried on with a rhythmic beat; every child knows that. Perhaps the child can also give the answer as to why this is so. Perhaps beat and rhythm are old acquaintances, inevitable habits of life, from the life in the womb onwards. Probably the unborn child is restricted to a small number of perceptions, and among these the feeling of beat and rhythm takes first place. The child swings within the mother's body, now less, now more, according to the mother's movements, according to her manner of walking and the rapidity of her steps. And without interruption the heart goes on inside the child, beating out, in accent and rhythm, strange melodies to which it listens, perhaps with its ears, certainly with the general sensation of the body, which feels the vibration and stores it up in the unconscious.

I am very much tempted here to give a little consideration to this phenomenon, how not only man's conscious deeds are subject to rhythm, his work, his art, his gait and his actions, but also his sleeping and waking, his breathing, his digestion, his growth and decline, yes, everything. It seems that the It expresses itself in rhythm just as it does in symbol, that it is an absolute property of the It, or at least that we, in order to be able to contemplate the It and its life must ascribe rhythmical properties to it. But this leads too far away from my subject, and I would rather direct your attention to the fact that the march brought me to thoughts of pregnancy, a note already sounded in the mention of the globe on my watch chain. For this globe, I scarcely need to say, is certainly indicative of the expectant mother, as one may see from the expression, "Mother Earth," and from the roundness of its surface.

And now I understand why I tap the beat with my heel instead of with my toes. The heel stands, for everyone, from childhood on, in an unconscious relationship to childbearing, for we have all grown up familiar with the story of the Fall of Man. Read it over once again. The surprising thing in it is that after the eating of the apple, Adam and Eve were ashamed of their nakedness. That proves that we have here a symbolic narrative concerning the sin of sexual indulgence. The Garden of Eden in the midst of which "stands" the tree of life and of knowledge—"to know a woman" means to sleep with her—speaks for itself. The snake is a primitive phallus symbol everywhere repeated. Its bite is poisonous, it impregnates. The fruit picked by Eve, which, by the way, has been significantly represented for hundreds of years as an apple, although the word apple is not given in the Bible, this fruit which is beautiful to see and good to eat, stands for the breast, the scrotum, the buttocks. If one grasps these associations it is at once clear that the curse, "The woman shall bruise the head of the serpent and the serpent shall bite the woman in the heel," signifies the relaxation, the death of the member through the outpouring of the semen, and the "stork bite" of our childhood, birth. That I am using my heel to tap out the beat shows how deeply my unconscious is engaged in thoughts of pregnancy. But in thoughts of castration too, at the same time. For in the bruising of the serpent's head are contained both relaxation and castration. A man is made shorter by a head, the member is shorter by a head after the act of begetting.

144

You can follow this up further, if it gives you any pleasure, in the legends of David and Goliath, Judith and Holofernes, Salome and John the Baptist.

Sexual intercourse is a death, the death in the woman, an idea running through the stories of all time. And Death cries sharp and shrill to my hearing, with the hoot of the owl: *"Komm mit, komm mit."* ("Come with me.") And then again the masturbation motif is heard in the motor's horn: is not the motor a recognized symbol of masturbation, even if its very invention is not due to the urge to self-gratification? That the electric tram—through the association of friction-electricity and human transport —combines within itself the symbols of masturbation and pregnancy, may be deduced from the fact that women, more sensitive to symbols than men, more closely akin to art, always step wrong in getting out of an electric tram —in order to fall.

And now another aspect of the march problem becomes clear to me. Many years ago I used to hear this rhythm on returning from an officer's funeral. It always gave me extraordinary pleasure that soldiers who had just buried a comrade should come back into life with gay music. So it should be everywhere. So soon as the earth lies over the dead, there is no more time for mourning. "Close the ranks."

Do you think me hard? But I think it hard to wish people to be sad for three whole days. Indeed, so far as I have learned to know men, even three days are intolerable. The dead are always right, according to the proverb, but fundamentally they are always wrong. And if one looks into it a little, one discovers that the whole business of mourning is pure dread, the fear of ghosts, on the same ethical plane as the custom of carrying the dead man feet first out of the house: he is not to return. We have the feeling that the spirit of the dead stays near the body. One must weep or one offends the ghost, and ghosts are revengeful. Once the body lies deep underground, no ghost can come forth any more. For greater assurance a heavy stone shall be rolled on his breast. The phrase about a weight pressing on one's chest proves how convinced even we moderns are, of the continued life of the dead within the grave: how we picture to ourselves the weight of the gravestone on the dead, and transfer that feeling to ourselves, probably as a punishment for the cruel incarceration of our dead relatives. In case a dead man should really rise up, foot traps in the shape of wreaths are laid on the grave, and these will keep him from escaping.

I do not want to be unjust. The words "rise up" prove that yet another train of thought is revealed in the choice of the three days that elapse before the burial of the corpse. Three days are the period before resurrection, and three times three are nine, the number of pregnancy. And the hope therein, that the soul of the dead man has meantime found the way to heaven, where it is truly far distant, happily placed and out of the way, also has a meaning.

Man does not mourn the dead; that is not true. And if he does mourn in his inmost soul, he does not show it. But even then it is doubtful whether his mourning is for the dead or whether his It is sad about something else and only takes the fact of the death as a screen in order to rationalize its grief, to find a reason to suit Mrs. Grundy.

You don't believe it? Men are not so wicked? But why do you call it wicked? Did you ever see a little child mourn for the dead? And are little children wicked? My mother once told me that after my grandfather's death—I was then three or four years old—I ran around his coffin, clapping my hands and shouting, "There's grandfather inside." My mother did not think me wicked on that account, and I do not think I am entitled to be more moral than she was.

But why, then, do people mourn for a whole year? Partly to vaunt themselves before other people, but more than all, before themselves, in the manner of the Pharisee, to deceive themselves. They vowed to this dead man and to themselves that they would always be faithful, would never forget him. And a few hours after his death we are already forgetting! So it is well to keep ourselves reminded by black clothes, by memorial announcements, by the setting up of effigies, and by wearing the lost one's hair. Mourning makes us seem good to ourselves.

Shall I give you a little hint in private? Two years after the death of husband or wife, look for the grief of the afflicted survivor; either he (or she) is also dead, that is not uncommon, or the widow is a buxom, happy lady, and the widower has married again.

146

Do not laugh at that! It has a deep meaning and is really true.

Ever yours,
PATRIK TROLL.

✳ LETTER XIX ✳

Again you have all kinds of things to which you take exception. That doesn't please me, and I am therefore going to speak plainly. Why do you think it far-fetched that I should compare Eve's apple with the buttocks? That is no invention of mine. The German language invented the simile, and the Italian and English as well.

I will tell you why you are irritated and scold me. You are just as much ashamed as if in your own person you were German science which so prudisly refers to *"more ferarum,"* "in the manner of beasts," and does not blush in this way to give a slap to its adherents. For it knows perfectly well that all young men have loved *more ferarum,* or at least that they have wanted to. And it also knows—at least it ought to know—that the masculine weapon of love is three-sided, and the feminine sheath is the same, and that the weapon fits the sheath quite perfectly only when it is thrust in from the back. Do not give ear to the chatter of pharisees and hypocrites. Love does not exist for the sake of reproduction. Sexual intercourse ought to bring pleasure, and in all marriages, with the most chaste of husbands and the purest of wives, it is practiced in every conceivable form, including *more ferarum.* Only certain people have not the courage for that and merely dream about it instead. But I have not noticed that these people are any better than the others, who do not conceal their childlike naïveté from their loved ones. There are those who speak of the beast in man, and they understand by "man" what they call noble, but what on closer inspection turns out not to be noble at all; intellect, for instance, or art, or religion, in short, everything that they can place for any reason in the brain or the heart, above the waist; and "brutish" they call everything they find in the abdomen, and above all, what is between the legs, the buttocks and the sexual parts. If I were you I should consider such people very carefully before making friends with them. May I make another ill-tempered remark? We educated Europeans always behave as if we were the only people on earth, as if what we did was right and natural, and what other races, other ages did, was wicked and perverse. But read Ploch's book about woman. There you will find that hundreds of millions of people have different sexual customs, different modes of intercourse from ourselves. However, these are certainly only Chinese, Japanese, Hindus, or even Negroes. Or go to Pompeii. There a dwelling house has been excavated—the house of Vettier it is called—in which the common bathroom used by parents and children is adorned with a frieze representing every kind of sexual indulgence, even that of animals. Certainly, these were only Romans and Greeks, but they were almost contemporary with St. Paul and St. John.

All these things have importance. You do not guess what a role they play in our daily habits and in disease. Take only that phrase *"more ferarum."* No one would have had the idea of the enema if it had not been for this "animal play." Neither would fever temperature have been tested from the anus. And the childish theory of birth from the bowel which in a thousand forms has entered in the healthy and pathological alike—but I will not speak of that, it would take me too far afield. I would rather give another example. Can you recall in what manner a girl runs? She keeps the top part of her body straight, and kicks her legs backwards, while a boy thrusts his thighs far out and bends his body forward as though he wanted to pierce his quarry. You make great use of the word atavism. What do you think; could not this curious difference in running be atavistic, a heritage from primeval times, when man hunted woman? Or is it that the It thinks the sexual attack must come from behind and it is therefore good to kick out? It is difficult to decide. But that brings up other differences that are amusing to note. In building with blocks on the floor the boy kneels, but the girl squats down with knees outspread. The little boy will fall forwards, the little girl backwards. If a man who is seated tries to catch an object falling from the table he closes his knees together, whereas the woman will jerk them apart. In sewing, a man makes a big sideways stitches while the woman stitches delicately from below upwards, exactly corresponding to their movements in sex-intercourse, and the child sticks its needle in without any skill, and, in accordance with the childish theory of impregnation through the mouth, from above downwards. Have you ever observed, by the way, the connection between sewing and the masturbation complex? Think about it. You will find it useful in either case, whether you suppose that sewing recalls symbolically masturbation or whether you believe, as I do, that sewing was derived from masturbation. And if you are thinking about dress, devote your attention for a moment to the heart-shaped line of the girl's décolletage, to the rose and the brooch, to the necklace, and the frocks, which are certainly not worn to put obstacles in the way of the love-act, but to challenge it. Fashion teaches us to recognize the characteristics of those periods of which we should otherwise know nothing. Look at the modes of hairdressing with parting and curls; all are creations of the It, the It of fashion, and the It of the individual being.

To return to the trivial distinctions between men and women. The man bends if he wants to lift anything up, the woman crouches. The man raises and carries with the back muscles, the woman, in symbol of motherhood, with the abdominal group. The man wipes his mouth towards the side, away from him, the woman brings her table napkin from the corners to the middle of the mouth; she wants to receive. The man trumpets like an elephant when he blows his nose, for the nose is a symbol of the member, and he is proud of it and will not conceal it; but the woman uses her handkerchief with cautious daintiness; she lacks what the nose stands for. The girl fastens her flower safely with a pin, the man carries it in his buttonhole. The girl carries a nosegay pressed against her breast, the boy holds it hanging loosely from his arm: he shows thereby that the budding maiden has nothing that struggles upwards, is not a man. Men and boys spit, showing that they have a flow of semen; girls cry, and the overflowing eyes symbolize their organs. Or do you not know that the pupils signify children, that the eye is a symbol of the woman in which one sees oneself again, mirrored in miniature? The eye is the mother, the eyes are testicles, for the testicles also contain the babies, and the ray of passion shining from the eye is a masculine symbol. The man bows, makes himself a servant and says thereby: "The sight of you brings me the utmost pleasure so that I now relax, but in a few seconds I stand upright again, since the desire for fresh pleasure possesses me." But the lady curtsies, meaning, "Because I see you, all resistance vanishes." The little girl plays with her doll, the boy does not need it: he carries his puppet on his body.

There are so many habits that we never notice, so many that are well worth noticing. What does the man desire when he strokes his moustache? The nose is the symbol of the member, as I have already mentioned, and the dawning moustache draws our attention to the fact that we have before us a sexually mature man who possesses pubic hair; but the mouth is the symbol of the woman, and the stroking of the moustache accordingly signifies, "I should like to play with a woman." The smooth-shaven face accentuates childishness, harmlessness, since the child has not yet grown pubic hair, but at the same time it is to signify potency, since the man, as an upright being, is the phallus and the head symbolizes the hairless tip in erection. Do not forget that when you see baldheaded people, or when your women friends complain of loss of their hair. Either the potency of the man is there represented, or childishness. When a woman sits, she draws down her skirt. "You may see what my feet are like," says this action, "but I do not permit you to see more, for I am modest." If she lies down in the presence of a man she invariably crosses her feet. "I know that you are desiring me," that means, "but I am armed against attack. Only try it." All this has a double meaning, a playing which entices while it recoils, allures, yet forbids, and is the parallel in action of the curious "No, but!" with which the maiden wards off the caressing hand. Or take spectacles; one wants to see better but not to be seen. Here one is sleeping with an open mouth; he is ready for conception. There lies another all huddled up like the foetus. Every old man walks with short steps, he wants to prolong the way which leads to its end in the grave; he sleeps badly, for his hours are numbered, and soon he will have to sleep only too soundly; he gets long sight, he will not see what is close to him, the deadly black of print, or the thread so soon to be cut by the Fates. The woman is afraid she will be ill if she stands for long during her period; the bleeding reminds her that to her the best is lacking. She doesn't dance at such time; it is forbidden to carry out the sex-act even in symbolic form.

Why do I tell you all this? Because I am wanting to escape from a tedious explanation about the apple of Paradise. Still, I shall have to give it to you some time. But no, I can first tell you a little about fruits. There is the plum; it conceals the kernel, the child, inside, and shows its feminine character in its lightly marked cleft. And here is the raspberry; does it not look like a nipple? Or the strawberry; it grows deep hidden amid the green grass, and you must seek before you can find the sweet secret in the woman's keeping. But beware of the strawberry; the bliss of desire eats ever deeper into man's being, it is ardently longed for and yet fled from as guilt, and then one gets nettle rash, which is a manifold reproduction of the emotion, with its torment of irritation. The cherry? You find it on the breast, the man also carries it on his trunk, for all symbols are bisexual. And now the acorn. That receives scientific recognition (*Eichel* is the technical term in German for the gland of the penis), although it is so closely associated with the pig, which bears so many secrets in itself. Shall I reveal one to you? The reproving mother calls her dirty child a little pig. Do you then wonder if the child makes the mental reply, "If I'm a pig, then you are the sow"? And in fact, however difficult it may sound to you, the sow is one of the commonest mother symbols. That has a deep significance, for the swine is slaughtered, its belly is slit open and it squeals. And one, perhaps the most frequent, of childish birth theories is that the mother's body is cut open for the child to be taken out, a theory which is based on the existence of a strange line between navel and pubes, and which finds support in the crying of woman in labor. From the association sow-mother an astonishing connection is found with religion, at any rate in Germany, where the butcher hangs the pig up in his windows for show. There is a symbolic association with the Crucifixion. What a caprice of the It! Pig——Mother——the Christ. Sometimes it is shocking. Like the mother, the father is also made into an animal; he is an ox, obviously. For instead of approaching the child in love, he remains unmoved by his advances, and must therefore be castrated. Finally, I ought not to forget the fig, in every language an emblem of the woman's sex organ. And with that I return to the legend of Paradise.

What can it mean that the first human couple sewed themselves aprons of fig leaves, and moreover, why should the century-old tradition have made out of this apron a single fig leaf? I cannot read the thoughts of those storytellers of the Bible; about the fig leaf with which bare nature is covered I can but hazard a guess. There are five divisions in this leaf, and the hand has five fingers. It is conceivable that it was a hand that covered what was not to be seen. But the hand by the pubes? There, where it ought not to be? It seems to me like a joke of the It. "Since you are not allowed to live freely in Eros, do as nature teaches you, use the hand."

I know I'm being frivolous, but now I must become serious at last. You know that the projecting larynx of the man is called "Adam's apple." The idea would be that with Adam the apple stuck in his throat. But why only with him and not with Eve, who also ate of the fruit? She swallowed the fruit, so that a new fruit might come out of it, the child. Adam, however, can bear no child.

And there we are unexpectedly in the midst of the maze of ideas which children have about pregnancy and birth. You are genuinely of the opinion that a good child believes in the stork, and he thinks so, too. But do not forget that a child believes in Santa Claus and yet at the same time he knows that the presents from Santa Claus were bought by his parents in the shops. The child has considerable capacity for belief and nothing stops him from honoring the stork while knowing that the baby grows in the mother's body. That he knows, he must know, for two or three years ago he was still inside this body. But how did he get in, and how did he come out? Those are questions which have pursued us all, at first with wavering, but, little by little, with ever-increasing urgency. And one of the many answers we all of us found, since we knew neither the womb nor the vagina in childhood, was that the child was born out of the opening which lets out everything in the body, out of the bowel. For that also there are many explanations in children's minds. The majority think that the seed of a child is swallowed, just as milk is sucked from the breast. And out of these reflections, this never ending, exciting self-questioning and self-answering of the child, there grows the wish to suck the member of the loved one, to smell, to kiss, a wish which is doubly compelling because it receives in its fulfillment the mother's breast and the happiness of childhood; from the same source comes also the idea of naming the man's larynx "Adam's apple." And finally, one may even say that the same source accounts for the onset of goiter, which troubles you so much in your small daughter. Believe me, you, as a schoolgirl, had the same thickened neck. A thing of this sort disappears with time. Only with those people whose It is altogether possessed with the idea of conception through the mouth, and with the horror of carrying a child in the belly, it actually develops into goiter and into Graves' disease.

Thank heaven, I'm finished for today!

PATRIK.

✳ LETTER XX ✳

Certainly, my dear, I promise you to bring the story of the penholder and the watch chain to a conclusion today.

I must try to make out why my right nostril felt stuffy. Either my It wished not to smell something or other, or else it wanted to wash out of the nose a smell I had perceived. The latter is my own particular case. Many people get few impressions of smell: driven by what has become a fanatical frenzy for protection from disease, above all by the dread of tuberculosis, crowds of people have come to the conclusion that the nose is to be regarded primarily as a respiratory organ, since they imagine that it is tempting Providence to breathe through the mouth. For others again the nose is indisputably a phallus symbol, and so with various patients the purpose of the It in producing results must be understood in various ways. But in my own case, if something goes wrong with my nose, I have

153

to look for what it is I am not to smell, and since it is the right nostril that is stuffy, whatever is objectionable to my sense of smell must be on my right. However I fail, in spite of all my trouble, to find anything with an evil smell on my right. But my long years of wishing to believe in the purpose of the It have made me cunning, and I have devised all kinds of ready justifications of my theory. So now I say to myself: if there's nothing there that has a bad smell, perhaps there is something which reminds you of a smell in times past. At once I think of an etching by Hans am Ende which is hanging to my right and represents a coast scene, with reeds and a sailing boat in shallow water. Venice suddenly stands in front of me, although I know that the subject of the etching is taken from the North Sea, and from Venice I go to the lions of St. Mark and thence to a teaspoon I used a few hours before. And at once I think I know what smell I am fleeing from. Many years ago, when I became nephritic after a severe attack of pneumonia, my sense of smell grew so acute that it was intolerable for me to use a spoon, since, in spite of the most careful cleansing, I could still smell what it had been used for, hours or days beforehand. So may it be, even now in my thoughts, that I am fleeing from the illness, the kidney trouble? As a matter of fact, a few hours ago I unriddled the story of a young girl's illness, in which figured an evil-smelling chamber pot. I myself, however, am indifferent to the smell of urine. It cannot be that. But memory takes me back to my school days, to the common urinals inside the school building, the sharp odor of ammonia which is still distinct in my memory. And the thought of this school period still depresses me. I told you once that I had forgotten almost everything belonging to those days. But I know that during that time—I was all of thirteen or fourteen years old—I was still in the habit of bed-wetting, that I was frightened that my school fellows would make game of me on that account, a thing which can almost never have really occurred, and anyhow never amounted to more than a mild teasing. Thoughts emerge of emotional attachments to one or another of my friends, attachments whose sexual content, though suppressed, nevertheless found expression in phantasy. The moment revives when I learnt to masturbate; then an attack of scarlet fever which led to my first kidney trouble comes to mind; I remember that Hans am Ende was my chum

154

and that he, too, caught scarlet fever; and behind all this rises the shadowy but ever-brightening mother imago. I was a "mother's boy," a petted nestling, and the separation from my mother when I went to school brought real suffering.

Now I'm stuck, but even so I am helped by an experience I gained in my struggle to preserve my theory of the It: there, where the associations come to a full stop, is the solution of the riddle. With my mother, then. That, I might have been able to think out for myself, since everything that is to my right is associated with my mother. But, however much I think about her, I do not remember ever perceiving any revolting smell in connection with her; on the contrary, I have certainly no smell perceptions at all associated with her.

I try with the name Hans (Hans am Ende). One of my elder brothers was so called, and he was closely connected with my school life. And suddenly there thrusts itself in front of his, another name, Lina. Lina was my sister, the same of whom I told you when I was speaking of my sadistic inclinations. And there also the smell impression comes up, though truly not a revolting but a soothing one, unforgettable. I can remember of that time—we were eleven and twelve years old—only the excitement, but I met this smell once again, and from that I know how overpowering for me is its impression. And alongside that comes a second memory, that Lina shortly afterwards initiated me into the secrets of menstruation. She pretended to me that she was consumptive, showed me the blood, and laughed at me when she saw my horror, explaining to me the meaning of the bleeding.

When I got so far, the stuffiness in my nose disappeared; what I now add, serves only to clear up the associations. And first I have thought what Hans am Ende signifies. All my family have died, my brother Hans last; Hans at the end. With this brother I made my one and only sailing trip, which links up with the sailing boat at the side of the etching.

Then the darkness clears up which lies over the connection with the mother complex. My mother had the same name as my sister Lina. Then my astonishment grows that I have no smell memories associated with my mother when they are so strong in connection with my sister, and again I begin all sorts of juggling with ideas.

If two dogs meet each other, one begins snuffling at the hinder parts of the other; obviously they discover with the nose whether they are sympathetic to each other or not. Whoever has a sense of humor laughs at this doggy habit, as you do, but people who have not, think it disgusting. But does your humor hold, when I maintain that human beings do the same? You will know from your own experience that a man who smells horrid, whatever may be his good qualities, will be regarded as fundamentally unsympathetic; only it should on no account be forgotten that what is an evil smell to one person, is attar of roses to another. As a keenly observant mother, you will also have noticed that the child judges objects and people by their smell. Science, it is true, behaves as though mouth and tongue were used as the touchstones of what is pleasant and unpleasant, but science upholds many things, and we need not worry ourselves about it. I maintain that man uses his nose more intensively, and, if you like, more disgustingly than the dog, to find out what pleases him and what does not.

First there is the smell of the woman's body and of the blood flowing out from it, one of the first perceptions which man has. I mentioned that before in making clear the significance of the monthly period. Then follows a time when the little citizen's nose busies itself with the smell of his own urine and faeces, changing at times to the scent of his mother's milk and of her axillary hair, while the penetrating and unforgettable smell of the lying-in bed lasts on and has its influence upon him. During the time after his birth the mother renews her own memories of the infancy which gives her the opportunity of transferring her self-love to the baby. The long-forgotten enjoyment of the smell of the baby's wrappings revives. At the same time she breathes in the odors that come from the little one's hair and from its whole body. And that goes on for some time, for the child is small and the mother big, so that every time she has to do with him she first sees and smells his hair, a fact of some importance since around the organs of love is just such another growth of hair. But for the child, the field of operation is changing. In the first years it is the feet and legs that he smells, for the child is short and grownups are tall. Keep it in mind, dear, that the child first learns to recognize and love people's legs. It is significant, it explains a great deal, and it is never remarked. Then come years, long years, and if you were to count up every fleeting moment that dogs are smelling each other, you would still be far short of the period of years in which the child must be almost uninterruptedly smelling what is in front of it, that is, people's stomachs and round about. And that gives him great pleasure. And it is even discovered to be appealing, for what emotional writer forgets to mention the boy—or the man—who buries his face in his mother's—or his sweetheart's lap? Which, disrobed of its romance, says in effect: he puts his nose between her legs. That sounds crude, but it explains the beginnings of childish love and of love for woman. Nature has marvelous paths of bringing men to the arms of women, and this is one that everybody treads.

What has that to do, you will ask, with the fact that I retain no smell memories of my mother? That is quite simple. If the child is indeed compelled by the force of circumstances for years to go on smelling all the mother's abdominal activities, it must necessarily perceive the remarkable difference of smell which recurs every fourth week. It must share in the emotional disturbances of the mother during the time of the period. The fervent atmosphere affects him too, and heightens his incest wish. All sorts of inner conflicts arise from these exciting experiences, all sorts of vaguely felt, but deeply painful disappointments are associated with them, and are strengthened by the grief caused by the mother's caprice, ill humor, or migraine. Is it any wonder that I chose to take refuge by repressing?

Is what I am saying obvious to you? But think then, there are people who maintain that they knew nothing about the period until they were grown up. If I am not mistaken, many people say so, indeed nearly everyone. Where, then, did everyone leave his nose? And what is happening to man's memory, when he forgets such experiences, must forget them? One is surprised that man has so weak a sense of smell, but how it might develop if he did not stop up his nose with all the might of his unconscious! He is compelled to do that through the command of the grownups that he shall know nothing of sexual matters, and through the prudish modesty of the mother who is embarrassed if the child is inquisitive, for nothing gives one a greater sense of shame than to see that a loved person is ashamed of something. It does not need words for a child to be intimidated; involuntary movements, slight, hardly noticeable gestures and embarrassments have sometimes a much more serious effect. But how shall a mother avoid this appearance of embarrassment? It is the mother's lot to wound her own child in its deepest feelings, it is her destiny. And no amount of good will or forethought can alter it, not even in the very slightest degree. Alas, dear, there is so much tragedy in life awaiting the poet who will be able to express it. And perhaps this poet will never come.

One forgets what is hard to bear, and what we don't forget was not unbearable for us. That is a statement on whose content you should ponder, for it upsets a great deal of what is current opinion. We forget that we once sat in the mother's body, for it is terrible to think that we were driven out of Paradise, but also terrible to think we were once in the darkness of a grave; we forget how we came into the world, for the dread of suffocation was intolerable. We forget that we once learned to walk, for the moment when the mother's hand let go of ours was horrible, and the blessedness of this first independent achievement so overwhelming that we cannot preserve it in our memory. How should we bear to know that for years we dirtied our baby diapers and drawers? Just think how ashamed you are if you find a tiny brown spot on your linen, and think of the horror that descends upon you if in the street you cannot keep back what belongs to the water closet. And what should we do with the memory that there were people so terribly strong that they could throw us up in the air, who scolded us, without our being allowed to reply, who smacked us and put us in the corner, we who are town councilors, or doctors, or even fourth-form men. We could not bear it that this being whom we call "Mother" once denied us her breast, this person who claims to love us; who taught us to masturbate and then punished us for it. And alas, we should weep ourselves to death if we remembered that once there was a mother who tended us and sympathized with us, and that now we are lonely and have no mother. And through our own fault!

That we forget our acquaintance with menstruation— of which we must have learned through the smell perceptions of early childhood, if not through the sight of the blood, the towels, the chamber pot, the little discords, the migraine, the doctor's treatment—that we completely forget this knowledge is not more wonderful than that we also lose all recollection of masturbation, the masturbation of our first years. And at least one ground is common to both these gaps in our memory—the dread of castration. You remember that I held our castration-anxiety to be associated with a sense of guilt, arising out of masturbation and its prohibition. But the thought that the member can be cut off springs from the ideas of earlier years concerning differences of sex, because as children we take the vulva for a wound: the woman is a castrated man. This idea grows to certainty through the perception of the bleedings, which we smell. These frighten us because they arouse the fear that we ourselves can be made into women. In order not to be reminded of these bleedings, we must destroy our sense of smell and get rid of the memory of that smell of blood. That we cannot do, we can only repress. And life uses this repression and builds upon it the prohibition of sex-intercourse during the period. Since the bleeding woman arouses the repressed castration complex, we avoid fresh contact with her.

Here a second repressed complex comes into play which is similarly bound up with the sense of smell, the birth-and-pregnancy complex. Do you remember my once asking you whether you had ever noticed anything of your mother's periods of pregnancy and of her *accouchements?* You had just been visiting your sister-in-law Elizabeth to pay your respects to the new baby, and the characteristic smell of the lying-in bed still clung to you. "No," you answered, "never." You were even surprised at the arrival of your youngest brother, although, at fifteen years of age you had long been enlightened on such matters. How is it possible that a child should not see that its mother is growing fatter? How is it possible for a child to believe in the stork?

Both things are impossible. Children know that they come out of the mother's body, but they are forced, both by themselves and by grownups, to believe in the fable of the stork. Children see that the mother grows fatter, that she suddenly has body pains, brings a child in the world, bleeds, and, when she gets up, is thinner again. Children know whenever the mother is pregnant, and the birth never takes them by surprise. But all this knowledge and all these perceptions are repressed.

If you reflect what force must be employed in pushing aside all these impressions and the conclusions drawn from them, you will have a little insight, perhaps, into what I mean by insisting that repression is the chief business of life. For what I am saying here in connection with the particular case of pregnancy and birth, is happening every minute of our lives with other complexes. You cannot go into a room without setting the mechanism of repression in motion, without dismissing from your consciousness this or that perception of the furniture, of its color, design and ornament. You cannot read a book, or see a face, or listen to someone speaking without continually repressing, without pushing away memories, phantasies, symbols, affects, hatred, love, contempt, shame and emotion. And now, dear, think; what is repressed is not destroyed, it stays there, only it is pushed into a corner, out of which one day it comes of itself, or perhaps is only dragged out of its position, no longer glittering red in the sunshine but seeming to be black. Repression works its changes unendingly in these phenomena; what is now for the eye a picture by Rembrandt, is repressed and reappears the same moment as a play with the watch chain, as the spot by the mouth, as a treatise on castration, as the foundation of a state, a declaration of love, anger, fatigue, sudden hunger, embraces or a blot of ink. Repression is transformation; it builds up civilization and destroys, it composes the Bible and the legend of the stork. And looking into the secret of repression so bewilders the brain that one has to close one's eyes and forget that there is such a thing as repression at all.

PATRIK TROLL.

✳ LETTER XXI ✳

You blame me, my dear, for not keeping my promise, since I still am not finished with my watch-chain story. I should never have thought you were stupid enough to believe in my promises!

Far more just is your reproach that I constantly digress and fail to carry to a conclusion what I have started to say. I was speaking about the repression of smell sensations connected with a birth, and neither proceeded to point out that the penetrating smell of the lying-in bed, even if everything else is carefully hidden, must be perceived by the child, so that he invariably gathers experiences of birth by means of his nose, nor made it sufficiently clear why the perception of this smell is banished from the conscious mind.

Why is this so? First, because the mother, the parents, and grownups generally, forbid the child to understand things of this nature; perhaps they do not forbid expressly with words, but there is in the tone of the words, in the expression of the voice, a curious, and, to the child, a surprising embarrassment. For it is the predestined fate of man to be ashamed of having been, in human fashion, begotten and born. He feels his vanity threatened by the fact, his divinity. He would like so much to have been divinely begotten, to be God, because he was almighty when he was in his mother's body; he establishes the religious cult of the Heavenly Child, he invents a Heavenly Father, and exalts his incest repression until he has found consolation in believing in the Virgin Mary and the Immaculate Conception, or in some branch of science. He contemptuously calls begetting and conception animal acts, so that he can say, "I am not an animal, I have not the form of an animal; I am accordingly a child of God and divinely begotten." Since he does not succeed in believing this, he surrounds these processes with a hypocritical pretense of mystery, in doing which, like Judas, he must betray love. Yes, he has gone so far that he is not in the least ashamed to bespatter the moment of human union with evil-sounding lies, as if this moment were not heaven. Man would like to be anything else but mere man.

The second reason why we repress the smell complex connected with birth, and so deny a gift peculiarly human, our nose—for, first and last, it is the sort of nose we have which distinguishes us from the animals—the second reason is that we cannot bear the thought of having a mother. Oh, pray understand: if she pleases us, so long as she is what we want her to be, we gladly acknowledge her as our mother. But so soon as we are reminded that she has borne us, then we hate her. We do not want to know that she has suffered for us, it is unbearable to know that. Or did you never see the distress, the torment, of your children when you were sad, or when you even wept? Certainly, it is a fact known to me that my mother bore me; I speak of it as if it were the most natural thing in the world. But my heart does not acknowledge it, it cries out against it and says no! At times it weighs upon the breast like a stone. That is the unconscious memory of the struggle for breath during birth, say our know-all analysts. "No," whispers the defiant soul, "it is my sin against the mother who bore me, the mortal sins of ingratitude, of incest, of bloodshed, of murder. Did I do the things I ought to have done, that all might be well with me, and my days be long upon the earth? This hand caressed me, gave me meat and drink, and at times I have hated it, have often hated it, because it guided me; this skin warmed me, and I hated it because I was too weak to renounce willingly its warmth and its alluring softness, and because of that, against my better knowledge, in order to escape temptation, I imputed to my mother all kinds of wrinkled ugliness, I, Judas! This mouth smiled upon me and spoke, and I often hated it because it scolded me; these eyes smiled upon me, and I have hated them; these breasts nourished me, and I have bitten them with my teeth; in this body I dwelt, and I have torn it." Matricide! You know it, you feel as I do. There has never been a human being who would not have murdered his mother, and it is because of that, that we do not acknowledge that our mother bore us. The blood we shed cries to heaven, and we flee from it, from the fumes of the blood.

A third reason occurs to me, why we struggle away from the memories of birth and prefer to destroy our most distinctive sense, the sense of smell; that is the dread of castration. I know that bores you, but what am I to do about it? Since you want to learn what I think, I must repeat. For the castration idea runs through our lives like the sounds of speech. Just as the a and the b are always coming over and over again in speaking, so is this complex of being made into a woman continually coming up in us. And if you put a and b together you have ab (off), and I hope you laugh as I do over the joke in the associations of the unconscious.

But it is time to make a few final remarks on the birth theories of children, or we shall never get out of this tan-

162

gle. I told you before that the child knows that he lives in the body of the mother before coming into the world; yes, the younger he is, the better he knows that. And so it shall not be forgotten the Bible reminds us with, among other things, the words, "The babe leaped in her womb." Sometimes the place in which the unborn sits is quite clearly localized at the pit of the heart, that is, in the stomach. And that tallies well with our phrase, that the woman carries her child under her heart. Take an opportunity to tell that to your doctor; it may be useful to him, especially in treating stomach troubles, from sickness to cancer; and for you, too, it will be useful, that you may get to know your doctor. If he shrugs his shoulders and goes off, get another doctor, for yours is out of date, however able he may be. I know nothing is more unpleasant for you than to be behind the times. Among other ideas there occurs to me the one that pregnancy can take place in the heart itself. I told you of a case where this belief led to illness and retained its power up to the time of the analysis. People who believed in this sort of thing in childhood are the worse for it. For with this absurd idea, which is derived from such words of love as "I bear you in my heart," or "You are the child of my heart," is bound up the dark and dreadful consciousness that one has in truth torn the mother's heart. And that, too, should your doctor know, for his heart cases. To reveal the whole foolishness of the child I will add what I know from eye patients, that the idea of eye pregnancies exists. Think of the word "pupil" only—the mother calls the child the apple of her eye. Or has the phrase "apple of the eye" arisen because the theory is general, and has established itself in the language? I know not.

Enough, the leading idea in any case is that of pregnancy in the stomach. And if I omit reference to the phantasies about the bursting or cutting open of the body, and about birth through the navel or in vomiting, there remains over and above for the child, the view that babies come to light through the anus. I told you this before, but you must stamp it well on your memory, for to this are due all cases of constipation, and thence arise as well all parsimonious traits, and therefore barter and exchange and ideas of property, and thence, as a good windup, all neatness and orderliness—and many a thing besides. You must not laugh, dear, when I speak thus. It sounds monstrous even to me, as soon as I say it aloud. And yet it is true. The It doesn't bother itself the least little bit about our aesthetics, our intellect, our thoughts. It thinks in its own way, independently, makes game with ideas so that all reasoning becomes foolish. "For me," it says, "a child is the same as the sausage, which you men produce, and the same as the gold which you possess. Yes, and something I was nearly forgetting; a child is also the same for me as the little tail that distinguishes the boy from the girl, which I have brought from the back to the front to suit my own fancy. At the back I let it fall out once in every twenty-four hours; I castrate it. At the front I leave it with those whom I recognize as men; from the others I take it away, I force them to rub it off, cut it off, tear it out. For I need maidens too."

This I have told you many times before. So much the better for remembering. Now we will see what the child thinks about conception.

But first we must get it clear how it is that he finds time and opportunity for thinking over things. The outside world offers so much that interests a child's brain that already some impulsion to quietude must be in operation, if all impressions are to be worked over. And there I should certainly remind you of that little throne from which the household is ruled, as soon as its walls enclose a child. I have long wondered why no sage has yet given his learned attention to the significance of the chamber pot, and it is doubly surprising since Busch has recorded it in classic verse:

> *Der Mensch in seinem dunkeln Drang*
> *Erfindet das Appartement.*

> His dark mysterious urge, that would not be prevented,
> Has forced man on, and so the closet was invented.

Seriously, you cannot overestimate the importance of this vessel, which adapts itself throughout life to physical requirements, and through the voluntary prolongation of the business serves the desire for meditative solitude. And first of all, there is the daily ritual of the infant.

I cannot tell you how often, either of my own wish, or because I was obliged for some reason to stay, I have seen families, stern father, decent mother, pleasant children, watching the baby's delivery, in dumb devotion, broken only by one or the other giving at times an encouraging grunt. And if I am not mistaken, it was your little Margaret who knew how to arrange things so that she had to use the chamber pot every time visitors were in the house. How cleverly she understood how to win the attention of everyone present by a quiet but firm refusal to finish her task! And then at the end, with a graceful lift of her night-dress, she would show her hidden treasures, in doing which she did not fail, as a final item in her performance, to call attention to her bottom by its pleasing exhibition.

Such a procedure is common, is the rule, with children. And because we invent learned names for things we are unwilling, for reasons of propriety, to recognize as part of the Universal Good, so that we can treat them as morbid desires from which we ourselves, while full of pity, are far removed, we call this urge to display our sexual secrets, exhibitionism. I've nothing to say against that, but now medicine, the law, the church, and unfortunately also that chaste prostitute, society, have decided that there must be people who are "exhibitionists," that is, people in whom the desire to exhibit their sexual organs has been exalted into a disease. You must let me quarrel with that. The truth is that the exhibitionist is in the same class as all those other people labeled with the final "ist," with the sadist, the masochist, the fetichist. They are in essence the same as ourselves, who call ourselves healthy; the sole difference is that we allow our desire to play only where custom permits, while the "ist" is out of date.

Some years ago a man went from house to house here at about six o'clock in the morning; he would ring the bell, and when the maid opened the door, would throw back his long military cloak, which was his only garment, and present to the horrified girl his erect member, to which for its better showing, he had tied a lantern. That we called morbid, that we named exhibitionism. But ask what happens in barracks. And why do we not give the same name to evening dress, which seems to reveal a good deal, or to dancing, which is quite certainly a representation of sex intercourse, or at any rate of erotic behavior? Certainly there are fanatical and pharisaic hypocrites who maintain that people dance merely for the sake of the exercise. I might answer this one-sided, exaggerated defense of morality with an equally one-sided, exaggerated attack on morality, and say: "Exercise itself, whether it be walking, fencing or dancing, is taken for the sake of its erotic quality." Today, people wear full trousers, but a few decades ago one could not wear them tight enough, with the result that the shape of the masculine organ could be distinguished even at a distance, while at the time of the Reformation the soldiers had the shape of the scrotum marked distinctly enough outside their armor, and to this they sewed a wooden stick, the tip of which was covered with a red cloth. And today? The walking stick and the cigarette speak clearly. Notice how a beginner starts to smoke, how quickly he puts his cigarette into his mouth and out again. Watch a lady getting into a carriage and then talk about the disease of exhibitionism. Women crochet, that is exhibitionism; men ride, that is also; the girl puts her arm into her lover's, that is exhibitionism; the bride wears wreath and veil, it is an exhibitionist symbol of the approaching bridal night.

You will have noticed how closely related are the impulses of exhibitionism and symbolism for me, for I feel justified in calling crochet exhibitionistic in character, since the needle, the member, is put into the stitch, the hole; riding has the same significance, for the identification of horse and woman is deeply planted in the unconscious of all thought; and it is hardly necessary for me to say that the bridal wreath stands for the vagina, the bridal veil for the hymen.

The purpose of this digression into exhibitionism is probably clear to you. I wished to convey by it that there is no essential difference between sick and healthy, that it depends on the choice of every doctor, and every sick man, what he will call diseased. That is for the doctor a necessary view. Otherwise he gets lost in the impassable tracks of the desire to heal, and that is a fatal mistake, for in the last resort it is the It which heals, the doctor merely gives treatment. We can discuss that at some other time. Today something else is on my mind.

There is a sort of counterpart to exhibitionism, viz., peeping. One understands by that, it seems, the impulse to catch a glimpse of sexual objects of one kind or another. And this impulse has been raised in the case of the so-called voyeurs to the dignity of a disease. That is, as I said, a matter of taste. I have not much use for people who ignore the erotic side of life, and I do not believe in the sincerity of the boarding school mistress who saved herself from the sight of the boys' swimming bath by means of her open sunshade. It is certain that these two impulses, to show and to see, play a great part in human life, and have an influence upon what is human, as well as upon what is all-too-human.

Suppose these two impulses, which are so perverse, were absent from the life of humanity, what would happen then? Where would be the drama, with its theater and raised curtain, where the church with its festivals, the garden with its flowers, and the house with its treasure of furnishings and pictures? Believe me, there are times when I do not know whether I ought to laugh or cry. And when I am in this state, my eyes get keener, and I gradually compose myself with the reflection that these things provide me with interest, and with material for my discussions with you.

PATRIK TROLL.

✳ LETTER XXII ✳

Thanks, my dear, this time you have arrived quickly at the heart of the matter. The story of little Else coming in her nightdress into the drawing room to say good night and, on being reproved by her mother with "Shame on you, Else. When visitors are here you oughtn't to come into the room in your nightdress," immediately lifting up this last little garment, in order to bring shame on herself, fits well into our little collection; and Ernst, who cut a hole in his sister's little frock, so that he should always be able to see how a "she" looked down below, is an excellent parallel to the stage custom of making a spyhole in the drop curtain. Perhaps this will help you to understand why I brought the stage into connection with exhibitionism and voyeurism. The "act" is truly an act, a symbolic sex-act.

There you have also at the same time my answer to your contentious point about the multiple perversion of the child. I stand by my opinion, that this multiple perversion of the child is common property of human beings at all ages, and in that I will not allow myself to be in the least confused by what you say. Both perversions, exhibitionism and voyeurism, are certainly to be found in every child, of that there is no doubt. And I am not in the least mistaken about the significance of the fact, that, up to three years of age, children show a special preference for such perversions. I shall return to that, for I must certainly tell you in my most moving language about the way in which Nature uses those first three years that can never be remembered, in order to make the child a servant and an artist of love. But what is right to the child is approved also by the grownup. It cannot be denied that the lover likes to see his mistress naked, and that she is not unwilling to be seen, yes, that it is even an unmistakable sign of disease if she be unwilling. But isn't it funny that the sages, the judges, the ladies, in the serious business of the day, completely forget what they have done by night? And even with a doctor, who prides himself on being free from prejudice, this holds good. The dictum, "Whatever you blame, that you have done yourself," is absolutely true, true in the very smallest detail. We humans always act on the principle of the man who has stolen something, and then is the first and loudest to cry, "Stop, thief!"

Furthermore, the perversion is not limited to the sense of sight. It sounds mad if I talk about exhibitionism of hearing and smell, of voyeurism of taste and feeling, but it means something definite and actual. It is not only the boy who passes water with audible force, in order to prove his manhood. The curiosity, or the rage, amounting to disease, with which people will listen to the love whispers and moans of a honeymoon couple in the adjoining room of a hotel; the splashing when washing, or the characteristic slam of the door of the bedside cupboard, and the rustle of urination, you will know from your own experience. Mothers realize it, too, when they use their special whispering words "Wsh, wsh," that the child may ejaculate his urine, and we doctors all use the trick of turning on the water tap when we see that a patient is ashamed to use the chamber pot in our presence. And what a part is played in life by the letting out of wind! You are not the only one, my dear, to give a pleased smile in reading this at the memory of some amusing explosion. Truly, I am convinced that if you give this letter to your friend

Katinka to read, she would utter an affected "Fie!" and be willing to read further, and that Councilor Heavy-liver, since he has long ago buried his sense of humor in the dirty folds of his scandal-loving mouth, would censoriously enounce the word "swine." But anger proves, just as laughter does, that the emotional response is there, that the hearing exhibitionist has met the hearing voyeur.

Beginning with faecal gas one may without trouble find plenty of examples in the zone of the sense of smell. I leave you to think out for yourself the repulsive and the attractive smells which are given out by man himself, or which he attaches to himself, and will merely add a few observations on this subject. First, as may be deduced from the foregoing, the production or perception of smells by no means always bears the character of a sexual challenge. Here, too, the law of contraries is valid. In certain conditions the smell is produced to express hatred, contempt, aversion. You will admit that an evil smell given by the It to the mouth, to hands, to feet, to sexual parts, arouses more emotional response than a pleasant smell. I may remind you, to make clear this curious freak of the It, of a friend of ours called Anne. You know that she has wonderful hair, perhaps the most beautiful that I have ever seen. But I distinctly see you make a wry face. This lovely hair stinks like the plague. Or rather it used to, for now the most fastidious nose would find not the slightest ground for complaint in the scent of this hair. Anne has easily and quickly lost this fatal combination of the ugly and the beautiful, since she became aware that her It was particularly sensual, and had on that account created this beautiful hair, just as the most sensual of sensualists, the consumptives, do with their hair and eyes and teeth. On top of this It, life placed a second moralistic, anxious It, which created the smell in order to mar the seductive beauty with its repulsiveness.

One more remark on this point. You always maintain that people smell who don't wash. I have often heard you try to impress this view on your boy, who at ten years is suitably shy of water, and you drive your words home by means of a thorough examination of hands, ears and neck. May I ask you how often you wash your hair? And I can assure you it smells like new-mown hay. The It does not trouble itself at all with the foolish views of men. It stinks if it wants to, and it changes the evil into a good smell, if it so pleases. Now and then I am inclined to believe that people wash, not because they have a horror of dirt but because, like Pilate at the Judgment Seat, they want to assume a spotlessness which is by no means theirs. The little boy's protest, "I'm not such a pig as to need washing every day," is not at all so stupid. It is the same with the horror of dirt as with the horror of "Aa" and "Wee-wee." People wipe themselves very carefully, wash themselves whenever possible after every evacuation, whether solid or liquid, and never reflect that inside the body man carries these supposedly dirty substances around with him all the time. O thou wandering closet that callest thyself man, the more horror and disgust thou showest at faeces and urine, the more clearly dost thou prove thy pleasure in these things, and the more thou washest, the better I know thou dost believe thine own soul to be filthy. But why swallow thy spittle, if spittle is disgusting?

I won't torment you any longer with paradoxes, but will rather bring to your notice a curious type of exhibitionism, exhibitionism to oneself. You think of the mirror, and then of narcissism—for Narcissus invented the mirror; and masturbation—the mirror is a masturbation symbol; and if you have the same sort of juggler's brain as I have, you will reflect that people even make grimaces in front of a mirror, so an act of exhibitionism can be double-sided, can be both alluring and ugly.

But I was speaking of the water closet and of smell, and if you will, please name any one of your friends who does not look at her evacuations in the water closet—for considerations of health, be it understood. And certainly, believe me, there are refined people who bore in their noses when they are alone, for a hole will not rest until something is stuck in it, and the nostrils are no exception.

What could I not tell you of those acts of exhibitionism in gestures, in the voice, in personal habits! "Seek and ye shall find," it says in the Bible. But it also says, "They have eyes and see not; ears have they, but they hear not."

The associations of the sense of taste with unconscious erotism are difficult to bring to consciousness. It will be easiest to follow up the associations of children's comforters with the act of sucking. If one goes out from this starting point, with a little trouble one often finds lovers' habits which can be classified under the heading of taste. Thus the sucking of the other one's finger is an action which can be frequently observed. But the secrecy of such caresses tells clearly how greatly they are prized. One may be ever so modest, yet sucking will accompany the love-act, and the tongue for everyone, and not merely in the wonderfully changing expression of the word "love," is a voluptuous organ. But above all, it seems to me, the exposing of the breast is a challenge to taste, associated, it is true, with touch and sight, in the way all these sense functions are associated. And that leads me to point out a genuine act of exhibitionism on the part of the It, the erection of the nipples, which happens to the most chaste of maidens quite independently of any will of hers. For the time I will leave it to you to make conclusions about the man's erection from what you know of the nipples, but later, however strictly forbidden the subject, I must come back to it.

One thing, however, I have still to mention, in the sphere of taste erotism, and that is people's favorite foods. The preference for sweet, sour, bitter, fat, salty, for this food or that beverage, the offering, the pressing, the manner of eating, and the composition of the menu, show desires of curious kinds. Keep that in mind, and—do not forget this—it is just the same whether anyone is fond of roast pork, or whether it makes him sick.

Shall I now add some observations on the sense of feeling? You can fit these together yourself, can think over and try them out for yourself. The offering of the hand, or of the lips to another, the insinuating knee, and the foot touching under the table. But there are other things more difficult to understand. Certainly the erotic purpose of a stroking hand is quickly felt and quickly interpreted, but how does the matter stand with a cold hand? "Cold hands, warm heart," says the proverb, and proverbs seldom err. "See, I am cold," says such a hand, "warm me, I need love." The It lurks concealed behind, cunning as ever. "The man pleases me," it thinks, "but perhaps I do not please him; we shall see. If my cold hand does not frighten him away, if he takes loving hold of this wretched thing I offer him, then all is well. And if he stays remote, cold as my hand, then still he may be loving me, and only be frightened by the coldness." And then, too, for the It is subtler than you think, it will make the hand damp, and so will it really be the "touchstone" of love; for to want to hold a damp, cold hand, one must indeed value the owner.

This exhibitionist hand says openly and frankly, "See, even in the coldness the love fluid is flowing out of me, so ardent is my emotion. What floods of love will I pour over you, when you bring me warmth!"

You see, dearest, I am already in the deep levels of unconscious erotism, in the interpretation of the physiological processes, and there I should like to linger for a moment. For to me, as a physician, the unconscious exhibition of sexuality offers more of interest than instinct working simply in the conscious mind.

I find a convenient example in skin processes, which have given me considerable trouble. You know that, as a pupil of Schweninger's, I am still sought out now and then by patients with skin trouble, and among them there are always some who suffer from chronic, irritating eruptions. In earlier days I took no particular notice when I heard them say, at some point or other, in describing their symptoms, that they had a sensitive skin. But now I know that their eczema ceaselessly repeats the same assurance, only that it speaks more clearly, and also describes the type of sensitiveness. It says—at least I think I hear it, and the results seem to bear me out—"See how my skin longs to be gently tickled. There is such wonderful charm in soft stroking, and no one strokes me. But understand me, help me! How should I better express my desires than through the scratching I force upon myself?" That is pure exhibitionism in the realm of touching.

We have talked long enough, and the baby whom we left sitting on his little throne in solemn meditation, has meantime finished his business. I wanted to tell you what he was thinking of during this time, but have not done so because it isn't certain whether he was occupying himself just at this moment with thoughts about conception. I will make up for that later. But there is one thing more I must say before taking leave of you: the chamber pot—or the toilet, it is the same—is an important bit of furniture, and there are many, many people who occupy three quarters of their lives with it; not that they are literally sitting there, but they wake up in the morning with the thought, "Shall I have a movement today?" And a few hours after this mighty deed is done, they start again to think—and even to talk about it, generally at lunch—"Shall I have a movement tomorrow?" It really is a funny world!

Only think now: the little child likes to accompany father or mother, and to watch their doings in this quiet place. When it is bigger it seeks other children, that it may pursue its investigations and solve more riddles. Then comes the time of puberty, and again the most engrossing experience of these years, perhaps of the whole of life, is carried on in the water closet, masturbation. After adolescence people begin to grow stupid, and are content, instead of pursuing the wonders of life, to read the paper in there, or to improve their minds, until finally old age comes, and then, not infrequently, a seizure in the bathroom makes an end of all. From the cradle to the grave!

With affectionate regards,
PATRIK TROLL.

✳ LETTER XXIII ✳

I grant you, my dear, that it was wrong to say so much about exhibitionism, and I also agree that I stretched unwarrantably the meaning of the word. Let me explain that just at this moment I have one or two patients who indulge this instinct to the point of virtuosity. I had hoped you would overlook the form for the sake of the substance.

So, today, instead of trying to force into a system that which is without system, I will only set forth a few observations. You may draw your own conclusions.

The next time you have an opportunity, please observe your friend Helen's mouth and you will be able to learn a good deal. You know everyone thinks her mouth is particularly small; it looks as if a coin could be passed into it only with difficulty. But mention the word "horse" in her presence, and her mouth gets wide and she gnashes her teeth just like a horse. Why? Behind the house where Helen's parents lived there was a drilling ground used by a dragoon regiment. From the horses she derived her knowledge of male and female, and on one of these, as a tiny girl, she was lifted up by a corporal and so apparently had her first experience of voluptuous sensations. Imagine a five-year-old child standing by the side of a gelding; there she sees in front of her the great belly with a thing hanging to it which suddenly extends to double its length and lets a mighty flow of urine stream forth, truly an overpowering sight to a child!

So watch people, and you will read in their faces, the shape of their heads, the molding of their hands, their gait, a thousand tales. One man has protruding eyes; you may be sure he wants to show you from afar his curiosity, and his horror at the remarkable discoveries he has made. In another, the deep-sunken eyes withdraw themselves when his hatred of mankind grows great; they do not wish to see, and still less to be seen. The tears that are shed are not dedicated only to pain and grief; they imitate the pearl which lies hidden in the shell, in the woman's mother-of-pearl shell, and every tear is full of symbolic sensuousness; always, without exception. Every poet knows that; for centuries they have known it and told about it without consciously expressing it. Only those who should know it do not. Eros uses the eye for his service, and it must give him pleasing pictures. If too many are given he washes them out; he lets the eye overflow because the inner tension is too great to be released by means of the genital secretion, because the childish method of getting rid of excitement by urinating is not open to him, or because he is depressed on account of morality, he wants to make the person do penance in symbolic form for being ashamed of being erotic. Eros is a strong, zealous god who knows how to punish cruelly and mockingly. "You think it dirty," he rages, "that I have united the wetness between the thighs with man's greatest achievement, the union of man and woman and the creation of a new being. You shall have your way. You have mucous membrane in the bowel and elsewhere, so henceforth your ejaculations shall be diarrhoea, excrements, sneezing, sweating of the feet or underarm, and above all, urinating."

I understand that you will find all of this strange, but who shall stop me from phantasying as I like; from calling Eros today what I yesterday called the It; from conceiving this It as a wrathful god, although I described him as pitying, gentle, and tender; from ascribing to him a power that urges here and forbids there, and ever again seems to be meeting itself in contradictions? In this I do no other than men have always done. And it seems to me to be good for our well-ordered, superficial thinking, to have things thrown into confusion. "Everything must be revolutionized" is a stupid aim, but a just observation.

Shall I phantasy further? Peasants make the comparison between the mouth and the vaginal opening. Similarly—for our It has grown capricious and its power is boundless—the nose is the male member, and consequently it makes the nose grow big or little, pointed or snub, plants it straight or awry, according to whether it wants to express this or that desire. And now please make your conclusions as to the cause of nosebleeding, which is common at certain ages, of the hairs that grow out of the nostrils, of polypus and a scrofulous stench. The ears again have shells, and the shell, as I said before, is the symbol of the woman. The ear is a receiving organ,* its shape is not without interest for imaginative observers.

But you must not think that I want to give explanations. Life is much too multicolored for us to be able to recognize it, much too smooth for us to seize it. Perhaps I only want to poke a little fun at logic. Perhaps there is more behind it than that.

Have you ever noticed how difficult it is sometimes to get children to let you look into their mouths? The child is still naïve. It believes that the mouth is the opening to the soul, and that the doctor, whom fools, young and old, take to be a magician, can see all their secrets. And indeed something is sticking in his throat which no child likes to reveal; his knowledge of man and woman. At the back of the mouth are two arches (or are they two tonsils?) which surround an opening that leads into the depths and in between them a red structure is palpitating, getting shorter, getting longer, always changing; it is a little tail that hangs there. "The man with glasses, the Uncle Doctor, will know how I lie in bed watching when papa and mama believe I am asleep, and they play games with the opening and the piston that I ought not to know about. And, who knows, perhaps it is also written there what I did myself without anyone finding out." The throat inflammations of children are very instructive; you would not believe all that one can read in them.

* The German word *Empfangen* means both to conceive and to receive.

And now, let us consider, first, measles and scarlet fever. "I burn, I burn," the fever tells you, "and I am so ashamed! Only look how I have got red all over the body." Of course you need not believe this, but from whence comes it, then, that out of three children, two catch scarlet fever and one remains well? Sometimes a phantastic explanation is better than none at all. And it is not so altogether stupid. You must remember, however, that the age of passion is not youth, but childhood. But the blushing conveys a double meaning from the It: it draws a veil over the face so that no one sees what is going on behind it; one also sees how the fire of sensuality is blazing and how the piously trained It is driving the hot blood away from the bowels, from the sexual parts, from hell and the devil, up to the head, in order to load the brain more thickly.

I might go on telling you more, about pneumonia and cancer, about gall stones and hematuria, but we can talk about these later. For today, only one word more on the exhibitionistic impulse and its strength. A century ago there were as yet no women's doctors; today in every little town and at every street corner in a big city you will find a specialist. That is because, except in marriage, the woman of today has no opportunity to reveal herself. But illness excuses everything, and since the illness takes revenge for the guilty wishes, unconscious, half conscious and wholly conscious, it saves the victim from eternal punishment.

There is one form of exhibitionism which is historically important for the outcome of our correspondence, namely, hysteria, and in particular, hysterical cramp. I have already mentioned Freud's name, and I should like to repeat what I said in the beginning: Everything that is correct in this medley of letters goes back to him. Now, it is more than twenty years since Freud made his first basic observations on the It of an hysteric. I do not know how he now regards these phenomena, and so I cannot count on his support when I say that the It of the hysteric is more cunning than that of other people. Among other things, this It gets pleasure from reproducing publicly the secrets of Eros, before the eyes of all men. Compared with these performances the nude or the belly dances are as naught, and to give them undisturbed by self-reproach or by the outraged anger of those around, the It brings about a loss of consciousness and dresses the erotic behavior symbolically as cramps, horribly distorted movements of the buttocks, of the head, and of the limbs. Things go on then as they do in dreams, only that the It invites to its exhibition a respectable public over whom it lustily makes merry.

I am again drawing near to the subject of the theories of begetting and conception as conjured up by the child, as you once imagined them, and I, too. But first I must put one question to you. When, do you think, did you first learn of the difference in the sexes? Please don't answer, "At eight years of age, when my brother was born." I am convinced that at five years of age you could already distinguish a naked little girl from a naked boy, and even at three years, and perhaps still earlier. It will finally come out that you know just as little as I do about it. No one knows anything about it. I know a little boy of two and a half called Sam, who watched his baby sister being bathed and then said, looking down between his legs, "Sammy has," and turned his back on the baby girl.

And so we know nothing at all about the point of time at which the child comes to recognize the difference between the sexes, but that he has a lively interest in making sure of the matter before he is four, that he ponders over it and asks questions about it, even mothers know— an incontrovertible proof, for me, that this interest is extremely vivid. I told you before that every child, under the pressure of the castration complex, believes that all people are originally provided with the little tail, are male, and that those who are called girls and women are castrated males, castrated for the purpose of bearing children and as a punishment for masturbation. This idea is by no means stupid and is of incalculable importance in its results, since upon it rests the man's feeling of superiority, the woman's feeling of inferiority, and for this reason again the woman strives towards higher things, towards heaven, towards religion, while man strives ever towards the things ahead, towards philosophy, and searching the depths. This idea is associated, in the tangled and yet so logical thinking of the child, with the attentive examination of the male organ. In our primitive, economic fashion we meditate—you and I have done so, and everyone does

177

—on what use can be made of these amputated sex organs. The use of the appendage itself is the first mystery. Under certain conditions it appears to prolong its existence in the appendix. But then there are, in the testicles, two structures which are decidedly like eggs—but eggs are eaten. Therefore the eggs cut off from the males condemned to be females, are eaten. From such a conclusion the child turns away in horror, although in general he has little feeling for the woes of others. He thinks it senseless to mutilate people merely for the sake of eating the eggs, since the hens lay enough eggs for that. And so he searches for some other purpose, to make this amputation and eating reasonable. Then an early experience comes to the help of the reflective child; from eggs come chickens, the hen's children: and these eggs come out from the hen at the back, out of the hole in the hen's "bottie"; and out of the woman's "bottie," he knows already, children come. Now the matter is cleared up. The eggs that are cut away are eaten, not because they taste good, but because little children are going to come out of them. And slowly this circle of ideas closes up, and then out of the misty darkness of thought a terrifying person steps forth: the father. The father cuts off the mother's sex parts and gives them to her to eat. And out of them come the children. This is what is going on during those panting, bed-shaking struggles between the parents at night, the groans and the sighs are for this, this accounts for the blood in the chamber pot. The father is terrible, a cruel man, a man who punishes. But what is it then that he is punishing? The rubbing and touching. Then was the mother also doing this? That can hardly be possible, but it is not necessary to think that, for an experience comes to take its place. Every day the mother's hand rubs the childish "eggs" of her son, every day she plays with his little tail. "Mother knows how to rub, father knows and punishes her for this; so he will punish me, too, for I also play. But let him punish me, for I want to have children. I will play, then he will punish me and I shall have children. Thank heaven, I've an excuse for playing. But what shall I have to play with when my father has cut my tail off? It would be better to hide my enjoyment. Certainly it would be better."

And so anxiety and longing change and change about,

and slowly the child grows into a man, forever wavering between instinct and morality, desire and fear.

Good-bye, dear one,

Your
PATRIK TROLL.

✳ LETTER XXIV ✳

How nice of you, my dear, not to take my writing tragically, but to laugh at it! I have been laughed at so often and have so much enjoyed joining in the laughter that I often do not know myself whether I mean what I am saying, or am simply poking fun.

But it is written, Sit not in the seat of the scornful. I don't imagine that the mixture of phantasies that I recently set out for you as a childish sexual theory was ever really in the mind of a child, or at any rate, in any child's mind but my own. Fragments of it you will find everywhere, often changed almost beyond recognition, often incorporated in another series of phantasies. What I wanted to do was to make it quite clear to you, to impress it on your innermost soul, that the child is continually occupied with the mysteries of sex, of Eros, of the It; is much more deeply concerned with these than is any psychiatrist or psychoanalyst; that his development is essentially bound up with the attempt to solve these mysteries; in other words, that our childhood may very well be regarded as a school in which we are instructed by Eros. And now if you imagine the wildest phantasies that the child may have over birth, conception, sex differences, you will still not be able to imagine a millionth part of what the child, every child, actually dreams; indeed, on any given topic you will only be able to imagine what you yourself, as a child, once really thought. For this is the remarkable thing about the It—and I beg you to remember this—that it does not distinguish as does the

179

lofty intellect between reality and phantasy; for it everything is real. And if you have not yet grown quite stupid, you will understand that the It is right.

Yes, I can tell you something more, not much, but something, about the fate of that little tail that you must have imagined was eaten by your mother. From this little tail, the child hazards, there comes the sausage. Not all of the eggs that are swallowed give rise to pregnancies; most of them are changed in the stomach into a brown chocolate-like mass, like other kinds of food, and because this mass contains the eaten-up, sausage-shaped tail, it takes on the shape of a long sausage. Is it not strange that the three-year-old's brain already holds the theory of form, and the theory of fermentation too? You cannot attribute enough importance to this, for the associations—defecation, birth, castration, conception, and sausage, penis, power, money—are daily and hourly repeated in the world of our unconscious ideas; association makes us rich or poor, amorous or drowsy, busy or lazy, potent or impotent, happy or sad; it gives us a skin which sweats; it makes and unmakes marriages, builds factories, contrives whatever happens, and plays a part in everything, even in diseases. Or rather, it is in the diseases that this association allows itself to be most easily discovered; only one must not be frightened at the jeers of the wise.

For your amusement I will tell you of another idea hatched in the brain of the child, which seems not infrequently to survive in the adult. It is the idea that the tail when swallowed is sometimes transformed into a stick corresponding to an erection, that the little eggs are fixed on this, and so an ovary is made. I know of an impotent man—that is, he became so at the very moment when the member had to be inserted—who had the idea that in a woman's body there were sticks bearing rows of eggs. "And since I have a particularly big member," thought his vanity, "I shall break all these eggs with my thrusting." He is now potent. The noteworthy point in his story was, that as a boy he had a large collection of eggs, and in blowing out the eggs, which he took out of the nest away from the mother-birds, he now and then found one which already contained a young bird. His theory about the egg sticks (ovaries) went back to that. To the great logicians this is nonsense, but you do not consider it too trivial to ponder over!

I return to my associations with the situation in which I recently found myself in writing to you—you remember, when I was speaking about the watch chain. I still owe you an account of the itching on my right shinbone and the spot near my upper lip. In some curious fashion the word shinbone (*schienbein*) at once turned itself around into leg pads (*beinschiene*), and then there rose up before me the picture of Achilles, as I remember it from my childhood—perhaps from my eighth or ninth year. It is an illustration in Schwab's *Stories of the Greek Heroes*. And the words "unapproachable hands" occur to me. Where am I to begin? Where to end? My childhood wakes up and something within me is weeping.

Do you know Schiller's poem, *Hector's Farewell to Andromache?* My second brother, Hans—I mentioned him recently in speaking of Hans am Ende—yes, verily, he had a wound on his right shin. In tobogganing he had hit a tree. I must have been five or six years old at the time. In the evening—the lamp was already lighted—my brother was carried in, and I saw the wound, a deep wound a couple of inches long, all bleeding. It made a terrible impression on me; I know why, now. The picture of this wound is indissolubly united with another: black leeches are hanging on the edge of this wound, and one or two have fallen down from it; the Creation of Eve, castration, leeches, the penis cut off, wound, and womanhood. And my father put the leeches on.

Tobogganing—why do people toboggan? Did you know that rapid motion gave sexual pleasure? Since the nosedive was invented, every aviator has known it. It sometimes leads to erection and ejaculation; life itself tells you why for thousands and millions of years man dreamed he could and would fly, whence came the legend of Icarus, why angels and cupids have wings, why every father lifts his child up and lets him fly through the air, and why the child exults in it. Sleighing and tobogganing were for the boy Patrik a symbol of masturbation, and the wound and the leeches, its punishment.

To come back to Hector's farewell, and the "unapproachable hands." My second brother, Hans, and the third, Wolf—a fateful name as you already know—used to give a dramatic rendering of this poem, at which the family and any visitors we might have would form the audience. And then a riding cloak of my mother's with a

181

red lining, and trimmed with fur, was used to adorn Andromache; purple and ermine, that is the great wound of the woman, and the skin; the bleeding and the binder. What an impression it all made on me! Right at the beginning the words "To him brings Patroclus a dreadful sacrifice." "Patroclus—Patrik," and the sacrifice, Abraham's offering and the circumcision, and the weeping for the desolation now of Achilles' revenge, now of the castration. The little one, the penis, he shall no more "cast the spear," because dark Orcus has devoured Hector. Hector is the boy, and Orcus, the mother's womb and the grave; it has to do with incest, the everlasting wish of man and of little Patrik. Oedipus! What shudders went down my back at the words, "Hark, the enemy is thundering at the walls." I recognized this thundering, the fearful wrath of the father, Achilles. And Lethe's stream got mixed with the meadow brook from *Struwwelpeter's Paulinchen*, with the maiden's masturbation song, and with the bed-wetting stream of urine when I was deep in sleep.

Certainly, dear, I did not know this at the time, and did not know it with my intellect. But my It knew it, understood it all better, more thoroughly, than I understand it now, after all my efforts to know my own and others' souls.

Let me rather speak about that book, Schwab's Greek *Stories*. It was given to me as a Christmas present. My parents by that time had become poor, and so the three volumes were not new, but only newly bound. They had previously belonged to my eldest brother, a fact which distinctly increased their value for me. And concerning this brother many things come into my mind, but first I must finish this business with Schwab. One volume—it deals with the Trojan War—had the corners crushed. I had struck my brother Wolf with it, the brother five years older than myself, when he teased me into a rage and then laughingly held me with one hand. How I hated him, and yet how I must have loved him; how I admired him, the strong one, the wild one, the wolf!

I must tell you something. Whenever I am miserable in any way, perhaps my head or my throat is aching, the word "Wolf" comes up in the analysis. My brother Wolf is inextricably knit up with my inner life, with my It. There seems to be nothing more important for me than this Wolf complex. And yet years pass by without my thinking of him, and, too, he is long since dead. But he forces himself into my anxiety states, he comes into whatever I am doing. Whenever the castration complex comes to the surface, Wolf is always there, and something dark and terrible is threatening me. I remember only one single sexual experience which I can connect with him. Even yet I can picture the scene; it was out in the open and a schoolfriend of Wolf's was holding a playing card up to the light. Something peculiar could be seen when the light shone through it, something forbidden, for I still remember their frightened manner due to their sense of guilt. What was on the card, I do not know. But with this memory a second is inseparably connected, how my brother Wolf pretended to this same friend that his name was derived from the giant Wolfgrambar, and this had a dreadful effect upon me. And now I know that the giant is the personified phallus.

Suddenly there comes to my mind one of Kaulbach's illustrations to Reineke Fuchs, how the wolf Isegrim has broken into the farmhouse, is discovered, has thrown the farmer over and stands with his head under the man's shirt. I have not looked at this picture for at least forty years, but I can still visualize it clearly. And now I know that the wolf is biting off the farmer's sex organ. It is one of the few pictures that have remained in my memory. But Isegrim—Grim was the name of the boy from whom I learned to masturbate—significantly enough, meant to warn me, and told me what was deeply repressed.

How did the Fuchs epic come to choose the wolf as a castrating animal, and how did Kaulbach come to make a picture of this incident? What is the meaning of the story of Red Ridinghood, and of the Seven Kids? Do you know that one? The old goat goes out and warns her seven little ones beforehand to keep the door locked, and not to let the wolf into the house. But the wolf forces his way in and devours all the kids except the youngest, who hides in the grandfather clock. There the mother finds him on her return. The kid tells her of the wolf's wickedness and the two of them search for the robber, find him lying in deep slumber after his too heavy meal, and as there seems to be something moving about inside his belly, they rip it open, and all the six kids he has swallowed come to light again. Now the mother fills the wicked animal's body with great stones and sews him up.

The wolf wakes up thirsty and, as he leans over the brook to drink, he is overbalanced by the heavy stones and falls into the water.

I do not pretend to be able to explain the story so as to clear up all the secrets which the folk mind has put into its composition. But I can say a few things without being too daring. First the cutting open the belly, out of which comes forth the young life, is an easily intelligible birth symbol, since it links up with the idea commonly accepted by children that the body is cut open at childbirth and sewn up again. And along with that we have the explanation of the children being devoured without being killed: it is the conception. And in the mother's warning that the door must be kept locked, one can read the reminder that there is only one virginity to lose, and that the maiden should never allow entrance until "the ring is on her finger." But it remains a puzzle what the safe hiding of the seventh kid in the clockcase means. You know what a role the number seven plays in human life; one meets it everywhere, sometimes as a good number, sometimes an evil one. In that connection it is surprising that the expression "bad seven" is only used of the woman. It may be assumed, then, that "the good seven" denotes the man. That seems to be right, for while the woman, with head, body, and four limbs, has the character of "six," the man has also a fifth member, the sign of his lordship. According to this the seventh little goat is the male member, which is not swallowed up, but hides itself in the clockcase and then jumps out again. And it is open to you to decide whether the clockcase is the foreskin or the vagina which the seventh leaves again after the ejaculation. That the wolf falls into the brook at the end I cannot rightly get clear to myself; at the most, I could say that, as so often happens, it is a reduplication of the main theme of birth, as the hiding in the clockcase might also be interpreted as pregnancy and birth. We know from dreams that falling into water is a pregnancy symbol.

So far the story, brought out of its beautiful legendary form, is given more or less the aspect of plain everyday experience. There remains only the wolf, and you know that my personal complexes begin there. But still I will try to make something out of it. I should like to go back to the seven. The seventh kid is the boy. The other six are the "bad seven," the girl, with whom the "seventh" gets ill and is eaten up, and is bad because she masturbated and acted badly. Then the wolf would be the power which makes out of the seven "the six," which changes the boy into a girl, castrates him, cuts away his member. He would be identified with the father. If this is so, the opening of the door acquires another meaning, it is then the childish masturbation of the "seven," of the boy, who by his rubbing makes his "seven" sore, bad, so the wolf eats it up, that he may be restored to the world as a girl, with a wound instead of the member. The seventh little goat, to avoid masturbating, or at least the discovery of masturbation, awaits the time when he shall be sexually mature and therefore keeps his boy's nature. The word "bad" added to "seven" to denote the woman, in its further meaning of "sore" and "suppurating," supplies the association with syphilis and cancer, and helps us to understand why every woman dreads being visited by these two diseases. The eating of the kids leads on to the childish theory of conception through swallowing the seed, an association which reappears in the tale of "Hop-o'-My-Thumb," in the person of the man-eating giant. In the story of the Seven-league Boots, the connection between wolf and man or father is shown; for one would certainly not be mistaken in seeing a symbol of erection in these wonderful boots.

Now I must go back to something that I mentioned earlier, namely that the child does not like to have anyone look in his mouth. He is afraid of the uvula being cut off. In the name "Wolfsrachen" (wolf's jaws—cleft palate), you have the association between wolf and masturbation. With a cleft palate the uvula is missing which represents the male member, it is castrated. It symbolizes the punishment for masturbation. And if you have ever seen anyone with a cleft palate, you will know how dreadful the punishment is.

With that I come to an end. I do not know whether the interpretation pleases you, but it has helped me over the many difficulties of my "Wolf-Isegrim-brother complex."

Affectionately,

PATRIK.

❋ LETTER XXV ❋

According to you, then, "the bad seven" is the mouth, and there I entirely agree with you. There are men also, of course, who "jaw" terribly, but in the end it comes down to this: the seventh opening of the face is just as much a woman symbol as the great wound in the abdomen.

Since we are on the subject of numbers, let us go on playing with them. To begin with I must point out that the It, which has a marvelous memory for numbers, masters the simple rules of arithmetic in a way otherwise met with only in a certain type of idiocy, and that it finds just the same sort of pleasure as the idiot does, in solving arithmetical exercises in an instant. You will be able to convince yourself of this by means of a simple experiment. Talk to anyone you please on a subject that stirs the It; there are all kinds of signs by which you may determine that he is so moved. When you observe these signs, ask for a date, and immediately, with absolute certainty, one will be named which stands in intimate relationship with the complex which has been brought to the surface. Often enough the connection is obvious, so that the speaker himself is astonished at the capacity of his unconscious. Often all such connection is denied. Do not be misled by that. The man's conscious mind likes to deny—I had almost said to lie. Do not listen to his "No," but hold fast to the knowledge that the It never lies and never denies. After some time the correctness of the association will be proved, and at the same time a mass of psychic material will come up which, repressed in the man's unconscious, has brought about in him all sorts of evil and good.

I will describe to you a little number trick carried out

by my own It, which when I discovered it, amused me very much. For many years whenever I wished to express my impatience and displeasure, I used to say, "I've already told you that 26,783 times." You must remember that when we were last together, you teased me about it. That vexed me and I puzzled over the mystery of this number. It occurred to me that the cross sum of the figures in this long number is 26, exactly the same number that is separated from the other figures when they are taken away. With 26 I think of my mother. I was 26 years old when my mother died. Twenty-six was the age of both my parents when they married; in the year 1826 my father was born. If you take the cross sum of the other figures, 783, you hit upon 18. Isolate the first three figures as $2 \times (6 + 7)$ and you have the 26. Add the 2 to the last two figures 8×3 and again there is 26. I was born 13/10/66. These figures can be added to make 26.

I have analyzed the number 26,783 in yet another way. The 2 seemed to me to stand by itself, since I had unwittingly applied it to the two operations, with $6+7$ and 8×3. The other numbers group themselves, under the influence of the isolated 2, as 67, 78, 83. Sixty-seven was the age of my mother at the time of her death. Seventy-eight is the date I had to leave home to enter a boarding school. In '83 my old home was lost to me forever, for in that year my parents left the town where I was born, to settle in Berlin. In that same year an experience befell me, the effect of which lasted over a long period of my life. At recess between two periods one of my schoolmates said to me: "If you go on masturbating like this any longer, you will soon go crazy; as it is you are half-mad." These words became portentous to me not merely because my masturbation-anxiety was thereby intensified, but because I did not reply, and accepted in silence the disgrace of the public accusation of masturbating, as if it had left me unmoved. I felt it profoundly, but suppressed it immediately, with the help of the word "crazy." At this time my It took possession of the word, and has never since let go. Thenceforward all my freak thoughts seemed to be permissible. For me, half-mad means, "You are straddling between two possibilities; it is left to you whether you incline towards one side or to the other; you can look upon the world and upon life as a sane and ordinary human being, or as a madman, an exceptional individual who has forsaken ordinary standards." This indeed I have done with great thoroughness, and still do, as you know only too well. The two mothers—the wet nurse and my mother—found a new and necessary support, and my position between the two was made bearable to me through half-madness; it led me from the compulsion of doubting, to a patient skepticism and irony, to the world of Thomas Weltlein's thought.* It is possible that I am mistaken in the value I put upon this phrase, "half-mad," but it explains for me the curious qualities of my nature, which usually avoids two alternatives, but which nevertheless is able to follow two opposing, even contradictory trains of thought at the same time, undisturbed by contempt, every advice, every example, and despite my own inner disinclination. In a careful examination of the history of my life, I have found that this half-madness has given me just that amount of ascendency which my It required for the mastery of its problems. In this connection my medical career—for me at least—is significant. Twice I have adopted new methods in medicine, and have so absorbed and refashioned them that they have become my own personal possessions; once as the apprentice of Schweninger, the second time as the disciple of Freud. For me, each one of these men represents something mighty and inescapable.

The year '83 has crept in as especially important in its influence upon my external existence. This corresponds to its prominent position as the end figures in the mystery number 26,783. Soon after that remark about masturbation, I fell ill with scarlet fever, as a result of which I contracted nephritis. Later, as you know, I went through another illness of the same character. I mention this because this kidney disease—it holds true for me and for all people with kidney trouble—is characteristic of a double attitude toward life, of standing between two things. The kidney person—if I may use this expression—is facing two ways. His It is able, with more than customary ease, to be both childlike or grownup: a property both useful and dangerous; it takes its place between the 1—the symbol of the erect phallus of the grownup, of the father— and the 3—the symbol of the child. I leave it to you to

* Thomas Weltlein, the hero of *Der Seelensucher*. [A romance written by Dr. Groddeck, Int. Psychoanalytischer Verlag.]

go on with the endless chain of phantastic possibilities open to such a hybrid, and will merely observe that my own condition was revealed not only in the attacks of nephritis, but also in the fact that up to my fifteenth year I was a bed-wetter. And as a final word I would add: the hermaphrodite is neither man nor woman, but both, and that is my case.

And now we will play with numbers, and, as far as that is possible, we will be like children. But you must not get cross if grownup stuff pushes its way in. That cannot be helped. A child always wants to look big, and so he puts on his father's hat and takes his cane. What would happen if this wish to be big, this wish for an erection, were not present in the child? We should remain small, and never grow. Or do you think I am deceived in thinking that there is a certain connection between people's remaining little and their wanting to be little, their acting as if they did not know about erections, as if they were as innocent as little children; that the not-growing-tall arises from the wish to have an excuse to be still a child? We have this wish expressed in the rhyme, *"Ich bin klein, mein Herz ist rein"* (I am little, my heart is pure).

Sit down with me in front of the blackboard; we will both act as though we were learning to write numbers again. What goes on in a child's brain when he is made to write half a slateful of ones or eights? You can apply this also to the letters of the alphabet, to the *a*'s and the *p*'s and all the hooks and loops that tantalize a child's fancy. What does 1 stand for to you? For me it is a stick. And now the leap into grownupness, the father's stick, the penis, the man, the father himself, his sternness and power. Number 1 in the family; 2, that is the swan of Spekter's fable. Ah, how pretty it was! My sister had a long thin neck and was often teased about it. And she really was an ugly duckling that became a swan, only to die too soon. And suddenly I see the swan lake of my birthplace. I am eight years old, and am sitting with Wolf, Lina and a little girl friend, named Anna Speck, in a boat, and Anna falls into the water on which the swan is swimming. "My swan, my silent one, with tender plumage." Is that why I have occupied myself so much with Ibsen, because he composed this poem and I, in that trying time when I thought I was dying, used to hear it sung? Or is it Agnes in *Brand*? Agnes was my childish playmate and I

189

loved her dearly. She had a crooked mouth, and the story was that she had put an icicle into her mouth. And the icicle is symbolic. With her I jumped rope and with her is connected my family romance of kidnapped children and my phantasies of beating. Agnes and Ernest—that was the name of her brother who was my inseparable companion, but whom I later abandoned with contempt. And Ernest Schweninger. Ah, my dear, it is too much, too much!

Back to Anna Speck. Speck, Spekter's fables. "What kind of beggarman is that? He wears a coat as black as coal." The raven. And Raven was the name of my first teacher, whom I looked upon as a model of strength, and who once burst his breeches in jumping, an incident that came up again later in *Der Seelensucher*. And the word raven has been coming up for weeks in a patient's treatment which I want to bring to a successful issue, for it would be such a triumph as I have seldom enjoyed.

Spekter's fable of the swan. Did you ever see a swan swallow a large piece of bread? How it twists its neck down? Anna Speck had big, very big glands in her neck. And a thick neck signifies that something has got stuck there—the seed of a child. Yes, the seed of a child. I ought to know, for I myself for more than ten years had a goiter which as good as disappeared when I discovered the mystery of the half-swallowed child. How was I to think that this Anna would play such a part in my life? How should I ever have recognized her importance if it had not been for my faith in studying the It? And Anna was the name of the heroine of my first romance, and her husband was called Wolf. Wolf and Anna, they were both in that boat. And there, too, Alma appears again, whom you know as the friend of Lina's who interrupted my sadistic playing. Wolf had made a house with mattresses, in which he lived with Anna. But we little ones might not go with them into this mattress house. Alma, however, who was a knowing child, ran into the garden with Lina and me, when Wolf sent her away, and called out, "I know what the two of them are doing in there." I did not understand what Alma meant at the time, but the words remained in my memory, and the place where they were uttered, and I feel even now the shudder that ran through me then.

Anna, that is without beginning or end, alpha and

omega, Anna and Otto, spelt backwards and forwards alike, the being, the never-ending, eternity, the ring and the circle, the void, the mother, Anna.

It comes to my mind now that Anna's fall into the water must have meant a great deal in my life, since for years I had the masturbation-phantasy of Anna jumping from a high bank into my boat, and slipping so that her clothes flew up and I could see her drawers. How strange are the ways of the unconscious! For you must not forget that in the fall into the water there is a pregnancy symbol and a birth symbol, and Anna had a thick neck—like me.

That then is the 2, and the 2 is the woman, the mother, and the maiden with only two legs, while the boy has three. Three feet, tripod, and the Pythian oracle only speaks when she is seated on the tripod. But Oedipus guesses the riddle of the Sphinx about the animal which at first has four legs, then two, and finally is three-legged. Sophocles holds that Oedipus solved the riddle. But is the word "man" an answer to a question?

Two, thou fateful number that signifieth marriage, art thou also the mother? Or is 3 the mother? This 3 reminds me of the bird that my mother used to draw for us. *Vogel* (bird) and *Vögeln* (sex-act) go together. But when I see the 3 now lying down, it is for me the symbol of the breasts, my nurse, and all the many breasts that I still love. Three is the sacred number, the child, Christ the Son: the triune godhead, whose eye is shining within the triangle. Art thou truly only Eros' child, thou pattern of science, mathematics? And does even faith in a divinity spring from thee, Eros? Is it so, that the 2 is a pair, a married pair, and also the pair of testicles and of ovaries, of vulvae and of eyes? Is it so that the 1 and the 2 make 3, the all-powerful child in the mother's womb? For who is mighty, if not the unborn child, whose every desire is fulfilled before it is even felt? Who in truth is God and King and dwells in Heaven? But the child is a boy, for only the boy is the 3, two testicles and the penis. We're getting a little mixed up, are we not? Who could find his way aright through the labyrinth of the It? One is amazed and grows despondent, and yet casts oneself with shuddering pleasure into the ocean of dreams. A 1 and 2, that is 12. Man and woman, justifiably a sacred number, from which comes the 3, when it flows together into the unit, the child, the God. Twelve months are there, and the year is made up of them; twelve disciples are there, and in their midst is raised the Christ, the Anointed One, the Son of Man. Is it not wonderful, this phrase, "Son of Man"? And my It says to me, loudly and distinctly, "Explain, explain!"

Farewell, dear,

PATRIK.

✳ LETTER XXVI ✳

So the playing with numbers interests you, my dear? I am glad to hear that! You have so often given me a severe scolding that I need appreciation. And I am deeply grateful that you mention my name in the same breath as that of Pythagoras. Quite apart from the pleasure you bestow upon my vanity in so doing, it proves to me that you have the first requirement of a critic, the ability to compare, without hesitation, a Smith, a Jones, a Brown or a Troll with Goethe, Beethoven, Leonardo or Pythagoras. It makes your statements doubly worth while to me.

That you even quote further examples, pointing out that 13 is the number who partook of the Last Supper, and connecting the fear that the thirteenth guest at the table must die with the death of Christ upon the Cross, gives me the hope that your opposition to my It-talk will gradually disappear. But why must it necessarily be the Christ? Judas was also one of thirteen, and he, too, was destined to die.

Has it never surprised you how closely the two conceptions, Christ and Judas, are interwoven? I spoke to you once before about the ambivalence in the unconscious, about the human characteristic of showing hatred in love, treachery in fidelity. This profound and insurmountable inward duality of human nature has enforced the story of the kiss of Judas, in which are reflected the everyday affairs and experiences of mankind. I should like you to be quite convinced yourself of this fact, for it is of great importance. So long as you are not cognizant of it, are not permeated through and through with its realization, you understand nothing of the It. But it is not easy to arrive at such a realization. Think of the greatest moment of your life and then search until you have found the Judas intention and the Judas betrayal. When you kissed your beloved, up went your hand to smooth your hair that might have become disarranged. When your father died—you were still a youngster—it delighted you to wear a black frock for the first time. You counted proudly the letters of condolence, and with secret satisfaction you put the lines of sympathy from a reigning duke on the top. And when your mother was ill you felt ashamed of the sudden thought that came into your head of the string of pearls you would soon inherit; on the day of her funeral you thought the hat you were wearing made you look eight years older, and in that thought you were not concerned with your husband, but with the judgment of the crowd before whose eyes you wanted to play the part of the beautiful mourner, just like a real actress. And how often have you betrayed, as grossly as Judas, your dearest friends, your husband and your children, for the thirty pieces of silver? Think over these things a little. You will find that man's existence, from beginning to end, is filled with what our rash judgment brands as the worst and most contemptible of sins, treachery. But you also see at once that hardly ever is this treachery felt as guilt by the conscious mind. Scratch where you will the thin conscious layer with which the It covers itself, however, and you will see how the unconscious is continually sifting the treacheries of the last few hours; one it casts out, a second it puts ready for use the next day, a third it represses into the unconscious, so that it may brew from it the poison of future illnesses or the magic potion of coming achievements. Look attentively into this strange darkness, dearest. Here is a chink through which you can climb, almost despairingly, see masses driven like clouds by one of the active forces of the It, by the consciousness of guilt. This is one of the tools with which the It works on mankind, surely and without fail. The It uses this consciousness of guilt, but it takes care that its sources are never fathomed by man, for it knows that in that same moment when anyone discovers the secret of his guilt, the world will tremble to its foundations. For that reason it heaps horror and dread round about the profundities of life, makes ghosts out of the trivialities of the day, invents the word "betrayal" and the man Judas, and the Ten Commandments, and confounds the vision of the "I" with a thousand things which seem to the conscious mind to be shameful, in order that man may never believe the consoling words: "Fear not, for I am with thee."

And there you have the Christ. Just as treachery enters into every noble deed of man, taking part therein, so in all that we call evil, is there always the nature of the Christ—or however you may name this nature—the loving, the benevolent. To recognize that, you do not need first to tread the long road which carries the murderer's thrust back to man's primitive instinct, to try to press into the innermost parts of a fellow creature, out of love, to give happiness and to receive it—for in the last resort murder is only the symbol of the suppressed love rage. You do not need first to analyze a theft, in which you would again come upon the same all-transforming Eros, who in taking, gives. You do not need to consider the words of Jesus to the adulteress, "Thy sins are forgiven thee, for thou hast loved much." In your everyday life you will find everywhere sacrifice and simplicity enough to teach you what I was saying: Christ is, wherever man is.

But I go on talking and talking, and what I wanted to do was to make you understand that there are no contradictions, that everything is reconciled in the It; that according to its own pleasure this It can employ one and the same action as grounds for remorse or for the exaltation that follows a noble deed. The It is crafty, and it does not trouble itself about the stupid consciousness so confident that black and white are opposites, and a chair is really a chair, whereas every child knows that it is also a cab, a house and a mountain. The consciousness sweats and sweats in the effort to invent a system, and to put life into pigeonholes, but the It gaily and inexhaustibly creates what it wants, with its own power, and sometimes I think it laughs at the conscious mind.

Why do I tell you all this? Perhaps I too am making merry. Perhaps I only want to show you that one can start out from any point and roam over the whole of life—a little truth worth thinking about. And with that I make a bold jump back again to my story, for I still have some-thing to say about the spot near my mouth—perhaps the most important thing of all, in any case something strange, which will reveal more about your correspondent's repression than he himself knew for some years.

The spot near the mouth—I told you this once before—means that I should like to kiss someone, but I have some sort of feeling against doing so which is sufficiently power-ful to raise up the top layer of the skin and fill up the hole thus made with fluid. That is not much to start with, for, as you know, I like kissing, and if I were to consider all those persons who seem to me to merit a kiss, and who I am not sure would kiss me in return, my mouth would always be sore. But the spot is on the right side, and I tell myself that this is the side of righteousness, of authority, of family connections. Authority of my rela-tives; my eldest brother comes into my thoughts; and in-deed it is he against whom this spot was aimed. On that day my mind was occupied constantly with the thoughts of a particular patient. That surprised me, for it is cus-tomary for me to think no more about my patients once I have closed the door behind them; but soon I knew the reason for it. This patient resembled my brother. The desire to kiss is thereby explained, for it had to do with this patient, to whom I had transferred the feeling I had for my brother. This was made easier by the fact that my brother's birthday fell around that date, and that shortly before I had seen this patient unconscious. As a child I witnessed several times my brother's prolonged swoons; I can picture the shape of his head even now, and I have reason to think that my attitude to this patient was due to his resemblance. The likeness between the two became obvious to me in the immobility of their faces.

But the existence of the spot; one has to consider not only the wish to kiss, but also the opposite. That is quite explicable. In our family such demonstrativeness among the children was strictly forbidden. It is still unthinkable to me that we could ever have kissed one another. But the aversion to kiss is not merely a matter of family tradi-tions, it concerns also the question of homosexuality, and I must dwell a few moments on that.

I was, as you know, brought up in a boy's boarding school from the time I was twelve. There we lived in our monastery, quite shut off from the outer world, and all our capacity and need for love was directed towards our schoolfellows. If I look back upon the six years spent there, immediately there comes to me the image of my friend. I see us both, with arms tightly locked, as we walk through the cloisters; from time to time our furious discussion about God and the world breaks off, and we kiss each other. It is not possible, I think, to imagine to oneself the force of a vanished emotion, but judging from the many scenes of jealousy, which were accompanied, on my side at least, by phantasies of suicide, my affection must have been extreme. I know, too, that at that time my masturbation phantasies were almost exclusively concerned with boys' love. After I left school my affection for this friend endured until, a year later, I transferred it to a comrade at the University, from whom it made a sudden jump to his sister. With that my homosexuality, my affection for members of my own sex, was apparently extinguished. Thenceforward I loved only women.

I loved them very constantly, and very inconstantly, for I remember that for hours at a time I would stroll about the streets in Berlin for the sake of seeing some bit of femininity whom I had met by chance and never came to know, but who occupied my phantasies for days and weeks. The list of such dream loves is unending, and up to a few years ago was added to nearly every day. My actual erotic experiences had nothing in the world to do with these loves of my soul. For my masturbatory enjoyments I have never once, so far as I know, chosen any woman whom I really loved. Always strangers, persons unknown. Do you know what that means? No? It signifies that my deepest love belonged to one whom I was not allowed to know, in other words, to my sister, and before that, to my mother. But do not forget that my knowledge of this is only recent, and that until a short time ago I never believed that I could desire my sister or my mother. One goes through life without knowing the tiniest thing about oneself.

To complete the story of this love life with strangers, with unknown people whose acquaintance I never sought, I must add something else, although it is only distantly connected with what I wanted to speak about, namely, homosexuality. It concerns my attitude to the women to whom I am really bound by this tie of love. Not merely one of them, no, from every one, I have heard the same astonishing judgment: "When I am with you, I seem to be nearer to you than anyone else in the world, but so soon as you have said good-bye, it is as though you built up a wall between us and I were a total stranger to you; as if we had never met." I have not been aware of this myself, probably because I have never felt that anyone was not a stranger to me, but now I understand it. In order to be able to love I had to keep real people at a distance, and artfully draw close to the "images" of my mother and sister. At times that must have been really difficult, but it was the only way to keep my passion alive. Believe me, images are powerful things.

And that brings me now once more to my homosexual experiences. For with men it has been much the same thing. Thirty years long have I kept them at a distance; by what method I do not know, but that it was highly successful is proved by the list of my patients, which only in the last three years has once again included the names of men. They are reappearing now, because I am no longer fleeing from my homosexuality. For when all is said and done, it was my wish to escape from men that was the reason I was seldom consulted by them. Throughout those years I had eyes only for women, looked searchingly at every woman I met and loved her more or less, and during all that time, in society, in the street, in traveling, yes, even in meetings of men, I have never really observed a single man. I looked at them without seeing them, even if they were for hours before my eyes; they did not reach my consciousness.

All that has changed. I now look at men in the same way as I do women; they have become human beings to me, and I am equally pleased to deal with both; there is no longer any difference. Above all, with a man I am no longer embarrassed. I no longer need to keep people at a distance. The deeply repressed incest wish, which had so mysterious and powerful an influence, has now become conscious and disturbs me no more. At least that is how I account for the change.

To a certain degree the same sort of thing has occurred in connecton with children, with animals, with mathematics and philosophy. But that is another story, although it, too, is bound up with the repression of mother, sister, father and brother.

However true it may seem to me now to account for

my nature by this flight from Trolls, who are for me a special sort of people—for there are good people, and wicked people and Trolls—however enlightening it may be for me that I had to make a perverted use of the opera glasses through which I looked at my companions, put them artificially at a distance and make them into strangers so that they might resemble my images, it is still not sufficient to explain everything. It is not possible to explain everything. But one thing I can add: I need this subtle type of loving, this remoteness, because I am centered upon myself, because I love myself immeasurably, because I am what the learned call a narcissist. Narcissism plays a great role in men's lives. If I had not possessed it to so high a degree I should never have become what I am, and also I should never have understood why Christ said: "Thou shalt love thy neighbour as thyself." As thyself, not more than thyself.

Among us Troll folk there was a phrase which ran: "I come first of all, and then I come again, then nothing comes for ever so long, and then come other people."

And just think, how amusing! As a little boy of perhaps eight years old, I had an album in which my best friends wrote verses and their names. On the outside cover is written in my handwriting a modification of an old proverb:

> Whoever loves me more than myself,
> Let him write below myself
> Thyself.

That is how I felt at the time and I fear I have not greatly changed.

Ever your own,
PATRIK TROLL.

✻ LETTER XXVII ✻

Thanks for your letter, my dear. I will at any rate make the attempt this time to comply with your request that I should be objective. The phenomenon of homosexuality is sufficiently important to be methodically examined.

Yes, I hold the view that all people are homosexual, hold it so firmly that it is difficult for me to realize how anyone can think differently. Man loves himself first and foremost, with every sort of passionate emotion, and seeks to procure for himself every conceivable pleasure, and, since he himself must be either male or female, is subject from the beginning to a passion for his own sex. It cannot be otherwise, and unprejudiced examination of anyone who will consent to it, gives proof. The question, therefore, is not whether homosexuality is exceptional, perverse—that does not come under discussion—what we have to ask is, why it is so difficult to consider this phenomenon of passion between people of the same sex, to judge it and discuss it, without prejudice, and then we have also to ask how it comes about that, in spite of his homosexual nature, man is also able to feel affection for the opposite sex.

The first question is easily answered. Pederasty is threatened with penal servitude, is branded as a crime, has been looked upon for centuries as a shameful vice. That the majority of people do not observe it is explained by this prohibition. It is not more astonishing than the fact that so many children never observe their mother's pregnant condition; that almost all mothers are unable to observe expressions of sexuality in their little children; that no one observed the boy's incestuous desire for his mother until Freud described it. But to be able to recognize the universality of homosexuality is a long step from being able to judge it without prejudice, and the people who are able to do this prefer to remain silent rather than to enter into an argument with ignorance.

One might think that an age that is proud of its civilization, that learns geography and history by heart because it does not think for itself, that such an age must know that on the other side of the Aegean Sea, in Asia, open pederasty is the rule, and that such a highly developed civilization as that of ancient Greece is not to be thought of without its homosexuality. It must at least be surprised at that curious phrase in the Gospel concerning Christ's disciple, "whom Jesus loved," and who lay upon the Lord's breast. We make nothing of it all. To all this evidence we are blind. We are not to see what is there to be seen.

In the first place, the Church forbids it. Obviously she derives this prohibition from the Old Testament, the whole spirit of which was directed towards bringing all sexual activity into direct association with the begetting of children, and, as a result of priestly ambition, she purposely made this inherited human instinct into a sin in order to lord it over the stricken conscience. This was particularly opportune for the Christian Church, since it was able to deal with the root of Hellenic culture in its execration of male love. You know that there is an increasing feeling against penalizing pederasty, because it is felt that in this matter an evil has long been made out of what is an hereditary right.

In spite of this increasing insight we cannot expect a speedy reversal of our judgment of homosexuality—and that for a very simple reason. We all spend at least fifteen or sixteen years, most of us spend our whole lives, with the conscious or at any rate half-conscious realization of being homosexual, of having behaved as such more or less often, and of still behaving so. It happens with all people that at some time or other in their lives they make a superhuman effort to throttle this homosexuality, which in words is so despised. And the repression is not even successful, so, in order to carry through this lasting, daily self-deception, they support the public denunciation of homosexuality and thus relieve their inner conflict. With every reflection upon experience we come upon the same discovery: because we feel ourselves to be thieves, murderers, adulterers, pederasts, liars, we are bitter against robbery, murder and lying, in order that no one, ourselves least of all, shall come to the knowledge of our wickedness. Believe me, whatever man hates, despises, condemns, is in his own original nature. And if you want to make something really serious out of life and love, out of the nobility that is in your temperament, you must hold by the old proverb:

Blame not me!
Blame yourself alone!
And if I am at fault,
Then make yourself a better man.

I know of yet another reason why we are afraid to be honest in considering homosexual problems, and that lies in our attitude towards masturbation. The source of homosexuality is in narcissism, self-love and self-gratification. The being has yet to be born who is not prejudiced against the phenomenon of self-gratification.

It will surprise you that so far I have spoken only of homosexual love between men. That is easily understood since I was born at a time when people behaved—or did they really believe it?—as though, except in the case of outcast prostitutes, women had no sensuality in their nature. In the support it gave to this view one might say the last century was almost ridiculous, but unfortunately the results of this absurdity are serious. It seems to me as though the existence of the breasts, the vagina, and the clitoris, has only recently been rediscovered, and the idea become permissible that there are female faeces, faecal gas, and voluptuous sensations. But that is at present a secret known only to women and to a few men. For the great mass of the public the word homosexual appears to be derived from *homo*—man. That the love of one woman for another is an everyday affair, and is openly exhibited before everyone's eyes, is hardly noticed. Nevertheless it is a fact that any woman may kiss and hug any other female person of any age, without fear. Things of this kind are not "homosexual," any more than feminine onanism is "onanism." Nothing of the sort.

May I remind you of a little adventure we had together? It must have been about 1912. The dispute concerning the moral turpitude of homosexuality was at that time particularly keen, because the German penalizing laws were under review; a proposal had been made to include the female sex under paragraph 175. I was with you, and because we had been a little out of temper with each other, but quickly wanted to be friends again, I had taken up a journal and was turning over its pages. It was the *Kunstwart*, and it contained an article in which one of the most highly respected women in Germany gave her views on feminine homosexuality. She took up a strong position against the proposal to penalize love between women, saying that it would shake the whole structure of society to its foundations, and that in any case, if people wished to extend the penalties to women, they would have to multiply the supply of prisons a thousandfold. Hoping I had found a harmless topic of conversation by means of which we could chatter ourselves out of our mutual ill-humor, I handed the paper over to you, but with a curt, "I've read it already," you refused my olive branch. We made up then in another fashion, and that very evening you told me a story of your girlhood, how your cousin Lola had kissed your breast. I inferred from that, that you held the same views as that woman champion of the freedom of sapphic love.

For me the problem of homosexuality was cleared up then and there; this assault upon your breast showed me at once that nature itself insists upon erotic emotions between women, since little girls, after all, are fed by their mothers, and not by their fathers, and the fact that suckling at the breast is a voluptuous act, is known to every woman. That the lips which call forth this voluptuous pleasure are those of a baby and not of a grownup, at the most only makes this difference, that the baby caresses the breast more sweetly and tenderly than ever a grownup can. The writer of that article seems to me to have been right on the further point, that the foundations of human life would be shaken by the punishment of homosexuality, for it is on the sexual ties between mother and daughter, between father and son, that the whole world rests.

Now one may boldly assert—it is in fact being asserted —that up to the time of puberty, during childhood that is, people are one and all bisexual, and then most of them renounce love for their own sex in favor of love for the opposite sex. But that is not true. Man is bisexual all his life long, and keeps his bisexuality: at the most he consents at one or another period of his life, as a concession to the moral code in fashion, to repress a portion—and it is a very small portion—of his homosexuality, and in so doing he does not destroy it, but merely narrows its range. And just as no one is purely heterosexual, so no one is purely homosexual. Not even the most passionate pederast has escaped the destiny of staying for nine months in the body of a woman.

The expressions "homosexual" and "heterosexual" are nothing more than words, headings under which anyone can write what he will. They have no fixed meaning whatever, but are just something to talk about.

A much more important question for me than the love for one's own sex, which necessarily follows upon self-love, is the development of love for the opposite sex.

The matter seems simple in the case of the boy. The life within the mother's body, the years of dependence on woman's care, all the tenderness, joys, delights and wish fulfillments which only the mother gives or can give him, these are so mighty a counterbalance to his narcissism that one need seek no further. But how does the girl come to turn to the opposite sex? I fear the answer I give to that will satisfy you as little as it does me. Or, to speak more plainly, I know of no sufficient grounds to give you. And since I have a not unreasonable objection to playing with the word "inherited" for I know nothing more about inherited qualities than that they exist, and indeed exist in quite other ways than is generally supposed, I am obliged to hold my tongue about them. I should merely like to offer a few suggestions. And firstly, there is no doubt that the preference of the little girl for her father arises very early. Admiration for the superior size and strength of the man, if that is one of the sources of feminine heterosexuality, must be regarded as a proof of the child's innate power of judgment. But who is to establish whether this admiration is there to begin with, or only comes about in course of time? Exactly the same uncertainty disturbs me in regard to a second influence on the relation of the woman to the man, the castration complex. At some time or other the little girl discovers her natural lack, and at some time or other—certainly very early—she is conscious of a wish at least to borrow the manly weapon in the act of love, if she is never to grow one of her own. If one may derive feminine heterosexuality from the years of infancy, it is easy to find sufficient grounds for it. But the signs of the preference for the man, of sexual preference, appear at such an early stage that one cannot get much out of arguments of that kind.

I notice that I am beginning to babble, and so instead of giving you any more learned talk I would prefer to tell you something else about myself and the number 83. In the year '83 came that ominous remark about masturbation of which I spoke to you; soon afterwards I was taken ill with scarlet fever, and when I got well from that there came upon me a great passion for the boy with whom I walked in the cloisters and whom I kissed. I have cause to preserve the year '83 in my unconscious.

One other trifle I have still to record. I spoke about my eldest brother's fits, which I consider specially significant in the development of my homosexuality. One of these fits, which remains the clearest in my memory, took place in the toilet. The door must have been broken open, and I remember the figure of my father, axe in hand, just as well as I do that of my brother, sunk down behind, sitting there unconscious with his body exposed. If you remember that the breaking open of a door contains the symbolism for a sexual attack upon the human body, that here, therefore, to my symbolic feeling, the homosexual act was carried out; that, further, the axe revived my castration complex, then you have a connecting point for all sorts of trains of thought. Finally, I offer also for your consideration the fact that the parallel between giving birth and defecation here comes into force, and that the toilet is the place in which the child is best able to observe the sexual organs of his parents and family, and in particular, of his father or elder brother. The child is accustomed to being taken there by grownups, and it happens often enough that his escort takes advantage of the opportunity thus offered to relieve himself. In this way the child's unconscious gets used to identifying the bathroom with his examination of the sexual organs, just as later it puts this room and masturbation into the same pigeonhole of repression. You will certainly know, too, that the homosexual is specially fond of using public lavatories. All sexual complexes have some close connection with the evacuation of faeces and urine.

It comes to my mind that I broke off my consideration of the sources of heterosexuality to give you memories of my brothers and a bottom complex. The reason for that lies in today's date. It is August 18th. For about four weeks, that patient who reminds me of my brother has been telling me that, from August 18th onwards, my treatment will have no further effect on his progress. As a matter of fact, his condition today has become even worse. Unfortunately he cannot supply the unconscious ideas which make this date critical for him, and I, on my side, feel uneasy because I do not know the reasons for his resistance, and foresee all sorts of future difficulties.

The question how the little girl's preference for the man arises, is to me, for the time being, unanswerable, and I leave it open for you to reply. For my part I hazard the question that the woman's erotism is much freer than the man's in relation to the two sexes: it seems to me as if she had a fairly equal capacity of love for either sex, which can at need be transferred from one to the other without any great difficulty. In other words, it appears that, in her, neither homosexuality nor heterosexuality is very deeply repressed, that such repression as there is, is pretty superficial.

It is always dangerous to assign opposite qualities to men and women; one ought not to forget in that connection that in reality there is neither man nor woman, that everyone is rather a mixture of man and woman. With this reservation I am inclined to think that the problem of homosexuality or heterosexuality has little significance in women's lives.

I hazard yet one more guess; that the bond between women is stronger than that between men, which seems to me obvious and to be explained by the fact that self-love and love for the mother are directed towards one of the same sex. Opposed to that, so far as I can see, there is only one important factor which attracts her to the man, the castration complex, the disappointment at being a girl, and the resultant hatred of the mother, and the wish to be a man, or at least to give birth to a boy.

The case is different with the man. He is concerned, I think, not only with the question of homosexuality and heterosexuality, but with another that is inextricably interwoven with this, that of incest with the mother. The impulse, which is repressed, is towards a passionate relationship with the mother, and its repression, under certain conditions, drags all inclinations towards women along with it into the unconscious. Perhaps you would like to hear more about that later? Unfortunately it is all pure conjecture.

PATRIK.

✳ LETTER XXVIII ✳

It's not a bad idea of yours, that these letters should be published. Many thanks, my dear, for firing my ambition. To be sure, you've taken away half the pleasure I derived from writing them, and if you really think that I should revise and brush them up, I'll have nothing at all to do with it. My profession gives me quite enough to do. I've scribbled these letters to please myself, and work is no pleasure for me.

But I hope you do not mean this seriously. I can quite well imagine you were perfectly serious in what you wrote about my errors and exaggerations, my contradictions and superfluous witticisms, which you think are well enough in a correspondence between friends, but not suitable for publication. That attitude harks back to the time when you passed your examinations as a teacher. I always liked you when you suddenly became solemn: I could imagine you in school raising an admonitory finger and in mocking fancy I put your right hand behind your back, made you hold a cane in it, and stuck a pair of spectacles on your nose. And then this figure, transformed into a lovable woman, seemed to me so irresistible that I intentionally encouraged you to go on preaching for quite a time, simply in order to revel in the contrast between what you are and what you were pretending to be. However, today, I will treat your serious intentions in like manner.

Why should I interfere with the pleasure my fellow men will find in discovering the erroneous statements contained in these letters? I know what a dreadful effect the quite perfect people produce—we Trolls would call them oppressive angels—and I know how much I enjoyed exposing any sort of stupidity myself, hence I am not so uncharitable as to grudge this enjoyment to others. Besides, I count on giving so much that is useful that no one will bother about the rubbish. I want, or rather I am obliged, to believe that; otherwise my own self-esteem would desert me, and I really could not live without that. My behavior is much the same sort of thing as I was trying to describe to you in talking of spots on the face, or the evil-smelling breath. One is not quite sure whether one's affection is returned, one would very much like to find out, and one creates for oneself something or other that is calculated to put people off. "If I am still pleasing to the object of my adoration when I have a cold in my nose, or sweating feet, then there is no doubt of her love," thinks the It. The bride thinks so when she becomes peevish; the bridegroom thinks so when he starts drinking be-

fore going to his beloved; the child thinks it when it behaves badly, and so does my It when it puts mistakes into
my work. I shall let the mistakes remain as they are, just
as they stood in my earlier publications, in spite of all advice, friendly and hostile.

Some years ago I sent a manuscript to a good friend in
whose judgment I had much faith. He wrote back a charming letter with many encouraging words of praise, but he
thought the thing was much too long and much too blunt.
It resembled an embryo, with its sex organs disproportionately developed; I must make it shorter, then it would
be a fine child. And in order to discover what to strike
out, I must follow the example of the man who was on
the lookout for a wife. When he noticed that he was
beginning to fall in love, he contrived to go to the toilet
immediately after the presumptive queen of his heart.
"If it smells nice to me then I do love her. But if the
smell is horrid, then she's not for me." I followed my
friend's recipe, but all that I had written smelt to me like
new cakes and I crossed nothing out!

I'm going to make a proposal to you. We will let the
stupid bits alone, but you shall write and tell me whenever you find a mistake, and then, a few letters later, I
will correct it. In this way the conscientious reader, with
his pedantic attitude, will get his fun, and then a few
pages further he'll be annoyed by reading the correction,
and we'll have our fun. Agreed?

Now as to the faults that I'm to get rid of altogether.
First, there is the story of the creation of Eve. That has
always offended you, and now you suddenly open fire
with the heavy artillery of science, and prove to me that
this legend did not spring from the soul of the race, but
owes its existence to the tendentious work of the priests,
in the Old Testament. Very likely you are right: at least
I once read that, too, but it left me cold, like a good deal
else. For me the Bible is a wise and entertaining book,
with beautiful stories in it, which are doubly remarkable
because people believed in them for thousands of years,
and because they have been of immeasurable significance
in the development of Europe, and for all of us were a
part of our childhood. As to who invented them, that is
of interest to me as a matter of historical importance, but
it does not stir my human emotions.

I grant you the stories were invented by the priests.

There you are right. But you argue from that, that these Creation legends cannot be used for the purpose I tried to make them serve, as evidence for the childish theory that the woman comes into being through the castration of man. There you are wrong. I am not bold enough to maintain that the child has the idea of the castration creation from the beginning, but think it much more probable that, originally at least, he knows about the birth mechanism just what he may have learnt of it through self-experience. And then on top of his original knowledge, just as it happened in the Old Testament, the priests of childhood, parents and others, laid the castration idea, and just as the Jews and Christians have believed the fairy tales of the priests for thousands of years, so the child believes in the fairy tales made up from his own observations and by the lying lips of his preceptors. And as the belief in the creation of Eve from Adam's rib helped to bring about the thousand-year-old contempt for women, with all its consequences, good and evil, and still does so, in the same way the castration belief works continuously on and on in our own souls right up to the end. In other words, it matters little whether an idea grows up of its own accord or is forced on us from without. What does matter is whether it penetrates to the depths of the unconscious.

I am going to take this opportunity of making a Trollish remark about the creation of Adam. He was given a soul, as you know, by Jehovah's blowing the breath of life into his nostrils. That particular way, through the nose, has always struck my attention. Judging from that, I said to myself, it must be something with a smell that gave life to Adam. What sort of a smell it was became clear to me when I read Freud's story of little Hans. It became clear to me, but you need not, of course, accept my explanation. The little Hans, in his childish fashion, holds the view that the "lump," the sausage in the toilet, is more or less the same thing as a child. Your obedient Troll has the idea that the ancient Divinity also created man out of his own "lump," that the word "dust" is substituted for faeces only out of regard for decency. The breath of life would then be blown, with its living fragrance, out of the self-same opening as the faeces. Certainly the race of man has proved itself worthy of such an origin!

Well now, most honored lady, in telling Adam's story

have I rightly explained the childish theory of birth from the bowels, or has that grown out of the extraordinary relief which even the poets of the Bible felt after an evacuation?

The second error you have pointed out to me has made me thoughtful. It could easily be omitted, but I am going to leave that in, too. Let me explain why. In speaking of the castration complex I recounted an episode from Reineke Fuchs, and in this I have ascribed to Isegrim the Wolf a role that is actually played by Hinz the cat. The causes of this confusion, I think, are involved, and I doubt whether I can unravel them.

One thing is clearly obvious; the wolf complex in me is so powerful that it claws at things which do not really belong to it. To complete what I have already said about it, I will tell you of an incident of my childhood. Lina and I, when we were about ten and eleven years old, once acted Red Ridinghood with other little friends. I was cast for the wolf's part, and I acted it with tremendous verve. Among the audience was a little girl of five called Paula. I hated this Paula, who was a pet of my sister's, and felt wicked satisfaction when she set up a howl of terror at the wolf while the performance was going on. We had to stop. I went up to her and took off my wolf's mask and quieted her. It was the first time that anyone had been terrified by me, and so far as I know, the first time also that I felt a malicious pleasure. And it was the wolf that produced the terror. That experience has remained in my memory, partly, too, because there were among my fellow players in addition to my sister, the oft-mentioned Alma and a namesake of mine, Patrik, in whom I first saw an erection.

This Patrik was really a friend of my brother Wolf's, and therefore some years older than I. He was, however, for some reason or other left behind in the lower classes, which I attended, when Wolf was transferred to the Gymnasium. We younger ones used to bathe a good deal at that time in summer, and we shared a common dressing room. Here my namesake produced an erection for us, and also made some sort of masturbatory movements. This experience has remained only dimly in my memory; I have a feeling as though I had not understood all that was going on, had only looked at it calmly, as something new.

On the other hand, another display remains in my memory. This same boy tucked his penis and scrotum to the back, nipped them between his legs, and then pretended to be a girl. As a boy I often repeated this performance before the looking glass, and every time it gave me a curious voluptuous sensation. I consider this experience particularly important because it shows the pure castration desire, free from any admixture of anxiety. For my part, I personally have never been able to doubt the existence of this desire. But since the day my namesake showed me how to become a girl, I have also observed other men, and have been able to make sure that the anxiety-free wish to be a girl is common to them all. If one thought it worth the trouble to go further into the matter—and a doctor ought to at least have that much scientific curiosity—one would easily discover among one's friends and acquaintances conscious phantasies similar to those I have told you of, and if for once it really appears that these desires are entirely driven out of consciousness, all one needs to do is to bring such sexually normal people to an analysis of their modes of eating, still more of drinking, of brushing their teeth or cleansing their ears. Their associations then soon jump over to all sorts of other habits, to smoking, to riding, to boring in the nose and other things. And if all this is denied through the successful resistance of the will-to-be-male, there are familiar types of illnesses, of constipation, with its pleasure-yielding obstruction of the faeces by means of the anus, hemorrhoids, which transfer the desire to this entrance of the body, the swelling of the abdomen, with its pregnancy symbolism, the enema, the morphine injections, and the manifold use of inoculations, so fashionable in our repressed age; headaches, with their relationship to labor pains, work and the creation of work, of the child of man's spirit. Put my opinion to the test, rouse up here or there a man's resistance, and one day, usually very soon, there comes up the memory; what was repressed becomes conscious, and then it is as with us less normal people.

But I go on chattering and say nothing about why I made the wolf the castrator, instead of the cat, and why I put a peasant instead of the priest who was deprived of his sexual organ in that illustration from Reineke Fuchs. It is easy to see the reason for the second muddle.

From *Pfarrer* (priest) to *Pater, Vater* (father), the one who is to be castrated, is only a step, and the sound of *Pater* suggests the name Patrik. The threat to my own person in the animal's bite sufficiently accounts for the repression and falsification of the memory. The singular humor of the It is manifest in this. It lets me get rid of the anxiety connected with *Pater*-Patrik, but at the same time it makes me substitute a peasant, and George—Hodge—is, as you know, my second Christian name. So do we mock ourselves.

But why have I changed the harmless, domestic cat into the dangerous wolf? *Pater* and *Kater* (male cat), they rhyme, and whoever is given to rhyming, goes on to *Vater* (father), and the unconscious often likes to rhyme. The father therefore was repressed: he truly was more terrible than the wolf. He had knives enough, for he was a doctor, while my brother Wolf at the most had a pen-knife, and on Sundays there was placed next to papa's plate a whole set of carving knives, some of which had a wicked likeness to the knife of that giant who ate men's flesh. It might easily have occurred to him to test the sharpness of this knife on my little penis; after he had been grinding it for a time, it looked quite dangerous. It occurs to me now, too, why he seemed to me like a cat. One of his adorers had praised his fine legs, and to please her he used to swagger round in high boots. Puss-in-Boots, that was who he was, and I was reading this story at the time with unusual delight, and had secured a cutout puzzle of little picture scraps giving gaily colored scenes from this fairy tale.

Now the case is clear. For anyone who suffers from castration-anxiety, the father is worse than the brother. The cat he sees daily is worse than the wolf whom he knows only by hearsay in fairy tales. And then the wolf only eats sheep, and I no more thought of myself then as a stupid sheep than I do now; but the cat eats mice—as is shown by women's fear of mice.

Behind this dread that the father-in-boots might eat up my little mouse, something else still is hidden, something dreadful, something devilish. Puss-in-Boots overcomes a sorcerer who transforms himself into an elephant and then into a tiny mouse. The symbolism of erection and re-laxation is obvious, and since I certainly did not know of these phenomena from my own physical experience at the age when I read the fairy tale and saw the Kaulbach illustrations, I incline to the conclusion that the sorcerer who changed into an elephant and a mouse was my father, his castle and kingdom my mother, and I myself the puss-in-boots, as well as his owner, the miller's youngest son. As I realized that I could not destroy the whole of this man-elephant, it seemed reasonable at least to devour the symbol of paternity, the mouse, the father's member. And actually there seems to come before my eyes the picture of myself at that time, wearing my very first pair of Hessian boots. In the fairy tale, as in the picture, I saw my own castration, and, more horrible still, the criminal wish to devour the father's mouse in order to succeed in getting possession of the mother: both were repressed, and what remained was the dangerous rivalry with brother Wolf. And in this way we get a new light on the substitution of Hodge-George for *Pfarrer-Vater*. The wish to castrate the father will surely be punished with my own castration. My It, it appears, has a more or less sensitive conscience, so it repressed the crime but insisted on the expiation, and in this way made it as though the wish had never existed.

Let me draw your attention now for one moment more to the boots: they appear also in the story of Hop-o'-My-Thumb, and may be looked on as an erection symbol. Now you ought to try to find what meaning they have for you. First the boots might stand for the mother; indeed, according to my idea they are the mother, and also the woman, for she has two openings, the anus and the vagina, which are the boot legs. Since they make a pair, they may also be the testicles, the eyes, the ears, perhaps also the hands, which in their preparatory play lead on in seven-leagued strides to erection and masturbation.

Here I reach the third reason for the repression, masturbation, an entirely personal reason which finds no support in the fairy tale but only in my own experience. At that time I learned that now and then the male cat ate up his own children. If I am to be the cat, then my penis was my own child, which as the mouse is weakened to the point of destruction by the boot play of both hands in masturbating. Evil habit!

You see, if I take the trouble, I can invent fairly satisfactory reasons for my error, but it goes against the grain to do it. I claim the right to make mistakes, since I consider truth and reality to be doubtful blessings.

With every good wish to you and yours,

Patrik.

✳ LETTER XXIX ✳

You do not reply, my dear, and I am all in the dark as to whether you are cross, or whether, as it is so prettily put, you "haven't time." I will take a chance and go on with my theories regarding the symbolic significance of animals although I don't know whether or not you approve of the letters being published with their mistakes left in.

I spoke about your sensations at the sight of a mouse, but I finished only half of what there was to say. If the mouse merely signified running up under the skirt, women's fear would not be so disproportionately great. The mouse, as a thieving animal, is the natural symbol of masturbation and, in consequence, of castration. In other words, the girl has the vague idea, "My penis is running about there on four legs: as a punishment it was taken away from me, as a punishment it was given a life of its own."

There you have something of a belief in ghosts, of superstition: if ever one goes into the origin of ghost stories, one very soon arrives at the problem of erotism and guilt.

This peculiar symbolization of the mouse as a member, slipping about freely, brings me to its relative, the rat, which appears with the wolf and the cat, as a castrator symbol. Rather strangely, it seems to be the most dreaded and the most horrifying symbol of the three. In and of itself, the rat is less dangerous than the wolf or even the cat. But it combines within itself both the castration threats, that against the father and that against the child. Because it nibbles off anything that juts out, it is dangerous to the child's own nose and penis, but in nature and form it is the personification of the father's amputated member, the specter of that impious wish to destroy the father's masculinity. And because it gets into everything and forces its way into every dark place, it is at the same time the symbolic guilt and the parents' insistent curiosity. It lives in the cellar, in the drainpipe, in the woman. Hateful, hateful!

In the dark cellar there lives also the toad, moist to the touch, and flabby. And popular belief takes it to be poisonous. "Little toad, pretty toad," that is something which is not for the daylight, the little pet belonging to the girl who is just growing up; it has not yet the steady warmth of love, but is only moist from hidden desire. The contrasting symbol is the thieving little mouse with its soft fur, the precocious girl, who makes for the larder. And at once one thinks of the word "kitten" used in every language to denote the woman's pubes, or as a name for the sexual parts, and for the sleek woman, *chat noir*, the cat which catches the mouse, plays with it, and eats it up, just as the woman devours the man's mouse with her organ.

Did you ever see the childish drawing of the woman's organ which hobbledehoys will make on walls and benches, in their foolish longing? There you have before your eyes the source of the expression "beetle" for a loving girl, but it also makes clear why the spider is used as a term of insult for a woman; the spider, which spins its web and sucks out the blood of the fly. The familiar spider proverb, "*Matin chagrin, soir espoir*," expresses the woman's attitude towards her sexuality; the more ardent the bliss of her night of love, the more despondently will she, on waking, look upon the man to see what he is thinking of her abandonment. For more and more insistently life forces upon women a morality which seems to condemn all sensuality.

Symbols have a dual significance: the tree, if you are considering its trunk, is a phallus symbol, one that is quite respectable and sanctioned by custom, for even the primmest miss is not too shy to contemplate her family tree upon the wall, although she must know that the hundred organs of procreation of all her ancestors are leaping out at her from the picture, all swelling with power. But as soon as you think of the fruit, the tree becomes a woman

214

symbol. Before I forget it, I must tell you that for some weeks I have derived much amusement by asking everyone what kind of trees are growing near the entrance to my sanatorium. Up to the present I have not once been given the right answer. They are birches; their shoots are made into canes, which we feared and still more desired, for in all the many naughtinesses of children and of grownups, there lives the yearning for the burning sting of blows. And at the entrance gate, so that everyone strides over it, there stands a cornerstone, projecting and round like a phallus. That, too, nobody has noticed. It is the stone of stumbling and offense.

Pardon the interruption. Other symbols, too, have a double meaning. Thus the eye both receives and emits rays, and the sun, in its fertility, is the mother, but in its golden radiance is the man and the hero. So it is, too, with the animals, and most of all with the horse, which is sometimes equivalent to the woman, on whom one rides, who carries about during pregnancy the fruit of her body, and sometimes the man who bears the burden of the family upon him, and will give to a crowing youngster a trot on his knee or his shoulders.

This double application of animal symbols is supported by a curious proceeding on the part of my unconscious, originating from the castration complex. If I pass by a wagon drawn by cattle and glance at it, I do not know whether the draft animals are cows or oxen. I have to look for quite a time before I find the distinctive signs. And it is not only I who am like this, but many, many other people, while those who can distinguish a cock from a hen canary are just as rare. I go rather far in this respect. If I am looking at a fowl run, I can tell the large cock from his hens, but if young cockerels are there too, I find it difficult to distinguish them, and if I meet a single fowl by itself, I am puzzled. I do not remember ever consciously noticing a stallion, a bull or a ram; for me a horse is just a horse, an ox is an ox, and a sheep is a sheep, and if in theory I know what a mare is, or a gelding, and which is a sheep or a wether, still I cannot make use of this knowledge in practice without an effort, nor can I make sure when or how I got hold of the information. Obviously this is the effect of some early prohibition connected with an unconscious anxiety as to my own castration. At the ripe

215

age of fifty-four, I became the owner of a fine tomcat. What a shame that you could not witness the amazement that befell me when I came to notice his testicles!

This brings me back again to the subject of castration, and I must say a few more words about animals, which, in symbolic form, have a strange life in the dim regions of the human soul. Do you remember how we went to Kleist's grave in Wannsee together? It was long ago, we were both still young and enthusiastic, and had hoped to get I know not what lofty emotions from this visit of ours to the dead poet whom we loved. And while you were gazing, full of devout reverence, at the holy mound from which I was plucking an ivy leaf, a wretched caterpillar fell on the back of your neck. You shrieked, turned pale, and trembled, and Kleist and all else were forgotten. I laughed and nonchalantly took away the caterpillar, but if you had not been so taken up with your own terror, you would certainly have noticed that I removed it with the ivy leaf, because it would have made me creep to touch it. Of what avail are courage and strength against the might of the symbol? If at the sight of such a little, many-legged, crawling penis, there falls upon us the whole weight of mother incest, masturbation, and the castration of one's father and oneself, we turn into four-year-old children and we can do nothing against it.

Yesterday I walked across the park, where, as you know, there is always a great assemblage of carriages, of youngsters playing, and nursemaids. A fat-cheeked little girl of three or so looked radiant as she carried a long earthworm to her mother. The creature was winding about between her little fingers, and the mother shrieked out, struck at the child's hand, exclaiming "Ugh! ugh!" and knocked the horrid worm far down the slope with the tip of her umbrella. Growing paler, she kept on scolding while busily wiping the infant's hands. I should like to have got angry with the mother, only I understood her too well. A red worm, that crawls into holes; what is the use of Darwin teaching about the beneficent labor of the worm, in the face of that?

"Ugh! ugh!" That is all the mother's knowledge of training children amounts to. Everything the child likes must be made disgusting to him. And one may not remonstrate against it. The joy in passing water and in defecating must not be suffered; otherwise, people think—I don't know with what truth—the child will never learn to be clean. Only the It understands the psychology of life, and the only literary interpreters it makes use of are the few great poets.

However, I do not want to speak of these, but to consider the effects of the "Ugh! ugh!" of the earthworm incident; you can apply what I say to people's ideas about other outlawed animals, plants, people, ideas, activities and objects. On these I leave you to your own reflection. And do not forget, as you reflect thus, to get a clear idea of the difficulty of all research into nature. Freud has written a book about the forbidden things in human life; he calls it *Totem and Taboo.* Read it! Then let your fancy roam a little over all that is tabooed. You will be horrified and yet astonished at what, in spite of this, the spirit of man has accomplished. And finally you will ask yourself what may be the reason that the It plays such a curious game with itself, why it creates obstacles merely in order to surmount them with a great deal of trouble. And finally through doing this you will win to joy beyond your power to imagine, the joy of reverence.

You know, training gets rid of nothing; it only represses. Even that delight in the earthworm cannot be destroyed. There is one curious form in which it returns, the form of a body worm. The germs of this visitor, I imagine, are everywhere in our intestines, they come into everyone's body, often and often, but the It cannot use them, and so it kills them. One day, however, the It of this person or that becomes a child, has childish phantasies, and remembers its interest in the earthworm. Straightaway it makes an image for itself out of the eggs of the body worm. It laughs at the mother's "Ugh! ugh!" and snaps its fingers at her, and at the same time it remembers that the worm is also a child, so it laughs still more and plays at being pregnant with the intestinal worm, and another day it will play at castration, or at having children. And then it makes the body worm leave the body through the bowel opening.

Now please, dear, read this passage aloud to your medical adviser. You'll have great fun in seeing the sort of reception he'll give to this seriously intended theory of a serious-minded colleague, concerning the disposition to disease.

I still have to tell you a story about the slug. It concerns

217

someone we both know, but I shall not tell you her name, or you would probably tease her. I was once going for a walk with her when she suddenly began to tremble, all the blood went out of her cheeks, and her heart began beating so hard that one saw the veins pulsating in her neck. The sweat of fear broke out upon her forehead. What was it all about? A slug was crawling in our path. We had been speaking of fidelity, and she had complained of her husband, whom she suspected of dalliance. She had long had the idea, she said, of tearing off his member and trampling on it. So the slug was this torn-off member. That seemed enough to account for everything, but for some unknown reason I was dissatisfied and stuck to it, in spite of everything, that there must be some other hidden motive. One must have been unfaithful oneself, to feel such raging jealousy. Then it shortly became clear how no one feels jealousy unless one has been untrue oneself: this friend has not been thinking of her husband's organ, but of mine. We both laughed over that, but as I could not help being the schoolmaster, I gave her a little lecture. "You are between Scylla and Charybdis," said I. "If you love me, you'll be unfaithful to your husband, and if you stick to him you'll deny me and your great love for me. Small wonder that you cannot go on, since you see that you will soon be forced to trample on the slug, either his member or mine." Such incidents are not rare. There are people who fall in love in their youth and hug this first love to their bosoms as an ideal vision, but marry someone else. If now they become dissatisfied with their bargain and have injured their partner in any way, they bring forth this ideal, make comparisons with the reality, bewail the fact that they married the wrong one, and presently find all sorts of grounds for proving how wicked the person is whom they have married and grieved. That is clever, but unfortunately, too clever! For the reflection follows that they were unfaithful to their first love in marrying another, and unfaithful to the second in holding fast to the first. Thou shalt not commit adultery!

Such behavior, which is of some importance, is difficult to understand. I have long searched for a reason why people like this—they are anything but rare—get themselves into this situation of perpetual infidelity. My friend solved the riddle for me, and it was on this account particularly that I told you the story of the slug. She had on the inner side of the upper thigh, right under the bend of the leg, a small penis-like outgrowth as long as my finger. This worried her terribly. From time to time it got sore. Some strange chance determined it that this soreness came on several times during my treatment, and disappeared every time when repressed homosexual trends had come to the surface. She had long been advised to have the growth removed, but had not had it done. I pressed her until the fact came out, broken into a thousand splinters, that she wore this little tail out of love for her mother. All her life long she had insisted that she hated this mother, but I had never believed her, although she never tired of telling me stories to prove her hate. The reason for my disbelief was, that her undeniably strong affection for me bore all the signs of a mother transference. It went on for a long time, but finally there emerged a sort of mosaic picture, partly damaged, of course, in which everything was portrayed, the ardent love for the breast, for the mother, for her arms, the repression in favor of the father, associated with a pregnancy, the springing up of hatred with its homosexual remnants. I cannot give you all the details, but the result was that this woman, whom I saw again the following year, was operated upon and felt no further dread of infidelity or of slugs. You can believe what you like, but for my part I am convinced that she brought about the growth out of love for her mother. And now I have still to add that the slug is a dual symbol, the phallus, by reason of its shape and its feelers, the female organ, by reason of its slimy secretion. Scientifically speaking also, it is double sexed.

I must tell you a little story about the axolotl too. You have seen this creature in the Berlin Aquarium, and know how much it resembles an embryo. In front of the axolotl's tank in that aquarium once, a woman standing near me nearly fainted. She, too, pretended she hated her mother. She was very fond of children, but she had come to hate her mother while the latter was pregnant, and in spite of all her longing she had had no children. Look carefully at childless women, if they really love children. There is one of life's commonest tragedies. For all these women—I venture to say, all—bear hatred towards their mothers in their hearts, but crushed into a corner there mournfully sits the repressed love. If you can help it to escape from its repression, that woman will seek and find a man to give her a child.

I could go on talking in this fashion, but my attention is captured by a spectacle of which I will tell you. The best comes at the end. As I write I am sitting on that terrace crowded with carriages which I mentioned before. In front of me two children are playing with a dog, a boy and a girl. The dog lies on his back and they are tickling his belly, and every time, in response to the tickling, the dog's little red penis shows itself, and the children laugh. Finally they have carried their play to such a point that the dog ejaculates his semen. That makes the children thoughtful. They run to their mother and pay no more attention to the dog.

Have you noticed how often grownups will tickle a dog with the toe of their boot? Memories of childhood! And since the dogs cannot talk, one must watch them and see what they do. Many of them react to the smell of menstruation, and many masturbate by rubbing against people's legs. And if dogs say nothing, question people. You must ask with confidence or you will get no answer, for the dog is not merely an animal, but a symbol of the father, of the penis.

Would you like to know still more about animals? Good. Station yourself for a few hours in front of the monkey cage at the zoo, and watch the children: you may even spare some of your glances for the grownups. If in those few hours you have not learned more of men's souls than you will find in hundreds of books, then your eyes are not worth carrying in your head.

Every good wish from your trusty

TROLL.

✳ LETTER XXX ✳

So that was the reason for your long silence! You have again considered the question of publication, and you approve of my side of the correspondence appearing in print, but refuse to allow your own letters to be included. So be it, and may the Lord have mercy upon us!

You are quite right. It is time I gave some serious explanation of the It. But words are fixed and rigid, and so I must ask you every now and then to go right around one of the words I've written and consider it from every point of view. You will then find some meaning in it, and that is what counts, not whether this meaning is right or wrong. I will make an effort to remain objective.

I must first impart to you the sad tidings that, in my own opinion, there is no such It as I have been presenting to you, that it is a fiction of my own imagination. Because I concern myself alone and entirely with the individual man, and shall continue to do so for the rest of my life, I must act in such a way as if there were, apart from the Universal Nature of God, individual beings called men. I must behave as though such an individual being were somehow divided by an empty space from the rest of the world, as if it stood alone and independent of everything outside its own imaginary boundaries. I know that this is not so, but nevertheless I shall continue to suppose that every man is his own It, with definite boundaries and a beginning and an end. I emphasize that because, most excellent lady, you have made several attempts to seduce me into talking of the World Soul, Pantheism, the Divine Nature. For that I have no inclination, and I hereby solemnly declare that I am concerned only with what I call the It of the man. And exercising my authority as letter writer, I make this It start at fertilization—at which point of this extraordinarily complicated business is immaterial to me—and I will leave it to you to pick out some one moment in the whole process of dying, and to take this as the end of the It.

Since at the start I grant you an admitted error in my hypothesis, it is open to you, of course, to find as many conscious and unconscious errors as you like in my explanations, but do not forget that this original mistake of separating individuals, living or non-living, from the Universal, is a part of all human thought, and that our every utterance is burdened with it.

And now a difficulty arises. This hypothetical It unit, whose origin we have placed at fertilization, contains within itself, as a matter of fact, two It units, a male and a female. And then I look beyond this perplexing fact and see that these two units, which proceed from the ovule and the spermatozoön, are again no units at all, but multiplicities, coming down from the time of Adam and the animal world, in which male and female lie in inextricable confusion; though never mingled, it would seem they are always side by side. I must ask you to remember this, that these two principles never merge, for it follows therefrom that every human It includes within itself at least two It beings, which, bound as they are into some sort of unity, are yet in certain ways independent of each other.

I do not know whether I need to display to you, as I have done to other women—and men, too, of course—the full extent of our ignorance concerning the further development of the fertilized ovule. For my purpose it is enough to say that after fertilization this egg divides into two parts, into two cells, as science prefers to call these beings. These two then divide again into four, into eight, into sixteen cells, and so on, until finally there comes to be what we commonly designate a human being. Into the details of this process, thank heaven, I need not enter, but shall content myself with pointing out something which seems to be important, however incomprehensible it remains to me. In this tiny little being, the fertilized ovule, there is something or other, an It, which is able to take charge of all this dividing into multitudes of cells, is able to give them distinctive forms and functions, and to induce them to group themselves as skin, bones, eyes, ears, brain, etc. What in the world becomes of this It at the moment of division? Obviously it divides itself, also, for we know that every individual cell is able to exist and to divide independently. But at the same time there remains as well a something that is general, an It which binds the two cells together, which in some way or other influences their destiny and is itself influenced by them. Considerations of this kind have forced me to accept the hypothesis that, in addition to the individual It of any man, there must also be an innumerable number of It beings belonging to the individual cells. And kindly remember in this connection that, just like the individual It of the whole man the It of every cell conceals within itself a male and a female It, as well as all the tiny It beings of the ancestral chain.

Please don't become impatient. It is not my fault if I

show the tangle in things that are taken as simple in our daily thought and speech. Some divine being will lead us, I hope, out of the thicket which threatens to choke us.

In the meantime I will further confuse you. It seems to me as if there were yet other It beings. In the course of their development the cells join together to form tissues, epithelium, connective tissue, nerve substance and so forth, and each of these separate structures appears again to be its own It, which is able to affect the general It, and the It units of the cells and of other tissues, and is in turn influenced by them in its vital activities. And even that is not all. New It forms appear in the various organs, the spleen, liver, heart, kidneys, bones, muscles, brain and spine, and beyond these again we meet other It powers of the organic systems, for it seems these form artificial It unities as it were, which have their own strange nature, although one might suppose they were merely names and superficial phenomena. And so I must believe, for example, that there is an It of the upper and of the lower half of the body, of the right and of the left, one of the neck and one of the hand, one of man's interior and one of the surface. They are beings which we could almost believe originated in our speaking, thinking or acting, which we could almost take to be the creation of the much esteemed intellect. But do not believe that. Such a view only springs from the hopeless, hesitating endeavor to try to understand anything in the world. So soon as we attempt to do that, there is some assuredly malicious It sitting in hiding which will play tricks on us, and laugh itself to death over our pretensions, over the desire of our nature to be great.

Never forget, dear, that our brain, and therefore our intellect, is itself the creation of the It. Certainly it is one which can work creatively on its own account, but nevertheless it begins to function comparatively late, and its sphere of action is definitely limited. Long before the brain comes into existence, the It of any man is already thinking, thinking without the brain, since it has itself first to construct the brain. That is something fundamental, something we ought never to forget and yet always do forget. In the assumption that one thinks only by means of the brain, an assumption undoubtedly false, is to be found the origin of a thousand and one absurdities, the origin also, it is true, of valuable discoveries and inventions, the origin of everything that adorns life and everything that renders it ugly.

Have you had enough of the tangle we have got ourselves into, or shall I tell you something more still? That new It beings continually reveal themselves in never-ending variety, almost as if they were newly born? That there are It beings of the bodily functions, of eating, drinking, sleeping, breathing, walking? That an It of pneumonia or of pregnancy will reveal itself, that these strange beings fashion themselves from one's profession, from one's age, from the place one visits, from the toilet and the bed chamber, from the school, from confirmation and marriage, from art and from habit? Confusion, endless confusion! Nothing is clear, all is dark, inescapable entanglement.

And yet, and yet! We master all this, we step into the middle of these foaming waters and dam them up. We seize hold of these powers somehow or other, and pull them hither and thither, for we are men, and our grasp can at least achieve something. It arranges, organizes, collects and completes. Over against the It stands the "I" and however else it may be and whatever else one may say, for men there remains always the verdict, I am I.

We cannot do otherwise, we are forced to imagine that we are masters of the It, of the many It units and of the one common It, yes, masters even of the character and the actions of a fellow creature, that we control his life, his health, his death. Assuredly this is not so, but it is a necessity of our organism, of our human existence, that we should believe it. We live, and because we live we have to believe that we can train our children, that there are causes and effects, that we are able to be useful or harmful in accordance with our thoughts. As a matter of fact we know nothing whatever about the connection of things, we cannot determine for twenty-four hours ahead what we shall do, and we have not the power to do anything of our own design.

But we are compelled by the It to take its doings, its thoughts, and its feelings for affairs of the conscious mind, of our own design, of our "I." Only because we are immersed in error, are blind, and ignorant of every little thing, can we be physicians and treat the sick.

I don't know exactly why I write you all this. Perhaps to excuse the fact that in spite of my firm belief in the all-powerfulness of the It, I am still a physician, that in spite of my conviction of the determination of all my thoughts and deeds by forces lying outside consciousness, I nevertheless always continue to treat the sick, and act before myself and others as if I were responsible for the success or failure of my treatment. The essential quality of man is conceit and overestimation of self. I cannot rid myself of this quality; I am obliged to believe in myself and my doings.

Fundamentally, everything that goes on in a man is done by the It. And it is good that it is so. And it is also good, at least once in a lifetime, to stand quietly by, and as far as possible to give oneself up to the consideration of how things happen outside our knowledge or our power. For us physicians in particular, that is essential. Not in order to teach us modesty—what should we be doing with such an unnatural, inhuman virtue? It is purely pharisaical. No, but because otherwise we run the danger of being one-sided, of deceiving ourselves and our patients, by saying that just this or that mode of treatment is the only right one. It sounds absurd, but it is nevertheless true, that every kind of treatment is the right one for the sick man, that he is always and in all circumstances rightly treated, whether according to the methods of science or the methods of the old wife. The success of the treatment is not determined by what we prescribe, according to our lights, but by what the It of the sick man makes of our prescriptions. If this were not so, every broken limb that was correctly set and bandaged would have to heal. But that does not always take place. If there were really so great a difference between the doings of a surgeon and those of an internist, a neurologist or a quack, one would rightly boast of one's successes and be ashamed of one's failures. But one has no such right. We do it, but we have no right to do it.

This letter, it seems to me, is written in an unusual vein, and if I go on with it any longer, in all probability I shall either make you miserable or reduce you to laughter. And neither the one nor the other is what I am aiming at. I prefer to tell you how I came to take up psychoanalysis. Then you will understand more quickly what I am driving at, and will get an inkling of what sort of thoughts I entertain about my profession and its mode of existence.

I must first make known to you my state of mind at the

time, which can best be summed up by saying that I had become mentally bankrupt. I felt old, I had tired of everything I used to hold dear, and above all, my work as a physician had become distasteful to me. I pursued it merely for the sake of an income. I was ill, of that I myself had no doubt, only I did not know what ailed me. It was not until some years afterwards that one of my medical critics told me what my trouble was: I was hysterical. The accuracy of this diagnosis I accept with all the more certainty, because it was made without any personal knowledge of me, simply from the impression given by my writings. The symptoms therefore must have been very clear. During this time I undertook the treatment of a lady who was seriously ill, and it was she who compelled me to become an analyst.

You will forgive me if I do not go into a long account of this lady's troubles. I should not enjoy doing that, because unfortunately I have not succeeded in fully restoring her, although in the course of the fourteen years during which I have known her and she has consulted me, she has become better than she herself ever expected. But in order to assure you that in her case it truly was a solid, organic, and therefore a "real" illness, not simply an "imaginary" one, an hysteria, that I was treating, I will mention the fact that in the years immediately preceding our acquaintance she had undergone two severe operations and that she was handed over to me by her latest scientific adviser as a candidate for death, with a plentiful stock of digitalis, and other truck.

That she responded to my somewhat overstrenuous examination with abundant hemorrhages from the bowels and womb did not surprise me; I had too often experienced things like that with other patients. But what did surprise me was, that in spite of her considerable intelligence, she had an absurdly poor vocabulary. She would employ circumlocutions for nearly all useful objects, so that, perhaps, for a wardrobe she would say "the thing for the clothes," or for the stovepipe, "the arrangement for the smoke." Moreover, there were certain movements she could not tolerate, such as plucking at the lip, or playing with the tassel on a chair. Various things that seem to us necessary for everyday life were banished from her sick room.

When I now look back upon the whole picture of the

illness as it then presented itself, it is difficult for me to believe that there ever was a time when I understood nothing about all these things—and yet it is so. I felt that in this patient I had to deal with a difficult combination of so-called physical and mental symptoms, but how she had got into this state or how one was to help her out of it, I could not tell. Only one thing was clear to me from the start, that there was some mysterious bond between me and the patient, which enabled her to place confidence in me. I did not then know of the idea of "transference," but was merely glad of the apparent suggestibility of my charge, and blindly continued my usual treatment. Even at the first consultation I achieved a great improvement. Up till then she had always refused to be alone with the physician during treatment; she wanted her elder sister to be with her, and in consequence, all inquiries were pursued through the intermediacy of the sister. For some strange reason she at once concurred with my suggestion that on my next visit she should see me alone. Only later did it become clear to me that this was due to the nature of the transference. It was her mother whom Fräulein G. saw in me.

Here I must interpolate something about the It of the physician. It was at that time my habit to insist with great emphasis, without any fear of consequences, upon my smallest orders being obeyed. "You had better die than fail to carry out my instructions to the last letter," I used to say, and I meant it quite seriously. Stomach patients who suffered from vomiting or body pains after eating certain dishes, I fed exclusively on these dishes until they had learned to tolerate them; I compelled others who lay in bed unable to move, owing to some inflammation of the veins or the joints, to get up and walk about; I treated apoplectics by making them bend over every day, and people I knew must die in a few hours, I dressed and took out for a walk; it happened once in my experience that one of these crumpled up, dead, in front of my door. This method of enforcing an infallible, authoritative suggestion, in the manner of the kindly, all-powerful father, I had seen in my own father, had learned from that great master of the art of the father-doctor, Schweninger, and had had something of it in me from birth. In Fräulein G.'s case everything went on quite differently from the start. Her childlike attitude towards me—indeed, as I understood later, it was that of a child of three—compelled me to assume the mother's role. Certain slumbering mother virtues were awakened in me by the patient, and these directed my procedure. Later on, when I came to look into my own medical activities more searchingly, I discovered that often before I had been forced by mysterious influences of this kind to adopt some other attitude than the paternal one towards my patients, although consciously and theoretically I held the firm conviction that the doctor must be friend and father, must control his patients.

And now I was confronted with the strange fact that I was not treating the patient, but that the patient was treating me; or, to translate it into my own language, the It of this fellow being tried so to transform my It, did in fact so transform it, that it came to be useful for its purpose.

Even to get this amount of insight was difficult, for you will understand that it absolutely reversed my position in regard to a patient. It was no longer important to give him instructions, to prescribe for him what I considered right, but to change in such a way that he could use me. But it is a long step from understanding this principle, to fulfilling the conclusions to be drawn from it. You yourself have observed me as I took this step, have seen for yourself how I changed from an active, exploring physician into a passive instrument, have often blamed me for it, and still do so, impetuously urging me again and ever again to advise here, to explore there, to help by command or direction. If you would only stop it!

So far as helpful activities go, I am hopelessly lost; I avoid giving advice, I take pains to free myself as quickly as possible from any unconscious opposition to the It of the patient and its wishes; in so doing I feel happy. I see results, and have myself become healthy. If I have anything to regret, it is because the road I tread is all too broad and easy, so that out of pure curiosity and foolish wantonness I turn aside to lose myself in bogs and caverns, and thus bring trouble and injury to myself and those confided to my care. It seems to me that the hardest thing in life is to let oneself go, to wait for the voice of the It in oneself or another, and to follow that. But it is worth while. One gradually becomes a child again, and you know, "Except ye be converted and become as little children, ye shall not enter into the Kingdom of Heaven." At five and twenty, one should give up trying to be big; up till then one really needs it, if one is to grow, but after that it is only required occasionally for the sake of the erection. To allow oneself to relax, and to conceal this relaxation, this ease, this freedom from erection, neither from oneself nor from other people, that should be the important thing. But we are just like those soldiers with the wooden phallus of whom I told you.

Enough for today. I have long been wanting to have your opinion as to my progress in growing childlike, in getting rid of the "I." I myself have the feeling that I am still at the beginning of the process generally called "growing old," which seems to me to be like "growing childlike." But I may be mistaken, though I am somewhat reassured by the angry words of a patient who revisited my consulting room after two years' absence: "You have put on mental fat!" Please make known your verdict to your faithful

PATRIK TROLL.

✳ LETTER XXXI ✳

I would never have believed, most honorable lady, that you could be such a scold! It's clarity you want, that is all! Clarity! If I could get clear about the It, I should think I was no less than God. Permit me, please, to bear myself more modestly!

Let me go back to what I was telling you about my becoming a psychoanalyst. After Fräulein G. had recognized in me her "mother-doctor," she grew more trustful. She made no fuss about anything in the treatment that my work as masseur entailed, but there remained the difficulties in speech. Gradually I accustomed myself—for my own amusement, it seemed—to her roundabout expression, and behold! to my great astonishment, I noticed after some time that I was seeing things I had never seen before. I learned to recognize the symbol. It must have come about very gradually, for I do not remember on what occasion I first grasped that a chair is not only a chair, but a whole world; that the thumb is the father, that it can wear seven-league boots, that the outstretched forefinger becomes an erection symbol, that the heated stove is an ardent woman, the stovepipe a man, and that the black color of the pipe gives rise to unspeakable horror, because death is in the black, and so the harmless stove signifies the sexual union of a living woman with a corpse.

What am I to say further? I was seized with intoxication such as I have never experienced before or since. The symbol was the very first thing I learned in the whole field of analytical knowledge, and it has since never lost its importance to me. A long, long road of fourteen years now lies behind me, and if I try to look back upon it, it is full of strange discoveries of symbolism, richly varied and shot through with changing colors. The shock of the change which this insight into symbolism brought in me must have been immense, for in the first few weeks of my tutelage I was driven to seek the symbol in the organic modification of human expression, in what we call physical, organic disease. That mental life is one continuous symbolization was to me so obvious that I impatiently pushed aside the masses of new thoughts and feelings— new to me, at least—that arose in me, and in mad haste pursued the working of symbolization in organic disease. And this working was, to me, magical.

Think now, I had behind me my twenty-year-old medical practice, dealing only—an inheritance from Schweninger—with chronic cases that had been given up. I knew exactly what could be done on my former lines, and without hesitation I ascribed the increased success which now attended me to my understanding of the symbol, which I brought to my patients like a raging wind.

As well as the symbol, I acquired, by means of this patient, a practical knowledge of another peculiarity of human thought, the force of association. Perhaps in this, other influences were also at work, journals and communications, gossip, but the essential part came from Fräulein G. I immediately conferred this blessing, too, upon my patients; enough of my medical habits remained to lead me occasionally into error, but at that time, to me, everything seemed very good.

And so for a time it went on, but soon I began to meet with rebuffs. Mysterious forces of some sort suddenly barred my way, forces which later, under Freud's guidance, I learned to designate "resistances." For a time I went back to the method of command, was punished for that by unfortunate results, and finally learned more or less to find my way. Taking it all in all, my success went beyond expectation, and when the war broke out I had elaborated a technique which eventually met the requirements of my practice. When I was working for a few months in a hospital for the wounded, I tested my amateur, "wild" analysis—which I still stand by—and saw that wounds and broken bones responded to the analysis of the It in just the same way as nephritis or heart failure or a neurosis.

So far this has all been very nice and pleasant to write about, and it sounds quite plausible, but in 1913 in the middle of this stage of development comes something puzzling: an open attack on Freud and on psychoanalysis. You can still see it in black and white in my book *Nasamecu* on the healthy and the sick man. I always imagined, and do still, that I learned analysis through Fräulein G., but it cannot be entirely true, or how should I, at a time when apparently I knew nothing at all about Freud, have been familiar with his name? That I knew nothing that was true about him is evident from the words I used in making this attack. I cannot think of anything more stupid than those words. But where in the world could I have heard of him? It was only a short time ago that it came to my mind. My first ideas I got many years before I knew Fräulein G., from an article I had read, and a second occasion was when I heard the name of Freud coupled with the term "psychoanalysis," in the gossip of a patient who had picked up her knowledge somewhere or other.

My vanity prevented me from interesting myself in scientific psychoanalysis for a long time. Later on I tried to repair my fault, with a fair amount of success, I venture to hope, although there yet remains a weed here and there which I have not uprooted from my analytical theory and procedure. But my willful refusal to learn has also held a certain advantage. In that blind struggle, unimpeded by previous knowledge, I came by chance upon the idea that in addition to the unconscious of the thinking brain, there is an analogous unconscious of other organs, cells, tissues, etc., and that through the intimate connection of these separate unconscious units with the organism as a whole, a beneficial influence may be directed upon the individual units by means of the analysis of the brain unconscious.

You must not think that I feel quite easy in my mind as I write down these views. I have the uncomfortable feeling that they will not survive your kindly criticism, let alone the serious examination of an expert. But since it has become easier for me to give an opinion than to give proof, I will take refuge in opinion here too, and say: "Every sickness of the organism, whether it is physical or psychic, is to be influenced by analysis. Whether in a given case one should have recourse to analytical methods, or surgical, or mechanical, whether one should prescribe medicine or a special dietary, depends upon what one is aiming at. Of itself, there is no department of medicine in which Freud's discovery cannot prove its worth."

Your reference to the fact that I am a practicing physician and claim the title of doctor is so very trenchant, my dear, that I feel myself obliged to brag a little more about how I imagine I understand and cure disease. But first we must come to some agreement over what we shall call "disease." I think we won't worry about what other people understand by the term, but will make sure of what we mean ourselves, and I therefore propose to enunciate quite definitely, "Disease is a vital expression of the human organism." Take a little time to think whether you agree with this formula or not, and meanwhile I will continue as if you approved it.

Perhaps you do not consider the question particularly important, but if you had been trying for thirty years, as I have, to get a certain number of people every day to grasp this simple statement, and day by day for thirty years had found that it could by no means be driven into people's heads, then you would consent at least, when I emphasized its value, to understand it.

Whoever, like me, sees in illness a vital expression of the organism, will no longer see it as an enemy. It will no longer be his purpose to fight the illness, he no longer tries to cure it, he does not treat it at all. It would be just as absurd for me to treat disease as it would be to try to answer your teasing by pointing out the little naughtinesses in your letters very nicely and delicately, without answering it.

In the moment that I realize that the disease is a creation of the patient, it becomes for me the same sort of thing as his manner of walking, his mode of speech, his facial expression, the movements of his hands, the drawing he has made, the house he has built, the business he has settled, or the way his thoughts go: a significant symbol of the powers that rule him and that I try to influence when I deem it right. Disease is then no longer anything abnormal but something conditioned by the nature of this one man who is ill and wishes to be treated by me. One difference exists in the case of disease, namely that the creations of the It to which we are accustomed to give the name of disease are under certain conditions inconvenient for the creator himself, or for those surrounding him. But after all, a shrill voice or illegible handwriting can also be intolerable to one's fellow men, and an unsuitable house needs just as much rebuilding as a lung that is inflamed, so in the end there is no essential difference to be found between disease and speaking, or writing, or building. In other words I can no longer make up my mind to proceed with a sick man otherwise than with someone who wrote or spoke or built badly. I should try to make out why, and to what end, his It made use of the bad writing, speaking, building, of his sick state, what it was it wanted to express in this way. I should inquire from the It itself what grounds it had for acting in a way that was disagreeable, for me as well as for itself—I would discuss these and then view the result. And if one discussion was not enough I should repeat it again ten times, twenty times, a hundred times, until at last the It found this talking tedious, and either changed its behavior or compelled its creature, the patient, to depart from me, whether by breaking off the treatment or by dying.

Now I grant you it may be necessary, is so in most cases, to reconstruct or to pull down a badly built house as quickly as possible, to put a man to bed with pneumonia and nurse him, to get rid of the edema in a nephritic patient perhaps with digitalis, to set and immobilize a broken bone, and to amputate a gangrenous limb. Yes, and I have that same well-founded hope that the architect whose new building is reconstructed or pulled down immediately after he has handed it over to the owner, will examine himself, see his mistake and avoid it in future or give up his calling altogether, as that an It, when it has damaged its own work, lungs or bones, and thereby suffered pain and trouble, will be reasonable, and will have learned its lesson for the future. In other words the It can convince itself, by its own experiences, that it is foolish to spend its strength in producing disease instead of using it to compose a song, to carry on a business, to empty the bladder or to achieve the sexual act. But all this does not relieve me, whom my It has made into a physician, from the necessity of listening, when time permits, to the reasons of the disease-seeking It of a fellow man, of weighing them, and when it is possible and desirable, of refuting them.

The matter is important enough, looked at again from another point of view. We are usually accustomed to search for the causes of our experiences, according to whether they are pleasing or not, in the world outside, or within ourselves. If we slip in the street we look for and find some orange peel, or a stone, the external cause of our fall. On the other hand, if we take a pistol and put a bullet through our heads, we are of the opinion that we are acting from inward reasons, with intention. If someone gets pneumonia, we attribute this to infection, but if we rise from our chair, walk across the room and take some morphia from a cupboard in order to drink it, then we think we are being moved by causes within. I, as you know, have always believed I knew better than other people, and if someone has held forth to me about the well-known piece of orange peel that suddenly appeared on the path, despite all the police warning, and caused Frau Lange's broken arm, I have gone down to her and asked, "What was your purpose in breaking your arm?" And if anyone told me Herr Treiner had taken morphia the night before because he couldn't sleep, I have asked, "How and by what means did the idea of morphia become so overpowering in you yesterday, that you make yourself sleepless in order to have the excuse for taking it?" So far an answer to such questions has always been forthcoming, which after all is not so very wonderful. Since everything has two sides, we can always consider it from two points of view, and shall find, if we take the trouble, that for every event in life there is both an external and an internal cause.

This amusement of the would-be wiseacre has had some strange results. In its exercise I have been led more and more to seek out the internal cause, partly because I was born into a time which prated of the bacillus and only of the bacillus, even if it did not still bow down before the words "chill" and "disorder of the stomach," partly because the wish awoke in me very early—probably owing to Troll arrogance—to find within myself an It, a God, whom I could make responsible for everything. Since I had not been so badly trained as to claim omnipotence for myself alone, I attributed it to other people also, invented for them also this, to you, so offensive It, and was now able to maintain, "Illness does not come from without; man creates it for himself, uses the outer world merely as the instrument with which to make himself ill, selects from that inexhaustible supply to be found in the wide world, now the spirochete of syphilis, today a piece of orange peel, tomorrow the bullet of a revolver, the day after a chill, so that he may pile on his woes. And always for the sake of getting pleasure out of it, because as a human being he finds a natural pleasure in suffering: because as a human being he has by nature a feeling of guilt, and wants to remove it by self-punishment; because he wants to escape from something or other that is uncomfortable." For the most part these strange causes are all unknown to him, indeed they are all removed from the conscious mind, locked up in the depths of the It, into which we can never look. Between the bottomless depths of the It and our sane human intellect, however, there are layers of the unconscous which are attainable by the conscious mind, layers which Freud deemed capable of becoming conscious, and in which all sorts of nice things are to be found. And the strangest thing of all is that if one rummages through this, it not infrequently happens that we suddenly come upon what we call healing too—by chance it seems to be. "Not all our worth, nor all our pride." I must be forever repeating that.

And now, in conclusion, a story, according to custom, or perhaps two. The first is simple enough, and you will probably think me silly in attaching any value to it. Two officers in the trenches were talking of home, and one of them said how fine it would be to get a wound which would entail the necessary leave of a few weeks or months. The other was not content with that; he wanted an injury that would permanently incapacitate him so that he could stop at home, and he told of a brother officer who was shot through the elbow joint and thereby rendered unfit for service in the field. "That would just suit me!" Half an hour later he was shot through the elbow joint. The bullet got him at the moment when he raised his hand to salute. If he had not saluted, the shot would have gone past him, and there was no real need for him to salute, since the comrade whom he greeted had already met him three times in the previous hour. You need not attribute any significance to this: it is enough if I make a little song for myself out of it. And since I have the well-considered intention of finding an inner connection as often as possible between an incident of being wounded and the wish of the It, it has not been hard for me to read this into people.

Another man came to me for treatment long after the war. Among other things he suffered from slight epileptic seizures, and in describing them he told me the following story. He, too, was weary of fighting and was occupied in thinking how he might be lucky enough to get out of the mess without the consequences being too serious. It then occurred to him—and this thought too was not a mere chance, but was determined by impressions received shortly before—it occurred to him how as a student he had been compelled by his excessively strict father to wear skis, how uncomfortable these were for him, and how he had envied a schoolfellow who in skiing had broken his right kneecap and was consequently absent for two months. Two days later he was at his observation post directing his battery. They were being shot at by three enemy batteries, a light one that aimed short, a medium one that shot a good distance to the left, and a heavy cannon whose shells fell at regular intervals of exactly five minutes, just between the battery and his post. If he left his post immediately after this gun had fired, he could get back to his battery in safety, and this he did twice. Then there came an order from an officer in a safe position behind, that his battery must be moved. He was very angry at this order, and longed once again for his "Blighty wound," and—yes, I must accept what he told me, and I believe it too—he left his protected position exactly at that moment when the familiar interval between the heavy firing expired. The result was fortunate: two seconds later he lay on the ground with his right kneecap shattered, had a fit, and on returning to consciousness, was carried behind the lines. Of course this was pure coincidence. Who could doubt it? But the affair had a little sequel, which is the real reason for my telling you the story. You see, since that time, this man has had a stiff leg, not absolutely stiff, but enough so that on passive rotation of the joint, one could only get to about 20°. According to the verdict of the people who must have known, since they were learned surgeons and had mastered the Röntgen technique, and moreover they bore really honored names, this was due to the contraction of the scar on the kneecap. The day after he related this story, he could bring his knee round to 26°, on the day following still further round, and after eight days he was cycling. And yet nothing at all happened with his knee, except that he had spoken about it, and had been told of the strange healing power of the It. But he has not learned to kneel and that is a pity. His mother is a pious lady and would rejoice in his learning to pray once more, an exercise he carried on as a child with great zeal. But, it seems, he is still too much at odds with his father, in whose likeness he created for himself God, to bow the knee before him.

I have still another story to tell you. A young man recently visited me who was under my charge a long time ago. He suffered from frightful anxiety, which pursued him day in and day out. When he came to me he already knew that it was a castration-anxiety, and right at the beginning he told me of a childish dream in which two robbers came into his father's barn and castrated the black horse which was his favorite. (In contrast to his two brothers, this man had perfectly black hair.) As a growing child—I believe of nine years—he caught a heavy cold, and before that had lasted very long he'd had a piece of the septum removed. I know that: it is a trick of the It to castrate the father symbolically. And ten years later he had had both little toes amputated for no reason whatever and so had symbolically castrated his two brothers. But it had not helped at all; the anxiety remained with him. He only got rid of it after a troublesome analysis that lasted years. The funny thing about this case is, that this man has the vivid phantasy of enjoying sexual pleasure as a woman, and yet wishes to be heterosexually potent to an extraordinary degree. Still he has preferred the wish to be castrated, to become a woman, as he expressed it in his dream, to turn against his father and brothers, and has paid for this evil wish by the operations on the nose and toes, and by anxiety.

The It plays marvelous tricks, makes ill, makes sound, compels the amputation of healthy limbs and makes a man run up against a bullet. In short, it is a capricious, unaccountable, entertaining jester.

Affectionately yours,
PATRIK.

✳ LETTER XXXII ✳

No, my dear, that man's toes have not grown again in spite of the It and of analysis. That, however, does not preclude the possibility that some fine day a method will be discovered which, with the help of the It, will make it possible to re-grow amputated limbs. The experiments in getting different organs to go on growing after their removal from the organism prove that many things can be accomplished which thirty years ago we believed to be impossible. But I am going to make demands upon your powers of belief with something much stranger still.

What do you think about the "I," for example? "I am I," that is the fundamental proposition of our life. My assertion that this proposition in which mankind expresses its egoism is a mistake will not shatter the world as it would do if people actually believed it. But they cannot and will not believe it. I don't believe it myself, and yet it is true.

I am by no means "I," but a continually changing form in which the It displays itself, and the "I"-feeling is one of its tricks to lead man astray in his self-knowledge, to render his self-deception easier, to make of him life's pliant tool.

I! With the stupidity which grows with our growth, we

so accustom ourselves to the self-importance inspired in us by the It, that we quite forget the time when we naïvely held the opposite idea, when we used to speak of ourselves in the third person—"Emmy naughty girl! Smack Emmy!" "Patrik very good. Chocolate!" Which of us grownups could emulate a like objectivity?

I do not wish to maintain that the child's idea of the "I," the idea of his own individuality, first arises in the moment when he learns to use the pronoun "I," this symbol of mental impoverishment. But this much at least one can say, that the consciousness of the "I," the manner in which we grownups make use of the idea "I," is not inborn, but only gradually grows within man's mind, that he has to learn it.

You must make allowances for me if I skip over a good deal in writing of these matters. No one can find his way aright in the middle of the "I," neither will anyone ever be able to come to the end of it.

I am speaking intentionally of the "I"-consciousness as we grownups feel it. It is not absolutely certain that the newborn child is entirely without the consciousness of being an individual; indeed, I am inclined to think that he is so conscious, only that he cannot express himself in speech. I go so far as to believe that there is an individual consciousness even in the embryo, yes, even in the fertilized ovule, and in the unfertilized one too, as well as in the spermatozoön. And from that I argue that every single separate cell has this consciousness of individuality, every tissue, every organic system. In other words, every It unit can deceive itself into thinking, if it likes, that it is an individuality, a person, an "I."

I know this sort of argument confuses all our ideas, and if you put aside this letter unread, I shall not be a bit surprised. But still I must express what I believe: the human hand has its "I" as well, it knows what it does, and it knows that it knows. And every kidney cell and every nail cell has its consciousness just the same, and its conscious activity, its "I"-consciousness. I cannot prove it, but I believe it, and for this reason, that I am a doctor, and have seen that the stomach responds in a certain way to certain amounts of nourishment, that it makes a careful use of its secretion according to the nature and the amount of food supplied, that it thinks over what it will enjoy and to that end it uses the eye, the nose, ear, mouth and so on,

239

as its own organs, so that it may determine what to do. I believe it also for this reason, that a lip which does not wish to be kissed although the person's "I" desires the kiss, makes itself sore, puts a spot there, disfigures itself, and asserts its own opposing will in an unmistakable and highly successful manner. I believe it for this reason, that a penis will protect itself against a sexual intercourse desired by the general "I," by means of an herpetic eruption, or will avenge itself upon the overpowering might of the lustful sex instinct, by getting infected with syphilis or gonorrhea; that a womb will obstinately refuse to become pregnant, although the conscious "I" of the woman so greatly desires it that she is willing to be treated or to have an operation; that a kidney will refuse to work if it finds that the man's "I" desires something unreasonable; and that when the consciousness of the lip, the stomach, the kidney, the penis, the womb, can be persuaded into obeying the will of the general "I," all their hostile manifestations, the symptoms of disease, disappear.

In order that you may not misunderstand my otherwise confusing statements altogether, I must expressly emphasize one thing: the "I" that I claim for the cells, the organs, etc., is not just the same thing as the It. Rather is this "I" a mere product of the It, just as the gestures, the voice, the movements, the thinking, building, walking upright, getting ill, dancing, are all products of the It. The It unit at one time expresses its vitality in this manner, and another time in that, so that it transforms itself into a urine cell or helps to make a nail, or becomes a blood corpuscle, or a cancer cell, or gets itself poisoned, or avoids a sharp stone, or becomes conscious of some other phenomenon. Health, disease, talent, action and thought, but above all, perception and will and self-consciousness are only achievements of the It, expressions of life. About the It itself we know nothing whatever.

This is all pretty complicated! For if you picture to yourself how the It units and the It wholes are working with and against each other, and how they now here, now there, one time in this way, another time in that way, come together and separate from each other; how at one moment they make use of the general "I" in order to bring something into consciousness, and at the same time to repress this or that into the unconscious; how they bring one thing into the general consciousness, another again only into that part of the part "I," a third is shut up in a room from which it can be brought out into consciousness again with the help of memory or reflection, but by far the greatest part of life, of thought, feeling, perception, willing, acting, passes into the unsearchable depths—when you remember all this, you will find it easy to realize how vain it is to want to understand anything whatever. But heaven be praised, not only is it unnecessary to understand but the wish to understand is merely a handicap. The human organism is so strangely ordered that it will respond—if it wishes to do so, not otherwise—to a gentle word, a kind smile, a pressure of the hand, the cut of a knife, or a spoonful of digitalis, with results which only fail to astound us because they are so common. I have followed methods of medical treatment of every kind, at one time so, another time so, and have found that all roads lead to Rome, those of science and those of charlatanry, and so I do not consider it is of special importance which of the roads one takes provided one has the time and is not ambitious. And so habits have established themselves in me in the face of which I am powerless, which I am obliged to follow because they seem to me to be valuable. And pre-eminent among these habits is that of psychoanalysis, i.e., the attempt to bring into consciousness the unconscious. Others do differently. I am content with my results.

But I wanted to speak of the "I" and of its manifold nature. One usually understands by that term only what I have been calling the general "I," which I use as a starting point in my psychoanalytical experiments and alone can use. But even this general "I"—which we may as well now call the "I"—is not a being to be easily surveyed. Inside a few moments it will turn towards us the most diverse sides of its serried and scintillating surface. At one moment it is an "I" that comes out of our childhood, later it is twenty years old; now it is moral, now sexual, and again, it is the "I" of a murderer. Now it is pious, a moment later, impertinent. In the morning it is the professional "I," the officer or the civil servant, at midday perhaps the married "I," and in the evening a card player or a sadist or a thinker. If you consider that all these "I's"—and one could quote untold numbers more —are simultaneously present in the man, you will be able to imagine how great is the power of the unconscious in the "I," how exciting it is to observe it, what inexpressible pleasure it is to influence this "I"—whether it remains conscious or unconscious of us. Ah, my dear, it is only since I began to occupy myself with analysis that I have realized how beautiful life is. And every day grows more so.

Shall I tell you something that always fills me with amazement? That man's thought—the thought of the It, or at least of the unconscious "I" life—appears to be like a rolling ball. That is how it seems to me. I see nothing but beautiful round globes. If one writes down a number of words, just as they occur to one's mind, and examines them, one finds they have grouped themselves together into a spherical phantasy, into a poem in spherical form. And if one gets somebody else to try the thing, again one sees the sphere. And these spheres are rolling about, turning fast or slow, and shimmering with a thousand colors, with colors as beautiful as those we see when we close our eyes. Magnificent sight! In other words the It compels us to associate in geometrical forms, which rearrange their colored particles like those pretty optical instruments which, in turning, always make new figures out of their colored glass.

I ought now to tell you something about the onset of diseases, but on this subject I know nothing. And about their cure, I ought to speak, if I am to do what you wish. And of that, too, I know just nothing at all. I take both of them as given facts. At the utmost, I can say something about the treatment, and that I will now do.

The aim of the treatment, of all medical treatment, is to gain some influence over the It. It is the usual custom for this purpose to give direct treatment to groups of the It units; we reach them with the knife, or with chemical substances, with light and air, heat or cold, electric currents, or some sort of rays. No one is able to try more than one method or another, the results of which nobody can foretell. What the It will make of such a means can often be judged with some degree of precision; often again, we merely entertain some vague hope that the It will be good, will call our action satisfactory, and for its part will set the healing forces in motion. But mostly it is a groping in the dark, to which not even the most indulgent of critics can attribute any intention. This has always been the common practice, and the experience of thousands of years shows that it can achieve results, favorable results. Only one must not forget that recovery is brought about not by the physician, but by the sick man himself. He heals himself, by his own power, exactly as he walks by means of his own power, or eats, or thinks, breathes or sleeps.

Generally speaking, people have been content with this method of treatment, called "symptomatic treatment" because it deals with the phenomena of disease, the symptoms. And nobody will assert that they were wrong. But we physicians, because we are compelled by our calling to play at being God Almighty, and consequently to entertain overwhelming desires, long to invent a treatment which will do away not with the symptoms but with the cause of the disease. We want to develop causal therapy, as we call it. In this attempt we look around for a cause, and first theoretically establish, under the disguise of many words, that there are apparently two essentially different causes, an inner one, *causa interna,* which the man contributes of himself, and an outer one, *causa externa,* which springs from his environment. And accepting this clear distinction, we have thrown ourselves with raging force upon the external causes, such as bacilli, chills, overeating, overdrinking, work, and anything else. And the *causa interna,* that we have forgotten. Why? Because it is not pleasant to look within ourselves—and it is only in oneself that one finds some tiny sparks which can lighten the darkness of the inner causes, the "disposition"—because there is something which Freudian analysis calls the resistance of the complexes, the Oedipus complex, the impotence and masturbation complexes, etc., and because these complexes are terrifying. Nevertheless, in every age there have always been physicians who raised their voices to declare that man himself produces his diseases, that in him are to be found the *causae internae;* he is the cause of the disease and we need seek none other. To this claim people have assented, they have repeated it, and then they have again attacked the outer causes with prophylaxis, disinfection, and so on. Then some people came along with very loud voices, and never ceased to cry "Immunize!" This only emphasized the truth that the sick man himself creates his disease. But when it came to the practical application of immunization, once again people applied themselves to the symptoms, and what

243

was ostensibly a causal treatment grew into a symptomatic treatment unawares. The same thing has happened with suggestion, and, admit it at once, with psychoanalysis. Even this method uses the symptoms, and nothing but the symptoms, although its practitioners know that the man alone is the cause of the disease.

And there I have my jumping-off point. One cannot treat in any other way than causally. For both ideas are the same; no difference exists between them. Whoever is treating, is treating the *causa interna,* the man who has created the disease out of his own It, and in order to treat him the physician must watch the symptoms, whether he works with stethoscope and Röntgen rays, or looks to see if a tongue is furred, the urine cloudy, or whether he judges by a dirty shirt or a few cut-off hairs. It is the same thing in essence, whether one goes carefully through all the signs of the disease, or contents oneself with reading a letter written by the sick man, or with looking at the lines of his hand, or with dealing with him while he is in a somnambulistic condition. Always it is a treatment of the man and therefore of his symptoms. For the man, as he appears, is a symptom of the It, which is the object of the whole treatment; his ear is just as much a symptom as the rustling in his lungs; his eye is a symptom, an expression of the It, just as is the eruption of scarlet fever; his leg is a symptom, in the same sense as the grating of the bones which indicates the broken condition of this leg.

If then it's all the same thing, what sort of purpose is there in Patrik Troll's writing such a long book, full of statements sounding as if they claimed to be new thoughts? No, they make no such claim, they merely sound like that. In truth I am convinced that, in analyzing, I do no differently from what I did before, when I ordered hot baths, gave massage, and issued masterful commands, all of which I still do. The new thing is merely the point of attack in the treatment, the symptom which appears to me to be there in all circumstances, the "I." My treatment, in so far as it is different from what it used to be, consists of the attempt to make conscious the unconscious complexes of the "I," to do this systematically and with all the cunning and all the strength at my command. That is certainly something new, but it originated not with me, but with Freud; all that I have done in the matter is to apply this method to organic diseases. Because I hold the view that the object of all medical treatment is the It; because I hold the view that this It, with its own masterly power, forms the nose, inflames the lungs, makes a man nervous, prescribes his breathing, his gait, his activities; because, furthermore, I believe that the It can be just as much influenced by the making conscious of the unconscious "I" complexes, as by an abdominal operation; for these reasons I fail to understand—or rather, I no longer understand—how anybody at all can believe that psychoanalysis is applicable only to neurotics, and that organic diseases must be helped by other methods.

You must let me have my laugh over that!

Ever your
PATRIK TROLL.

✳ LETTER XXXIII ✳

Your words sound the note of release! "I have had enough of your letters," you say, to which I add, "And I enough of writing them!" Unfortunately you still express the wish—and your wishes are my commands—that I shall say quite concisely and conclusively what I understand by the term "It." I can say it no better than I have done before: "The It animates the man; it is the power which makes him act, think, grow, become sick or sound, the power, in brief, which animates him."

But you are not helped by such a definition. I shall therefore have recourse to my time-honored means of telling you stories, but you must remember, with these, that the events which I relate to you are selected from far-reaching associations, and are the occasional incidents which break the monotony of wearisome treatments; otherwise you will get the idea that I think myself a miracle worker. Nothing of the sort! On the contrary, the more I have to do with people, the more firmly rooted is my conviction that the doctor can do almost nothing by way of curing a patient, that the patient himself heals himself, and that the doctor, even the analyst, has only this one question to decide, by what artifice at any moment the It is contriving to remain sick.

It is therefore a mistake to suppose that the patient comes to the doctor in order to be helped. Only a portion of his It is willing to be healthy; another part wants to remain sick, and watches the whole time for an opportunity to be injured by the doctor. The principle that the most important rule of treatment is to avoid injuring, has impressed itself upon me more deeply with every passing year: indeed, I am inclined to believe that every case of death during treatment, every setback is to be attributed to some mistake of the doctor, into which he has allowed himself to be led by the villainy of the sick It. Alas, there is nothing godlike in our doings, and the wish to be as God, which is what really impels us to be doctors, takes its revenge upon us, as upon our first parents in Paradise. Punishment, curses and death attend it.

Here is a recent example showing what hostility the deep-hidden It of a patient felt against me, though his conscious "I" regarded me with admiration and gratitude. One night this patient had two dreams which contained much that was informative. To begin with, he said he no longer knew anything of the first dream. But since he pondered a long time over this forgotten dream, one might infer that the key to the riddle lay there. I waited patiently for a while to see if any memory whatever would emerge, but nothing came, so I finally challenged the patient to say a word haphazard. A little trick of this sort is often worth while. For instance, in such a situation, I once had the word "Amsterdam" named, and for about a year a successful, an astonishingly successful, treatment turned on this one word. Well, this patient named the word "house," and told me that on the previous day he had been looking at my sanatorium from outside, that it had a quite irrelevant tower, that a makeshift bridge had to be tacked on to it because the house was in a wrong position, and that the roof was ugly. I cannot dispute— nor will you, since you know the house—that he was wrong. And yet these reflections led on to quite other things, to things that were far more important, that turned out to be decisive for him and for my treatment. That was proved by the second dream. The patient said, "It was a thoroughly stupid dream," and with that he laughed. "I wanted to pay a visit at a house belonging to a shoemaker. In front of the house two boys were scuffling, and then one ran away howling. The shoemaker was called Akeley. No one was to be seen, but by-and-by some servants seemed to be about. The shoemaker, however, whom I wanted to visit, I did not see. Instead, after some time there appeared an old friend of my mother's, curiously enough with a head of black hair, although in reality he is completely bald." If the patient had not laughed in telling this, if he had not previously been criticizing the outside of my sanatorium, perhaps I should have been weeks in getting the meaning of it. As it was, it came out quickly. The word Akeley gave the first clue. It had been taken from a recently published work by Arno Holz, entitled *The Tin-smithy*, an extremely witty and erotic bit of foolishness.

Contempt for my person is to be found here, since the patient had been reading, a short while before, a book I had given him, *Der Seelensucher*, by our familiar friend Groddeck. This was *Die Blechschmiede*, the shoemaker Akeley was myself, the shoemaker's house, my sanatorium. It also came from this, that, as a matter of fact, on arrival the patient had been kept standing in the corridor for quite a time before anyone showed him to his room. He did not see me until the following day. This sort of criticism of the doctor who is treating him is to be found in every patient, it is always there, and the consistent nature of the disapproval, which is merely repressed, is evidence that we deserve it. There would have been no special point in relating this dream if it had not also given the reason for the patient's contempt of me. Instead of the shoemaker, there appears in the dream an old friend of his dead mother, who for some curious reason had black hair. This friend of his mother represents the father, who is given black hair because he is dead. The hate, then, is not for me but for his mother's friend, and behind him, for his own father. It is an amalgamation of three people, which shows clearly what a heaped-up mass of opposition my patient had transferred to me. But the mother's friend is also the patient himself, who rejoiced in a head of luxurious black hair. His unconscious showed him in the dream how altogether different it would be, if he were to give the treatment instead of the shoemaker Troll. He was not so far astray; the patient always knows better than the doctor. Only unfortunately his knowledge is not at the service of his thought, but can only be expressed in dreams, movements, clothing, nature, symptoms of disease, in short, in a language which he does not understand himself. And in truth, this identification of himself with the mother's friend, and with the father, revealed more than the patient guessed. Here was hidden the incest wish, the wish of childhood, the wish of every child, to be the lover of his mother. And now comes a strange turn. With a merry laugh, not in the least scornful, the patient said, "My mother's friend was called Lameer, he was a Fleming, his name has nothing to do with *la mère,* the mother."

No, truly? Yet I think it has. And that augurs well for the treatment, for if the patient identifies me not only with the friend and with the husband of the mother, but also with the mother herself, then he has transferred to me the feelings he has for her, too, a feeling that cannot have changed essentially since his sixth year, for the mother died at that time. Perhaps that is well, provided his attitude towards his mother was good, that he obtained help from her. But who is to know that? It may also be that he hated her even more than he loved her.

Here I must go back to the beginning of the dream, to the two boys scuffling in front of the shoemaker's house. These are easily explained. They represent the same thing at two successive moments, one of them being the phallus in a state of erection, the other, who runs away crying, the member as it ejaculates. Behind the first interpretation is a second, according to which the one boy was the dreamer, the second his brother whom he had ousted from the favor of their parents. And the third, most deeply hidden of all, is that the first boy is the dreamer himself who masturbates his penis, the other boy. This act of self-gratification takes place in front of the shoemaker's house, but the erotic phantasies of the dreamer, as the further progress of the dream shows, are concerned not only with the shoemaker, but with the mother's friend, that is, the father, and behind him, well concealed, with the mother herself, "Lameer."

I tell you this dream because, without knowing it himself, the dreamer gives in it the points for attack in the treatment. First he reveals to the attentive listener, long before he is clearly aware of it himself, that there exists a strong opposition to the doctor, that once again, therefore, we have reached the point which may be said to be the one and only feature of importance to the treatment. For it is in the serious conscious or unconscious recognition and removal of the resistance that the doctor's activity is essentially concerned, and this will be the more effective the more clearly he realizes the situation. Furthermore, the dream shows whence this resistance comes. It derives from the hostile attitude towards the friend and husband of the beloved mother, and before that again, from the struggle of the two rival brothers for entrance into the mother, who, behind several concealing veils, is yet clearly the owner of the house, of the sanatorium in which one gets well, of the mother's body, into which one enters. Finally, the patient also betrays the complexes which are affecting him, the Oedipus and the masturbation complex.

There you have a sample of the way in which the unconscious, the repressed material, attempts to make itself intelligible. But I am carrying coals to Newcastle—for you tell me you have been reading Freud's *Interpretation of Dreams*. Read it over again, and then several times more; you will be repaid in a way you do not anticipate yourself. In any case it is superfluous for me to go over the ground which the master himself has presented, and after him thousands of his followers, in ever new descriptions, to everyone who wishes to traverse it. Even the little story that follows takes a course which is known, or ought to be known, to you.

It concerns a little girl of eight years who for some time had been afraid of school, although previously she had gone there quite willingly. Arithmetic and knitting troubled her. I asked her what number was the most disagreeable to her, and she at once gave 2. She was told to write down a 2, and then she said, "The little hook underneath isn't easy; if I write it quickly, I leave it out." I then asked her what this little hook made her think of, and, without reflection, she replied "A meat hook," and then added "for ham and sausage," and then, as though she must obliterate the impression of this strange answer, or else explain it, she quickly added "I let the stitches drop in knitting and then a hole comes." If you start out from this last tag, "a hole comes," you will realize that the meat hook is a hook of flesh, that the child is therefore

249

passing through a period in which she is trying to explain to herself the fundamental difference between the two sexes. And in a very compressed form, through her anxiety, and through the mistakes she makes in leaving out the hook in 2 and letting her stitches drop, she lets us know of her theory that the woman, the 2 in the family, has no hook of flesh, but has lost it through overquick writing, masturbation; that through the quick movement of the needle, in and out, there has come the big hole out of which the precociously voluptuous girl makes her little pool, while the boy squirts his fountain out of the narrow opening of the penis. That is truly a difficult problem for a little girl's brain, and it is no wonder that arithmetic and knitting will not go right. On the next day the child showed more of her knowledge, which this time was of a reassuring nature. She complained that she had had dreadful pain in defecating, and so laid stress on the fact that, as a substitute for the abstracted penis, the girl can bear children, even if this means pain. And then, in her mysterious urge to explain herself more clearly, she began unprompted to relate, to the amazement of her mother who thought she knew nothing, how she had been present when a calf was delivered out of the body of a cow, and how three sweet little kittens had been born from the mother cat. It is droll to hear this bubbling out of a child's soul, if there is a leak anywhere in the layer which covers what is repressed.

In symbolic actions or mistakes of this kind, the unconscious is quite often expressed. Recently, for instance, I found one of my patients—he belonged to the so-called homosexuals—in a bad temper because he had broken his eyeglasses, without which he could not enjoy life. They had fallen from his nose as he went to remove a vase from the table. When I asked him to name other objects on the table, he mentioned the photograph of his friend, which was still lying there. As a matter of fact it was found buried under a heap of cushions and covers, with the back uppermost, so that one couldn't see the picture. It came out from this that the friend had been unfaithful to him, with a girl. Since it was not in his power to keep the youth away from the girl, he wanted at any rate to separate them symbolically, and therefore took away the vase, which represented the girl. There followed automatically on this the turning of the photograph over on its face, the covering it with cushions, and the breaking of the pince-nez. Translated into the language of the unconscious it means, "I will not see the faithless one any more. His back shall always be kept towards me, for that part of him has no use for a girl. Let the photograph be turned over so. It is, however, safer to protect the back. Let us cover it with cushions. That's good; now I shall see nothing more of him, especially if I put a cover on top. It isn't enough. I'm suffering too much. It is best to blind myself. Then I shall not have to observe his faithlessness any more, but can go on loving him." And with that, the poor dear broke his glasses.

The unconscious makes strange experiments with the eyes. It thrusts retinal impressions out of consciousness when they are unbearable. One day I asked one of my patients to look carefully at the objects on her writing desk and make a note of them. When I required her to tell me what was on the desk she enumerated everything until she came to the photographs of her two sons, which she failed to mention, notwithstanding my oft-repeated warnings that she had suppressed two things. When I asked her why she had omitted the two photographs she was astonished. "I did not see them," she said, "and that is all the more surprising since I dust them myself every day, and did it today. But there, you see, my poor boys are both in uniform. One has already been killed, the other is now at the front. When it is possible to suppress my grief, why should I arouse it afresh through my eyes?"

Another patient complained that he suddenly saw everything black before his eyes; that often occurs. I told him to go back in his recollections to the place where the black mist had descended upon him, and to tell me what he was seeing. "Stones," he replied. "I was going up steps, and it was stone steps I was looking at." That was little enough to start with. But as I kept obstinately to the point that the sight of the stones had caused his dizziness, he promised to look out for this. As a matter of fact, the next day he brought out that he had often been looking at stones on the occasion of other attacks. The matter was perhaps not altogether to do with the present, for he knew that he had first experienced an attack of a similar kind in Ostend, which had always seemed to him a comfortless collection of stones and of far too many cold-hearted people. When I asked him what

such a collection of stones and cold-hearted people signified, he said, "A churchyard." Since I knew that he had
been brought up in Belgium I tried to refer him to the
similarity of sound between *pierre* (stone) and Pière.
But he explained that neither a Peter nor a Pière had
ever played any part in his life. The next day he
brought up the matter himself and said that possibly I
was right. The home in which he lost his mother at the
age of six, and which was soon afterwards sold when the
father moved to Ostend, stood in the Rue St. Pière, and
even though the mother was not buried in the churchyard of St. Pière, still his nursery window looked out on
the gigantic stone masses of the church. He had been to
the church of St. Pière with his mother quite often, and
had always been confused by the stone masses of the
interior and the crowd of worshippers. After the word
Ostend, Russia came to his mind, the land of Russ (soot)
the black land, the land of death. Since that day when he
became conscious of the repressed complexes, he has
never again seen black before his eyes; on the other hand
his It has not abolished another measure of repression.
The patient, who was trained by his mother to be a Catholic, had abandoned his faith under the influence of the
desire to repress; in spite of the relief of the repression,
however, he has not again returned to the church.

Do you remember Frau von Wessels? How fond she
was of children, and how sad that she had no children
of her own? One day I was sitting with her by the edge
of the wood. For some time our talk had dragged, and
finally it stopped altogether. Suddenly she said, "What's
wrong with me? I can see nothing at all on my right, while
everything to the left is clear and distinct." I asked her
how long this condition had existed, and she replied, "I
noticed it while we were still in the wood." So I told her
to name any place where we had been during our walk,
and she mentioned some crossroads we had passed. "What
was to your right there?" I asked. "A lady walked past us
with her little boy. And now I can see everything clearly."
And then she remembered, laughing, how the whole way
before we reached the crossroads, she had entertained
me with the phantasy that she had a cottage far away
from everybody, with fowls and ducks and all sorts of
animals, and there she was living with her little son, while
the father only came for the day now and then, to visit

them. "If I had not known for a long time that you were right in your opinion that all diseases were created for some discoverable reason by the It," she said, "I should now have been convinced of it, for my one-sided blindness can only have been brought about by my not being able to endure the sight of that mother with her little boy."

Hysterical? Certainly, and no doctor and no educated person will hesitate about the diagnosis. But we two, you and I, have learned to smile at the term hysteria, we both know Frau von Wessels, and the most we can admit, out of deference to spectacled wisdom, is that this lady became hysterical for half an hour. But why should we bother ourselves further with such a stupid and diabolical word as hysteria? Let me rather tell you of what happened some years later.

One evening I met Frau von Wessels after the theater. She told me she had gone there on the chance of meeting an old acquaintance of hers, whose name she had seen some hours before in the visitors' list. I was surprised to see that the top of her left eyelid was much reddened and swollen. She had not previously noticed it, but she took out her pocket mirror, looked at the eye, and said, "I should not be surprised if the It wanted to play the fool again with a one-sided blindness." Then she began again to talk of the unexpected arrival of this former friend, but suddenly interrupted herself with the words, "Now I know why I have this swollen eye. It came when I read the name of this admirer of mine in the visitors' list." And then she told me how she had flirted with this man during her first husband's long and fatal illness. She mentioned all sorts of details connected with this period, and grew more and more taken up with the idea that her eye had become swollen so that she need not see the name that shamed her, accepting my suggestion also that her It was appropriately punishing her in the very organ with which she had sinned. The results seemed to prove that we were right, for when she went away, the swelling had vanished. The next day she had a fierce quarrel with her second husband about her stepdaughter, who was sitting on her left, and her eyelid slowly became swollen again. I talked to her later, and first she said that she, being childless, had not been able to tolerate the sight of her stepdaughter, and probably for this reason the eye had again swollen. This led to a new line of thought which she followed up for some time. Possibly the stepdaughter was also the cause of the eyelid being swollen the day before. Soon, however, she came back to her old idea that it must have been the name of her old friend in the visitors' list. "In a few days," she said, "it will be the anniversary of my first husband's death. I have noticed for years that I always become ill and wretched at this time, and I believe that I brought about this quarrel with Karl"—that is her present husband's name—"in order to have some reason for crying over my first husband. That is all the more probable since it has just occurred to me that the day before yesterday, that is the day before the swelling came on, I was in the hospital, and saw a man with kidney trouble who had the characteristic uremic smell, scraping the sediment from his tongue with a spatula, just as my dead husband used to do. That same evening I was sick when I looked at the horseradish sauce, and this went away as soon as I realized the similarity of the sauce to the secretion on the tongue. The sight of my stepdaughter was intolerable to me, because her existence brought before my eyes the fact of my infidelity to my first husband. For you can imagine that in that sad time I made a thousand vows never to marry again." Once more the swelling disappeared while we talked.

This time the inflammation of the lid was finally disposed of. But the next day, instead of that, Frau von Wessels appeared with an upper lip half an inch thick. Just over the top of the lip, right at the edge, a fiery-red spot had formed, which made the red of the lip look double its width. Half laughing, half angry, she gave me a letter which an acquaintance had written to one of her friends, and which this friend, full of disgust, had sent on to her, as friends are wont to do. There was to be read in this letter, after all sorts of other amiabilities, that Frau von Wessels, with her conspicuous and vulgar sensuality, was a real witch. "Look at my mouth," she said jokingly. "Can there be a better proof of my vulgar and sensual nature than these swelling, bright red lips? Fräulein H. is quite right in calling me a witch, and I could not punish her for lying." The matter interested me for various reasons, one of which I will tell you about later, and I devoted a good deal of time for some days to a thorough analysis, the results of which I will briefly set forth.

The matter did not rest with the death of her husband, nor with the stepdaughter, nor with the former admirer: the crucial point was with this very Fräulein H., whose letter had given her the swollen lip. This lady—let us call her Paula—an ancient enemy of Frau von Wessels, had been in the theater the selfsame evening—Friday, the 16th of August—that the left eyelid had become swollen for the first time, and indeed had sat to her left. Exactly a week before, also on Friday, August 9th, Frau von Wessels had been to the theater. As you know, such repeated visits are quite unheard of with her. Her second husband was with her, and to the left of her was sitting this same Paula, who, she knew, had fruitlessly endeavored to entangle Herr von Wessels. On that first Friday, August 9th, Frau von Wessels had encountered the malignant gaze of Paula's remarkable grey eyes, which in certain circumstances have a particularly hard and piercing look. Such grey eyes belong also to the wife of the nephritic hospital patient, with whose furry tongue she associated the sickness on Thursday evening, August 15th. On the occasion of her visit to this patient, whose uremic odor reminded her of her first husband, his grey-eyed wife had been there too. This lady is called Anna, but Anna was also the name of Frau von Wessels' eldest sister, under whom she had suffered inordinately as a child. And this sister Anna had the same hard, piercing eyes as Paula. And now comes the strange thing: this sister Anna had her birthday on August 21st. On the 15th, Frau von Wessels had looked at the calendar and determined to write; on the 16th she had wanted to write but had gone to the theater instead to see a ballet, *i.e.*, to see beautiful legs; on the 17th, she had again postponed her birthday letter, which she did not write until the 18th, the day she had the swollen lip. Finally, on the birthday itself, the swelling quickly disappeared, and the analysis, which up to that day made little progress, suddenly went on swimmingly, and all sorts of tangles were smoothed out.

Frau von Wessels told me, "At about fourteen years of age, when I first understood about pregnancy, I compared the dates of the birthday of my sister Anna, whom

I thoroughly hated at that time, and the wedding day of my parents, and as a result it seemed to me that she must have been on the way before they were married. From this I drew two conclusions, first, that my sister was not really legitimate—and this appears again in my inexplicable dislike, on August 17th, for my stepdaughter, for she is not my child, is therefore not legitimate, but was born before my marriage—and secondly, that my equally detested mother was a vulgar, sensual woman, an idea which I believed at that time to be all the more justified because during the previous six months—in my fourteenth year therefore—she had yet another child. As an analyst, you will certainly know what envy is aroused in the heart of an elder daughter by so late a pregnancy. I have always considered this calculation of pregnancy dates in connection with my sister Anna to be the most miserable thing I have ever done, and even now I find it hard to confess. As you have seen from my lip, I punish myself for the shameful deed against my mother, by expressing my own sensual nature to the whole world, once Fräulein Paula's accusation has been made. I know that my sister Anna expected me, in my birthday letter, to invite her here for October, but I don't want to have her here, although I feel wicked in hating the idea. The mouth, which will not utter, must be punished. But it must also be punished because about the same time as I reckoned up the dates of the wedding and the birth, I made it voice a wicked vow that I would never bear a child. This vow was made when I heard, by chance, the shrieks of a woman in the throes of childbirth. The association with the mouth is made clear through an acquaintance of mine, who after a long period of childlessness, has become pregnant, and whose lips, previously tightly pressed, are now full and red. I met this lady on August 15th, and talked to her about the coming baby. That is all the explanation I can offer for the mouth. As regards the eye, that is a very simple matter. Of my mother's numerous periods of pregnancy I noticed nothing at all, not even the last, although I was thirteen years old at the time, and knew very well how children came into the world. The attempt to make myself blind to pregnancy is therefore very old, and that I now take the opportunity by approved means to block up my good left eye—the right is almost useless—when the pregnancy complex in regard to my mother comes into the foreground, is not surprising. But there are still other things besides. For instance, I now know that in my visit to the hospital patient, it was not the uremic smell that upset me, but the smell of the faeces: that is, behind the memory of my husband's death was hidden the profoundly shameful remembrance of a moment when my mother was stroking my cheek, and I, instead of rejoicing in her tenderness, accused this loving hand of having a faecal smell; in other words, I transferred to her the habits which I as a child must have myself indulged in. I leave it to your facile mind to say whether the horseradish had anything whatever to do with my mother." Of this permission I took advantage. (*Meerrettich:* horseradish.) *Meer* seems to me to be associated with *mère,* and the radish is a recognized symbol for a man. The phrase, "to stick a radish in the bottom," ("to send him away with a flea in his ear") takes us on to the smell of the water closet. "The smell impression now leads me back again to the wife of this patient, and to her grey eyes, and to the hard eyes of Paula and sister Anna. The dread which I certainly have of Paula is due to these eyes so like Anna's, which frightened me. But when I say that I hated my sister Anna, I must make some reservation. Something in her I loved beyond measure, and that was her legs and her drawers. Even now I have in my possession a whole collection of Anna-legs in lace drawers, which I drew in the margin of my book during school time. In any case her legs have much to do with my love for the ballet, and you know that on the 16th I went to the theater to see beautiful legs. And now at once there comes an association which takes me back to my earliest childhood, beyond which I can only reach by the road of phantasy. The fear of hard eyes, namely, goes back to my grandmother of whom I had a terrible dread. The first thing she did when we went to see her was to lift up our frocks to see if we had on clean drawers. I understood, even then, that this practice was directed, not against me, but against my mother, and because of her enmity to mother, the old woman was revolting to my soul. None the less, I think it possible that this inspection of my drawers gave me voluptuous feelings. But notice, the charge of dirtiness which I took so hard from the old woman, I myself afterwards made against my mother when she stroked my cheek. That is bad. And something else still. One of my aunts—I heard the story in very early childhood—was repudiated by my grandparents because she became pregnant through her fiancé before their wedding. Again, the same accusation as I brought against my mother. My grandmother was an absolute witch, to me. And with this word 'witch' we come back to Paula and the events of the last few days. I knew that Paula, whose brain plays with all sorts of occult phantasies, ascribed telepathic powers to me and called me a witch. I have often applied the same term to my stepdaughter's own mother, whom I knew only by sight, or rather by sight and hearing. When I heard her voice for the first time, an icy fear seized me; I felt that there was something horrifying emanating from my childhood, in this voice. And when I saw the lady, it immediately came to my mind that she had my sister Anna's hard eyes, and then I knew also that her voice was like that of my grandmother, the witch. The remarkable revulsion I had against looking at my stepdaughter on the 17th, is connected with the fact that I was identifying her mother with my grandmother and sister and my enemy, Paula, so that she called up the worst, most deeply repressed memories. So far as I understand the matter, I must therefore seek for the causes of the mishaps to the eye and lip in conflicts with my grandmother, my mother, and my eldest sister, which were aroused from their sleep under the repression through the coming of the birthday and the meeting with Paula, while the yearly-repeated grief for my first husband is an attempt to cover up these complexes. The difficulty in seeing brought about the swelling of the eyelid in the same attempt at repression in another form, in a symptom of disease; I do not wish to see and consequently when, owing to the accumulation of phenomena, I can no longer be prevented from seeing the complexes, there comes the wish not to speak of them at least, and this is expressed in the swelling of the lip, and the resultant discomfort in speaking. The two things are at the same time the punishment for looking at beautiful legs, and for abjuring all pregnancy."

I leave it undecided, my dear, whether Frau von Wessels was right in her conclusions. Certainly she has even now suppressed a lot of material, and has scarcely interpreted a half of what she did give. I tell you the story, because here you have a not unintelligent woman describing, in her own vivid fashion, what I think about the mode of expression of the It through the symptoms of disease. But, as I have already indicated, I have still another reason for going into details in these things. At the time when Frau von Wessels had this experience with her eye and lip, and spoke about the uremic smell, there was in my sanatorium a patient with kidney trouble, who had this characteristic odor. I received him in the last stages of the disease and undertook the case in order to observe and make easy his dying, because the shape of his mouth with its tightly pressed, thin lips, seemed to me to be a confirmation of my belief that the It, in keeping back the urine, is saying the same as in the pinching together of the lips. For me, the uremia signifies the deadly struggle between the repressive will and the repressed material forever trying to force its way up, the important urine-secretion complex, which originates in earliest childhood and lies in the deepest levels of the constitution. The case did nothing essential in forwarding my phantastic, unscientific, researches—in which I have a personal interest owing to my own kidney disease. I had then to decide to bring some strange incidents in the progress of this tragedy into connection with my attempted interpretation of the It. And here I must mention that already, after the first few days of analysis, the constipation from which he had suffered for years before was converted into diarrhoea, the stench of which was indescribably horrible. One could, if sufficiently foolish, read into this the mocking cry of the It: "I will indeed give forth the bodily dirt which I used to hold back, but I am not going to surrender the filth of the soul." One could attribute a similar meaning to vomiting, which is certainly just as usual in uremia as diarrhoea; while on the other hand, with a little courage, one might say that the uremic cramp attacks, and finally the dying, are the means of compulsion adopted by the repressing It to prevent the complexes from reaching consciousness. Lastly, a remarkable edemic thickening of the lips, which I have never observed in any other case, and through which the mouth lost all its tight pressure, may be interpreted as the mockery of the It, which appears to restore freedom to the mouth, while in reality, by means of the edema, it prevents it from speaking. But all this is mere thought play, which I allow myself to indulge in, but for which I have not the least warranty in fact. During this time, however, I had a comical experience which I am able to interpret with a certain amount of confidence, since I was the person concerned. In the days when I was busying myself over Frau von Wessels' analysis and her swollen lip, my patient had his first uremic cramps. I stayed overnight in the sanatorium, and, as it was cold, I had a hot water bag in my bed. Before going off to sleep I was cutting a number of Freud's psychoanalytical *Zeitschrift* with a pointed paper knife, and turning over its pages. Among other things, I found therein a notice that Felix Deutsch had read a paper in Vienna on psychoanalysis and organic disease, a subject which, as you know, I have long been evolving in my mind, and which I have left to our mutual friend Groddeck to work up. Putting both paper and knife under my pillow, I began to phantasy a little on the subject, and in so doing soon got on to the uremic patient and my explanation of the withholding of the urine as a sign of repression. I went to sleep, at this point, to wake up the next morning with a strange sensation of dampness which made me think I had wet the bed. As a matter of fact, in my sleep I had stuck the paper knife into the rubber bag, and a small stream was issuing from it. Well, the following night I again slept at the sanatorium, and since I like to be munching something, I took some pieces of chocolate to bed with me, as I often do. What do you think happened? When I woke up the next morning, my bedclothes and night shirt were smeared all over with chocolate. It looked horribly like faeces, and I was so ashamed that I immediately took away the bed linen myself to avoid the charge of having relieved myself there; that led me to analyze this incident a little. For it then occurred to me that previously I had thought, in connection with the accident to the hot water bag, that it meant bed-wetting, and since I had been so much occupied with thoughts of the uremic patient, I explained the matter to myself this way: "Your It says to you that in spite of your kidney trouble you need not be anxious about ever getting uremia: for you see how easily you surrender urine and faeces, you hold nothing back, you suppress nothing, you are like a suckling babe, innocent and open with heart and reins." If I did not know the cunning of the It, I should have been content with this, but as it was, I did not allow it to satisfy me. All at once the name Felix shot through my mind. Felix, that is the name of the man who had spoken on psychoanalysis and organic diseases. But Felix Schwarz was also the name of a schoolfriend and this friend had died of uremia following scarlet fever. Schwarz (black) is death. The name Felix signifies happiness, and the union of Felix and Schwarz, happiness and death, can only be found in the moment of the utmost sexual delight, united, as it is, with dread of the death punishment; in other words it is the masturbation complex, this early complex, which is forever taking possession of me when I think about my kidney trouble. And now it seemed to me that the explanation I had found for the two mishaps was sufficient. Two hours later I knew better, for when I went to the bedside of my uremic patient, the thought suddenly came to me, "He looks like your brother Wolf." Up to then I had never noticed the likeness, yet now I saw it clearly. And darkly rose up before me the question, "What has your brother Wolf, or the word wolf, to do with your repressions? It is always coming up anew, however much you analyze yourself, and never do you find the answer. Even this one, that comes into your head at this minute, is not the last one, the ultimate."

Nevertheless I will not withhold it from you. When I was quite a tiny child—but old enough to remember—I often got a sore place in the cleft between the buttocks; i.e., I had a wolf (chafing). I then went to my mother and she would rub on some ointment. That certainly gave me an incentive towards masturbation, later, and was certainly itself a form of infantile masturbation in which, half-conscious, with fox-sly cunning, I made use of my mother's hand for this wicked deed, no doubt remembering the voluptuous feeling which every infant gets during his nurse's cleansing. And when I had got so far in my analytic play, it occurred to me that earlier in the day I really had produced a wolf (chafing) between my legs, in cycling. "So that is the wolf you have so long been searching for," I exulted, and I was happy, and able to help the wife of my patient over a bad half hour. But when I went out of the door, I knew, "Even that is not the solution! You repress, and however much your It and

261

your friends may praise your candor, still you are just as other men are. And only he is honest, who says, as that publican, 'God be merciful to me.'" But do you not think that even this ultimate conclusion is pharisaical?

Adieu, dear one,

I am your

PATRIK.

GEORG WALTHER GRODDECK was born in Germany in 1866. Although he spent his early years as a writer—he produced a novel, poetry, and a volume of art criticism—he became a doctor in middle life and, from that point on, thought of himself as healer rather than artist. He spent the remainder of his life as director of a clinic at Baden-Baden, and continued to write, but his plan for reviewing every aspect of knowledge in terms of the hypothesis presented in *The Book of The It* was cut short by his death in 1934. His other books, *The World of Man*, *The Unknown Self*, and *Exploring the Unconscious*, are collections of Groddeck's writings on science, cosmology, and art.

THE TEXT of this book is set in *Caledonia*, a Linotype face that belongs to the family of printing types called "modern face" by printers—a term used to mark the change in style of type-letters that occurred about 1800. The book was composed, printed and bound by The Colonial Press Inc., Clinton, Mass. Cover design by ABNER DEAN.